Discoveries and Inventions

From Prehistoric to Modern Times

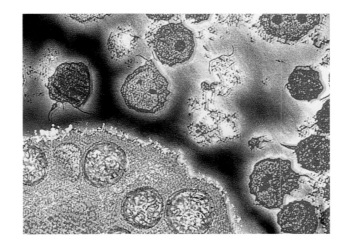

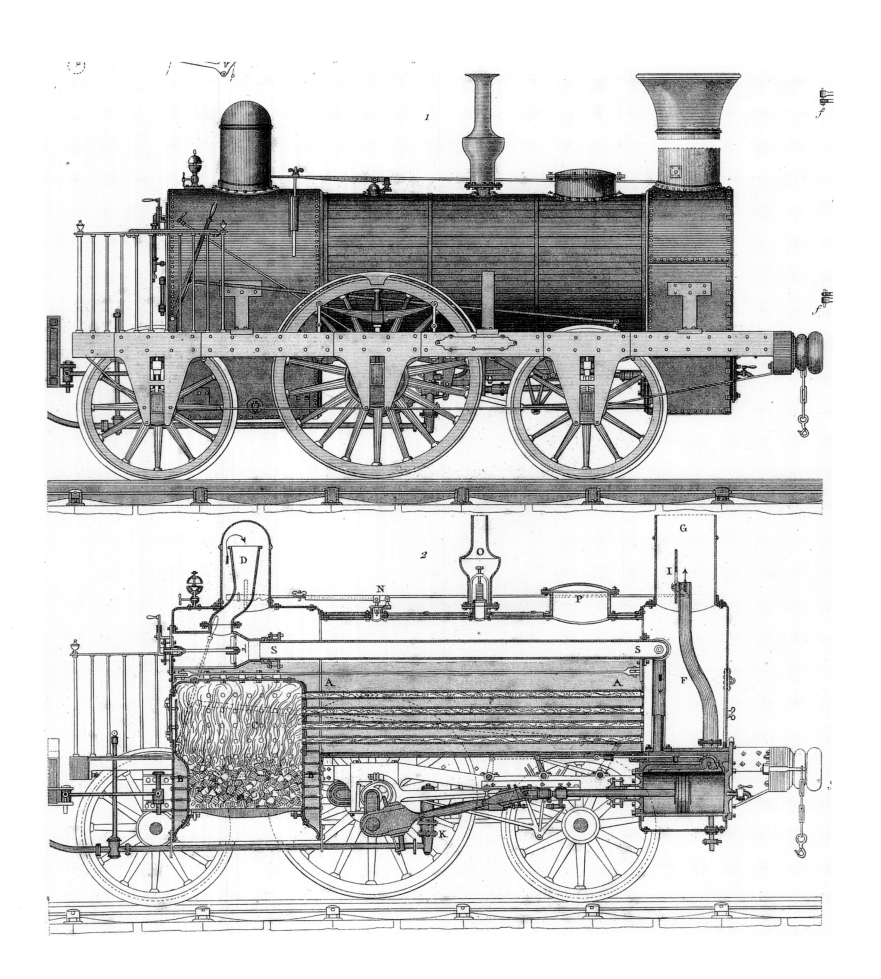

1

2

Discoveries and Inventions

From Prehistoric to Modern Times

Edited by
Dr Jörg Meidenbauer

REBO
PUBLISHERS

Contents

Introduction

Great moments of science

In this book the great discoveries and inventions of science are arranged chronologically, and the timeline accompanying each article serves to place its subject in a historical context. In producing this book it has been our aim, and at the same time a challenge, to provide an approachable and informative description of the scientific and human evolution of mankind, based on the vast array of facts available.

It is clear that opinions vary on how the history of science developed and the particular part played by individual inventions and discoveries. Opinions also vary as to what should be included in a work such as this. Here the attempt has been made to select the most important elements and processes in the development of science, describing them and highlighting their effects.

Albert Einstein, the patent office employee, enjoyed theoretical mind games and a little advanced mathematics. In doing so he revolutionized our view of the world as comprehensively as astronomers such as Galileo had done centuries earlier when, at the risk of his life, he proved that the earth was a sphere that revolved round the sun. It was only very gradually that Einstein's theories could be tested in the laboratory, among others by Werner Heisenberg, who discovered the "quantum leap" rather by accident. Now commonly used as a term to describe an important step forward in a development, in fact this term describes the "leaping" of atomic particles, a process of such infinite minuteness that it can only be observed with the most sophisticated instruments, using the most accurate measuring methods. But this discovery was a prerequisite for the development of nuclear energy, the most powerful and destructive force in the world.

The history of science is therefore no random succession of independent events. Every new answer to the mystery of the world brings up new questions to be answered. Questioning and searching for answers is part of the human race's yearning to find out more about itself and its surroundings. At the time, man's first walk on the moon was the most important milestone on the road to overcoming his own spatial limitations. But it was not the last. Many discoveries and inventions, often unnoticed, have radically changed our everyday life, often as much as highly acclaimed scientific achievements.

Everyday life in industrial countries would be unthinkable without cars, telephones, televisions, and computers, which are all the result of man's great creativity, persistent search for knowledge, and enthusiastic inventive mind. Printed books represent a medium that is often said to be on the verge of extinction at the hands of electronic media, but in reality they are still one of the most important sources of information and knowledge.

When a book was a unique handwritten item, as was the case in the Middle Ages, it was prohibitively expensive. Then, when Gutenberg's new printing process enabled multiple copies to be produced, books became more accessible, but still limited to an educated elite who could read. It is only in the "knowledge-thirsty" society of the last 200 years that books have become widely available to an increasingly literate general public. So today this book enables us to discover some of the great moments in the centuries-old saga of development and research that forms the history of science and invention, a story that contains a wealth of fascinating facts and remarkable stories.

In the beginning there was fire

China

At the dawn of mankind's history there was fire: torches lit up the darkness and flames provided warmth when it was cold. Meat and other foods could be cooked over the flames. The discovery and application of fire is one of the greatest achievements of *Homo sapiens*.

500000 BC

500,000 BC

> About 2.5 million years ago, *Homo habilis* begins to make simple tools.

> About 1.7 million years ago, humans begin to walk upright. The earliest finds of *Homo erectus* are made in Africa.

> 1.5 million years ago, *Homo erectus* reaches Europe, a fact confirmed by various tools found in France.

> The oldest find of *Homo erectus* in Asia is made in Indonesia.

Forest fires, thunderstorms, lightning, and floods have caused devastation on earth since time immemorial, and mankind has sought to bring these forces of nature under control, often without success. But human beings succeeded in "domesticating" fire quite early in the history of mankind and making use of it for their own purposes. They learned how to light a fire and how to keep it going. At first the flames were used to satisfy their daily needs, providing warmth, protection from wild animals, and for preparing food. Later fire was used to produce items of practical use and luxury objects, including ceramic vessels made from clay and tools, weapons, and jewelry formed from molten metal.

In Africa as early as 1,500,000 to 1,400,000 BC, man's ancestors made use of bush fires when they came across them, applying the flames for their own purposes. In the early Pleistocene era (730,000 to 200,000 BC) prehistoric man searched for natural fires since it was not then known how to create fire where there was none. Natural fires were caused by lightning and carefully kept burning when found.

A major step forward occurred towards the end of the mid-Pleistocene era (200,000 to 60,000 BC) when it was discovered how to light a fire to cook food. This has been substantiated by the discovery of waste material and animal bones on prehistoric sites. At the same time the first tents were made from animal skins and the raw material needed for stone tools was transported over distances as long as 200 miles. In the late Pleistocene era Neandertal man (60,300 to 40,300 BC) built carefully guarded camp fires and the first house-like constructions.

Fire radically changed the life of prehistoric people by providing protection, warmth, and nourishment. For instance, fire was used to thaw animal carcasses from their store rooms. When the nomadic lifestyle was abandoned for a settled one, new applications for fire were discovered, such as making clearings for cultivation by burning, and "firing" flaming arrows in the event of war. Fire was carefully guarded, since if it became extinguished the entire settlement would suffer. Magical or religious powers were ascribed to fire when people were still living in caves. Fire was considered a living being, one that had to be pacified with burnt offerings. Later civilizations gave names to their gods of fire, such as Girru, Hephaistos, and Prometheus. The guardian of the holy flame was highly respected. The ancient Romans worshiped Vesta as the goddess of the hearth, and women visited the Temple of Vesta in the Forum on her feast day. The eternal flame burning in the inner shrine was tended by "vestal virgins," young women whose lives were dedicated to Vesta and who were punished by death if unchaste.

Today it may be thought that fire has been tamed, but nature does not surrender control. Environmental pollution has led to climate changes, with the weather becoming hotter and drier. This in turn results in natural catastrophes such as large-scale forest fires. Inhabitants of the south-western United States are regularly plagued by widespread forest fires that engulf large areas, reducing them to ash and rubble.

Fire gives light and heat. Its important properties have contributed to the further development of mankind. But even though it is thought to have been tamed, it is a force of nature that can easily get out of control.

Numbers: counting with notches

Ancient cultures

Since time immemorial numbers have played an important part in mankind's everyday life. In order to orientate themselves in their surroundings and to plan how to manage their reserves, human beings invented a system of signs that clearly described how many inhabitants lived in a village or how many animals had already been killed.

30000 BC

AROUND 30,000 BC

> One hundred thousand years ago, *Homo sapiens sapiens* arises in Africa.

> Forty thousand years ago in Europe, *Homo sapiens sapiens* supersedes the Neandertals. He also makes instruments of stone, bone, and horn, and hunts with a spear thrower.

> The Paleolithic Age cave paintings from Lascaux and Chauvet in France are about 40,000 years old. They portray humans and animals.

Early numbers used the tally system of notation, such as notches on a wooden stick. These early "natural" numbers laid the foundation for the "whole" numbers 1, 2, 3… They were used for practical purposes: from about 30,000 BC Stone Age hunters carved a notch in a bone or piece of wood for each animal they had killed in order to keep a record of the total. For example, a wolf's bone 20,000 years old discovered in Dolní Věstonice in present-day Moravia carries 55 notches arranged in two rows of groups of five.

Such a method of counting in groups of five already points to the fundamental system of counting that uses parts of the body as an aid, normally the fingers. The decimal system of today is probably based on this archaic method of counting. Adding the toes created an alternative counting system based on 20 that was used by the ancient Egyptians, Greeks, and Persians. Many paintings and carvings discovered in Egypt depict people counting or haggling for goods at the market. The ancient Romans also expressed numbers by different movements of the fingers.

The number "0" on the other hand was discovered by the Sumerians and Babylonians. Their numerical system was based on the number 60, which is probably the origin of the division of the hour into minutes and seconds as well as the division of the circle into 360 degrees. The development of numbers is closely linked with that of the alphabet, since people also wanted to record the description of what they were counting, such as horses, slaves, apples or coins. This could be done by using pictograms or abstract characters.

An important prerequisite for the development of a complex number system was the naming of cardinal numbers that would lead to the definition of further numbers when put together: five and ten make fifteen, eight times one hundred make 800, and so on. This avoided the need for an endless number of terms for designating numbers, and it also meant that the same numbers could be combined in endless variations to create new numbers.

Numerology, the study of the influence of numbers that was much used by oracles, developed at the same time as the number system, and even today many people believe that certain numbers are endowed with magical powers. This superstition was widespread during antiquity, particularly in Byzantium. For instance, people would try to tell the sex of their unborn child or the date of their own death by using numerology. They also linked astronomical phenomena to numbers, the numbers 30, 12, and in particular 7 having important cosmic significance.

The Arabic numerals that are used today probably originated from India. Their most important characteristic is the use of zero as a number and the fact that the numerical value is determined by the position of the numbers.

Detail of the cave paintings of Lascaux. Even in the Stone Age people liked to convey the extent of their catch. In order to keep a count of the animals killed, the hunters developed a simple counting system of notches or lines.

Bow and arrow: vital for hunting and war

Paleolithic hunters

The bow and arrow are among the most important long-range weapons ever invented, only disappearing when firearms appeared. The bow and arrow was used for thousands of years for hunting or in war.

> From the Neolithic Age humans bury their dead – or in the case of head burial, just the head – with artistic burial offerings.

> The hunters of the Neolithic Age track mammoth, horses, reindeer, bison, and bears.

> About 25,000 BC, the Cro-Magnon people use needles made of bone to sew clothing.

At some point in the Paleolithic era (30,000–20,000 BC), hunters and warriors began throwing their spears from a distance instead of just using them in close combat. As an extension of this technique, a small spear – an arrow – released from a tensioned bow was considerably faster and more effective than a spear. By this means hunters and warriors could hit their prey or their enemy from much further away. During the Mesolithic era hunters used the bow and arrow to hunt red deer and roe deer as well as wild boar. They "sharpened

" their arrows by attaching points made of small pieces of flint or the thorns of plants.

Usually the bows were made from elm wood and were between 5 and 6 ft long. Unfortunately none has survived, since being made of wood they rotted long ago. However today there is indirect evidence of their use in the rectangular stone guard plate with rounded corners used to protect the arm from the snap of the bowstring when it was released. Cave paintings in Spain and southern France depict hunting scenes with hunters using a bow and arrow.

"Ötzi," the mummified corpse discovered on a glacier in the Ötzi valley, gave scientists further information on the use of bow and arrow during the transitional period from the Neolithic to the Bronze Age (3350–3100 BC). In a quiver made from chamois skin the "man from Similaun" had two arrows ready to shoot, still showing traces of feathers, as well as 12 tubular shafts measuring 33–34 in in length. The feathers were fitted to the arrows to keep their flight level, instead of tumbling over. Ötzi's bow was never finished: neither the grip part nor the notches for attaching the string had been made.

In Egypt simple bows existed very early on. The wall paintings in Tutankhamun's tomb (c. 1325 BC) were decorated with illustrations of an elegant composite bow, a quiver, and leather arm protection. By gluing several layers of wood or horn on top of each other and coating it with a

△ In ancient Egypt bows and arrows were used very early on for hunting as well as for fighting.

Bows and arrows have been used for hunting since the mid-Stone Age. Small fragments of rock or thorns were attached to the point of the arrow to make it sharp.

The lamp: light in the darkness

Neolithic culture

Automatically reaching for the light switch is taken for granted today. However, until the invention of electric light, people had to make do with fire, oil, or gas to lighten the darkness. Lamplight brightened dark homes and "lengthened" the day. It also played a significant role in rituals.

> After 10,000 BC: Stone Age people use simple calendars. They carve the phases of the moon onto pieces of bone.

> 10,000 BC: The population of Jericho build houses using bricks.

> In the Neolithic Age, about 8000 BC, people start to cultivate fields instead of hunting and gathering. They give up their nomadic way of life and start to build settlements.

The development of the lamp began with the "taming" of fire. By 75,000 BC, early peoples were using burning pieces of wood as primitive torches. The lamps of the Paleolithic period were somewhat more sophisticated: tallow and a wick made of plant fiber were placed in natural hollows in stones and lit. Depending on the size of the stone, people could even carry these lamps about with them.

In order to obtain better, more portable lamps, humans gave nature a helping hand. They scraped out hollows in stones for themselves. Soft soapstone was ideally suited for making lamps this way. From 20,000 BC onwards, animal fat and oil were the usual lamp fuels; the floating wick was still made out of plant fiber. These stone lamps were the forerunners of the simplest form of clay bowl lamp.

In ancient Egypt there were countless variations of bowl-shaped lamps made of clay, stone or metal. Alongside these there were luxurious unique pieces, such as the lotus flower lamp with three bowls carved out of a single piece of alabaster that was found in the grave of Tutankhamun (d. 1325 BC). Once this lamp had been lit, the light shimmering through the transparent material threw mysterious patterns on the wall. To prevent lamps from smoking, the Egyptians added salt to the lamp oil.

In ancient Greece, torches were usually used for religious purposes and this custom can also be traced back to the time of the Romans. In daily life, two types of lamps appeared for the first time that were to characterize the shape of lamps for many centuries, the open and the closed lamp. The closed lamp prevented the oil being spilled. To make them easier to use, these bowl-shaped lamps had a pinched "spout" in which the wicks were inserted. Many lamps of this period were decorated with shiny glazes or geometric patterns while lamps made of metal were often shaped to represent animals. The clay lamps of Hellenistic and Roman times were to be found in many types and variations, for instance, in the shape of a bird's head.

In order to intensify the amount of light available, a mirror was often placed behind the flame. Some of these were decorated with a profusion of pictures, erotic motifs being most popular. In almost every larger city in the Mediterranean countries and their provinces, workshops sprang up for the manufacture of lamps; thus a profitable branch of industry was born. Apart from the lamps with one spout there were special forms with many wicks in a row, or lamps in the shapes of ships, heads or animals. One specimen from Pompeii was even made of pure gold. Lamps were of great significance for Roman daily life as well as for their burial rites. At the time of the early and middle empires, it was the custom to place one or two lamps in the grave of the deceased so that he or she could find the way in the dark beyond. Towards late antiquity and the Byzantine period, people had a preference for glass lamps hung on wheel-shaped or metal lantern frames. Candles were also becoming more popular. As a result of this development, the manufacture of clay lamps started to diminish in many provinces or disappeared completely.

The first oil lamps were very simple and made of clay. There were numerous variations in ancient Egypt; for example, the specimen illustrated on the right is over 3 ft tall.

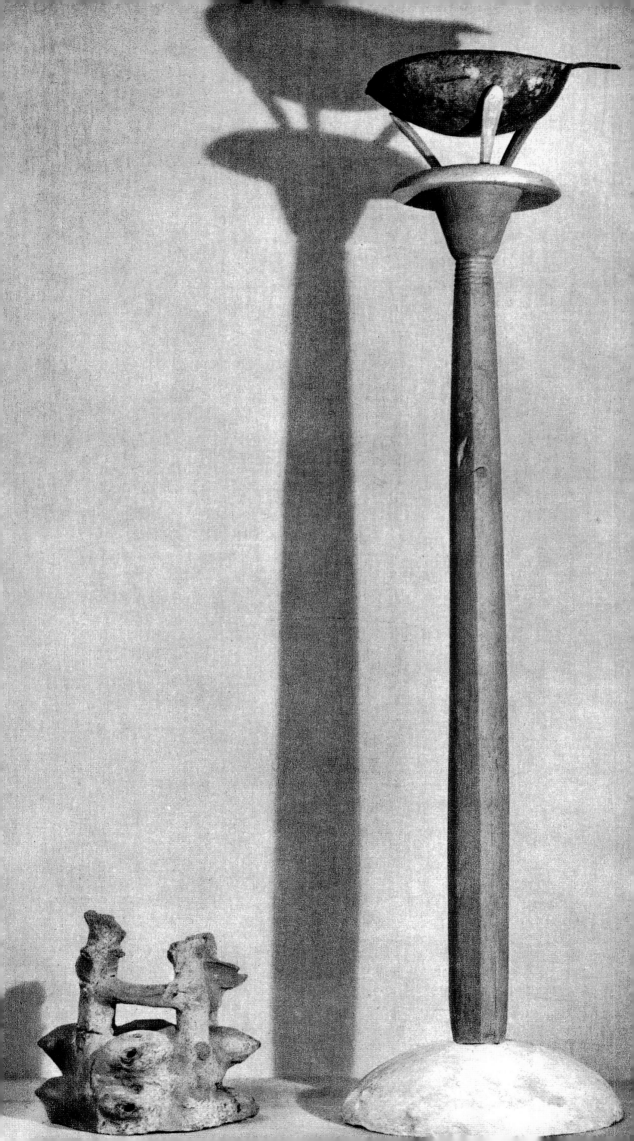

Irrigation: lush fields in spite of drought

Mesopotamia

AROUND 6000 BC

> From 7000 BC: The Egyptians and Mesopotamians begin to fire ceramics.

> From 6000 B.C:. People start using the iron from meteorites that they collect. It is heated and then hammered into shape.

> From 6000 BC: In Asia Minor, people are building rafts made of tree trunks.

The "fertile crescent," an arc-shaped strip of land running from Syria and Palestine towards the deltas of the Euphrates, Tigris and the Nile, is regarded as the cradle of civilization. However, it was only through intelligent use of irrigation that the land became fertile enough to enable the first great civilizations of mankind to flourish here.

In Mesopotamia, the "country between two rivers," agriculture and animal husbandry were the foundation of people's lives. Fields and plants, animals and humans, all needed water. The water supply in its turn was dependent on the natural lie of the land in the populated areas. Generally, there is more water to be found in mountainous regions, as rain clouds tend to "catch" on the mountain peaks and release their rain. The plains tend to be drier, especially if there are few rivers. Even at the edges of the river banks, agriculture still has to struggle with the problems of wet marshland and regular flooding.

In large areas of Mesopotamia it rained only occasionally, so that agriculture would have been unable to feed the population. However, the inhabitants adapted to the situation. To start with they learned to plant and utilize plants that could cope with dry conditions, and they also learned to use the water of the rivers for their needs.

Farmers established fields close to the rivers and developed plows that were suitable for the kind of soil found there. The early Mesopotamians dug irrigation ditches. By filling them in and digging them again when necessary, they regulated the water supply. In areas where the soil was sandier and the water drained away more quickly, the workers lined their canals with masonry or stone slabs. To collect and contain the precious element they also built dams, aqueducts, wells, and cisterns. After a time it was also necessary to drain the fields instead of watering them, to prevent them becoming too salty for agricultural purposes.

In order to keep the system of the irrigation canals functioning, the Mesopotamians had a large administrative structure and many laborers. To irrigate their fields they needed strict organization and a large number of workers. The matter of water supply often strained social relations between neighboring villages, and the struggle for the precious commodity sometimes ended in war.

Nevertheless, the advantages outweighed such negative side-effects. Their various techniques for distributing water enabled the Mesopotamians to harvest a surplus, until eventually the first advanced civilizations arose in the country between the two rivers and in Egypt.

△ The ancient Egyptians already knew how to build dams and canals and they were therefore able to use the waters of the Nile for agriculture all year round.

The development of early civilizations was closely connected with the invention of irrigation. In many regions, as here in Egypt, this situation did not change until the beginning of the modern era.

The loom: the first step towards fashion

Neolithic culture

The invention of woven clothes opened up a completely new way of dressing and indicating social rank. Clothes were no longer worn simply as protection against cold, sun, and rain; fashion and display became an integral part of human life.

AROUND 5000 BC

> From 5000 BC: People discover the use of an inclined plane and the power of leverage.

> From 5000 BC: On the Indian subcontinent, rice is being cultivated.

> 4500 BC: The farmers of Mesopotamia are using the plow.

Compared to the new woven garments, clothes made from animal skins or leather, which had been worn for thousands of years, were now considered impractical and heavy. There were obvious advantages in fabrics made of vegetable fibers such as cotton or animal fibers such as wool. Soon these were used to make light, durable garments that also had the advantage that they could be dyed.

The development of spinning and weaving skills is closely linked to the increasingly sedentary way of life during the Neolithic period. Traces of primitive looms have been found in all Neolithic cultures. Farmers cultivated textile plants such as flax and cotton, and they bred sheep and goats to provide the necessary raw materials for producing textiles. The Chinese even bred silkworms. Every family was involved in the weaving of fabric but only for its own use; these textiles were unique and the work of women and children. The commercial production of garments started only in Roman times, spreading more widely during the Middle Ages, when pre-industrial production methods and guilds developed.

The oldest example in the long history of the loom is the warp-weighted loom. The weaver would fasten the warp thread (the threads that run in a longitudinal direction) to a horizontal wooden beam, called the warp beam. In order to draw the threads as taut as possible, the weaver attached weaving weights made of clay or stone. To produce a length of fabric, the weaver also needed a device that would divide the warp threads into so-called "compartments" as required. In the simplest type of weave, plain weave, every second warp thread is raised alternately. The crossways weft threads are then introduced into this "compartment" and pressed against the already woven fabric. For the next row, the warp threads that had been left in place in the previous row are raised and the remainder lowered; the weft thread is then pushed through the compartment from the other side. The weaver proceeds in this way until the material is the desired length. Inserting the weft threads in the compartment is done either by hand or using a weaver's shuttle made from wood or bone to which the thread is attached. The earliest known example of such a shuttle came from the Neolithic Hemudu culture in China. This particular shuttle would have been used to weave silk.

The loom is one of the most important and successful inventions of mankind, whose importance is comparable to the wheel, the potter's wheel, and metalworking. The loom has developed from the primitive warp-weighted loom to the gigantic industrial looms of modern textile factories.

△ **This loom found in Crete was still being used in the 20th century. This shows that this simple technical device remained unchanged in many areas even after the introduction of industrialized weaving machinery.**

One of mankind's most important inventions, the loom was widely used in ancient Rome.

Astronomy: studying the stars in the sky

Mesopotamia, Egypt, China, Greece

The stars of the heavens always fascinated people in prehistoric times. It was usually for religious reasons that they wanted to find out more about the universe, but they were also driven by economic interests. The cycles of nature recorded in calendars made it possible for farmers to plan their agricultural tasks. This is why it was so important for astronomers to find out about the infinity of space and the movements of the stars.

Although ancient civilizations did not have the resources available today, their systematic observation of the sun, the moon, and the stars provided important information about the regular occurrence of certain natural phenomena. The identification of the four cardinal points was originally used in religious rituals to determine the direction for graves. The stone circle of Stonehenge in England, which dates from the Neolithic period, appears to illustrate the remarkable astronomical knowledge of its builders. Two groups of stones on the site have been positioned so that the point of sunrise on the summer solstice is precisely aligned along their axis. It also possible that the positioning of the stones played a part in the forecasting of solar and lunar eclipses, serving as a calendar.

In about 5000 BC agriculture and farming had developed to such a point that people needed a calendar to establish the seasons and the passage of the year. Farmers needed to know when to sow, harvest, and carry out other related agricultural tasks. Because the moon was more noticeable than the sun with its rapidly changing position in the sky and constantly altering shape, it was used by the Mesopotamians (and other civilizations) as the starting point of their calendar. They divided the year into twelve months, each of 29 or 30 days. In about 4000 BC they were already studying the seasonal changes in the constellations of the stars in the night sky, naming some of them after animals. Astrology then established a connection between constellations such as the bull (Taurus), the lion (Leo), and the scorpion (Scorpio) with particular events on earth.

The Egyptians developed the first solar calendar at the beginning of the 3rd millennium BC. One of the reasons was that the sun played a major part in their religion. They also studied the "heliacal rise" of stars, that is, the point in time when a star and the sun could be seen rising in the sky together. The heliacal rise of Sirius was a particularly celebrated event because it coincided with the flooding of the Nile that provided much needed irrigation. The position and alignment of the pyramids was also determined by astronomical aspects; the sides of the Great Pyramid of Cheops, built in about 2520 BC, face the four cardinal points, while its ventilation shafts point towards particular stars and constellations. The astronomical records of the Chinese go back as far as the Shang dynasty, about 1500 BC. By the 5th century BC the Chinese had developed a calendar based both on the solar year and moon phases.

From about 600 BC Greek scholars had been studying astronomical phenomena such as the spherical shape of the earth, the distance between the earth and the sun and the moon, and the circumference of the earth. However, with the decline of science in Greece, astronomy remained dormant in the West until after 1300 AD, when it experienced a new revival.

The mystery of the starry sky. Astrologers used the constellations for prediction since earliest times.

> 5000 BC: The first copper mines are dug on Mount Sinai in Palestine.

> 5000 BC: The Chinese are using the technique of flooding fields to cultivate rice.

> 4000 BC: The Phoenicians carry out dental treatment, fixing the front teeth to the adjacent ones with gold wire.

△ **Scientists tried to represent the constellations of the stars pictorially.**

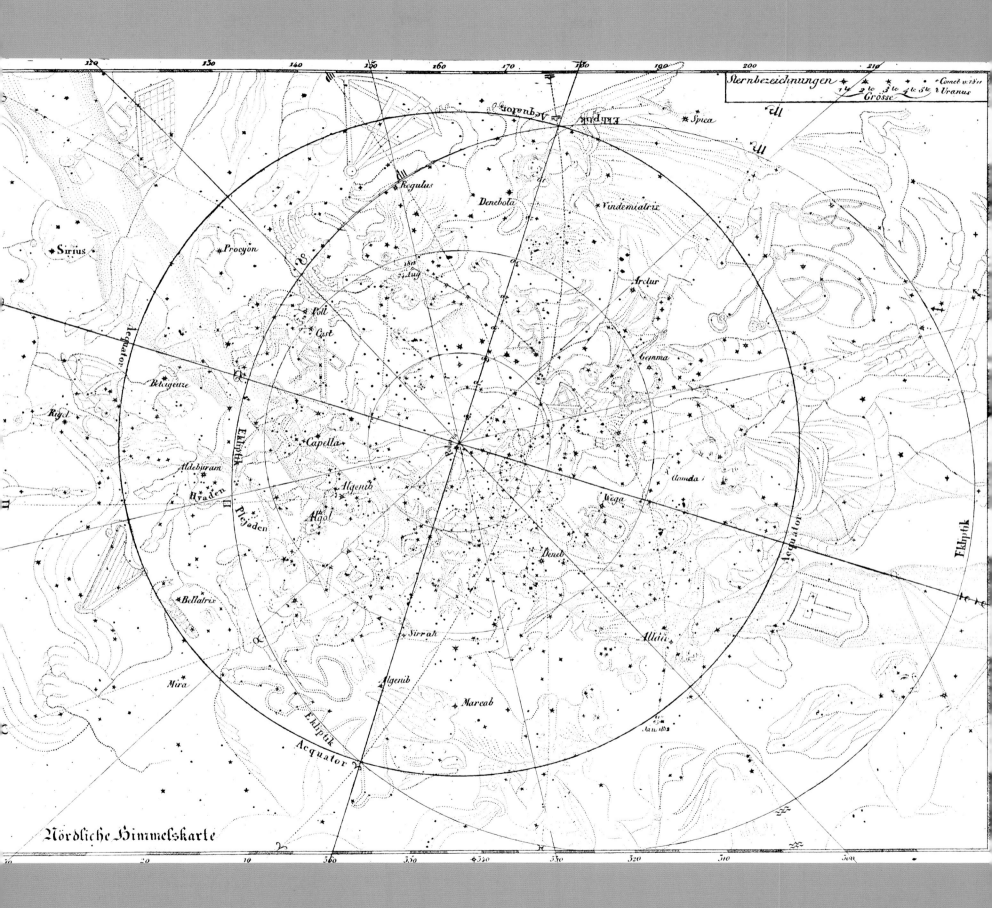

Sternbezeichnungen
Grösse   Comet v. 1811   Uranus

Spica

Regulus
Denebola
Vindemiatrix

Sirius   Procyon
Arctur

Poll
Cast
Gemma

Beteigeuze

Rigel
Capella

Aldebaran   Lamda

Hyaden   Vega
Algenib

Pleyaden   Algol   Deneb

Bellatrix

Sirrah
Alldii

Mira
Algenib

Marcab   Jan. 1812

Ekliptik
Aequator

Nördliche Himmelskarte

The sundial: man first measures time

Mesopotamia

Since the very beginning of mankind the sun has been the center of many civilizations, worshiped as a life-giving divinity. Once astronomers had found that the position of the sun in the sky varied, they were in a position to solve a problem that had long remained unsolved: how to measure time.

Before people could measure time in other units, their day was determined by the time between sunrise and sunset, which in turn determined the periods of work and rest. The best times for sowing and harvesting were established by observing of the position of particular stars or by the recurrence of natural phenomena. There were no other fixed points of reference for structuring the time between morning and evening. An important guide was the position of the sun during the day in relation to distinctive landmarks in the landscape. But unlike the moon, on whose phases calendars had been based, the bright sun could not be observed directly. It was by chance that the Mesopotamians noticed how the position of a shadow of the sun altered during the day: for example, the shadow of an obelisk moved steadily round the column. At sunrise the shadow pointed to the west, at midday towards the north, and in the evening to the east. In the morning and in the evening the shadow was longer than at midday.

Inspired by this phenomenon, the Mesopotamians and Babylonians constructed the first sundial. This consisted of a perpendicular shadow pointer, the gnomon, fixed to a horizontal plate marked with angular lines. The shadow of the gnomon moved over the marked lines, indicating the time. Based on the hexadecimal system, in which the numbers 6, 24 and 600 had a special meaning, the Babylonians divided the daily course of the sun into 24 hours of 60 minutes each. Since the hour was always the 12th part of the time span between sunrise and sunset, it was therefore sometimes longer and sometimes shorter, since the length of the day varies during the year. These were therefore termed "temporary" hours. The sundial measured (and still measures) the actual local time.

The Egyptians applied the Babylonian method to more convenient models. A fragment of a portable Egyptian sundial dating from 1500 BC shows six markings made to measure the length of the shadow on the long side of an angular plate. Using a table it was possible to translate the measurements into the correct time for a particular geographic latitude.

The ancient Greeks and Romans built their time-measuring instruments on the basis of the hollow hemispherical sundial that is thought to have been developed by the Babylonian astronomer Berosos in about 300 BC. Known as the hemicycle, the shadow pointer is placed inside a hemispherical bowl and throws its shadow on a semi-circular arc. Information about the time and date is displayed on a system of lines consisting of hour lines and diurnal arcs. It also enables the height of the sun and geographical latitude to be determined.

With the invention of the mechanical clock in the 14th century the sundial gradually lost its importance. Without it people would not have been able to plan important activities and it thus played a vital role in laying the foundations for communication and trade.

△ Today time can still be measured from the sun using the same principle as the Mesopotamians long ago.

It was the sun that enabled time to be measured for the first time. This sundial is set in a church window dating from relatively modern times.

·1·5·5·3·

M   8·16

9·15

10·14

11·13

20·20

13·11

14·10

tag   15·9   nacht
16·8

△ **The inhabitants of the African rain forest have long known how to build complex suspension bridges from the simplest materials.**

Bridge building: rivers and gorges become passable

People of all cultures

Bridges allow people and goods to cross safely over wide rivers and deep chasms. Alexander the Great would never have reached India without these constructions. Lacking them, the Roman emperor Trajan would never have arrived in Dacia, the capture of which marked the Roman Empire's greatest expansion.

Before bridges were invented, people searched for shallow crossings, known as fords, in order to cross wide rivers. In addition, since it was always dangerous to attempt such a crossing, they would try to calm the unpredictable elements by means of sacrifices.

Building a bridge of wood, stone or of temporary plant fibers posed a problem, however, for prehistoric humans. Such a construction had to carry the weight of several people and carts, and it also had to be able to withstand floods.

The simplest bridge construction is the beam bridge. A beam of wood or stone is laid across a narrow stretch of water or a ravine. When and where the first such construction, based on the "building blocks" principle, was built is a matter for conjecture. It was probably constructed over and over again at all times in various places.

In Neolithic times, houses constructed on stilts were being built close to rivers and lakes. Possibly the idea of a bridge arose from this tradition – a slab lying across uprights or buttresses. The most sophisticated wooden pile bridges were built by the Romans. Many of the iron bases used in their bridge foundations still exist.

The oldest existing stone bridges originated in Babylon and Egypt and date from 4000 BC. A stone slab was laid over vertical uprights, or sometimes between massive blocks of stone even more solid than the slab. The first bridge builders must have been working by trial and error as they would have had no knowledge of structural engineering. The bridges that came later had arches; they were made of piles of stones that reached out further and further to lean against each other. The Romans perfected this technique, which had originally been developed by the Etruscans. They were driven by the need to guarantee a smooth-running military and civil administration, for which a well developed route system was necessary. They constructed arched bridges with remarkable spans, such as the bridge over the river Tagus in Spain dating from about AD 200.

A further basic requirement of the Romans explains their preoccupation with bridge building. They needed large amounts of water for their hot baths, private households, and sewage systems. In order to transport this water, they built aqueducts – huge stone bridges for carrying water on structures of great length. The Romans were the first to make precise plans of the bridges they were going to build. They surveyed the land beforehand, used standardized blocks of stone, and calculated the size and angles of the wedge-shaped stones for the arches. However, by the time of the Middle Ages in Europe, there was no further use for this wonderful Roman achievement. The principle of the stone bridge remained, but the aqueducts fell into disuse along with the ancient way of life.

The principle of the stone bridge shaped like a semi-circle dates back to antiquity.

Fig. 12

Fig. 11

Fig. 8

Fig. 10

Fig. 14 a

Fig. 14

Fangedamm

Schöpfwerk

Rost

Belag

Mittelpfeiler

Fangedamm

30'7'

18'

40'

16'

26'

16'

9'3'

19'

12'

6'

25'

16'

10'

32'

16'

16'

8'

55'

Rad 27'7"

61'

153 F.

Rad 17'7"

Höchstes Wasser

Megaliths: monuments of the early Stone Age

Western and northern Europe

Few prehistoric monuments in Europe have fascinated people's imagination over the centuries as strongly as the megaliths. The stone circle at Stonehenge in the south of England is the most famous example. Contrary to previous belief, it is no longer certain that they were all astronomical observatories; many served instead as places of ancestor worship and cults of the dead.

AROUND 4000 BC

> 3400 BC: In Egypt, the first settlements completely surrounded by walls are built.

> 3200 BC: The people in Central and South America begin to cultivate maize.

> 3000 BC: Builders in what is today Peru construct the first houses with balconies.

The remarkable prehistoric monuments known as megaliths are to be found particularly along the coastlines of western and northern Europe, as well as in the British Isles. The name "megalith" comes from Greek and means "large stone." Many different variations of these colossal places of worship were built during the transition from the early Neolithic period to the Bronze Age (4,000–2,500 BC). But what were they for?

The search for the people who built these structures with great feats of strength and without any means of transport or knowledge of the wheel leads to the first European farmers. After the end of the Ice Age when the hunting and gathering way of life started to change, in about 5000 BC, people started to settle down. They tilled the fields and kept animals. Although village communities usually lasted only for one season, their places of worship, the megalithic monuments, were built to last. They were often built in a place within reach of several such villages, forming a meeting place and center for rituals.

It is particularly the circle monument of Stonehenge, built rela-

tively late (around 2000 BC), that encourages archaeologists in the belief that all the megalithic monuments served as celestial observatories. But this is probably only true of a few of them. The attempt to draw parallels to the cultures of the Middle East, such as the Babylonians or the Egyptians who were practiced in astronomy, leads nowhere. Nor can the theory that travelers from the Middle East built the megaliths be substantiated. An analysis of the various dates of building shows that many of the northern European megalithic constructions are actually older than the Egyptian pyramids or even than the tombs of Mycenae, which are often cited as an example. It is most probable, therefore, that the megalithic constructions are a purely European manifestation and originated at different places nearly at the same time.

The question of their meaning can be searched for in the stone circles themselves. In several, there are traces of burnt human bones. It is reasonable to think that they were used as a central place of burning, such as existed later on the cremation fields in the time of the Romans. As is also the case in Stonehenge, the graves belonging to the megalithic monuments themselves lie in a large circular formation around the monument. The secret of these mystical sites has still to be discovered despite the accumulation of new knowledge.

△ **The most famous example of a prehistoric megalithic construction is the stone circle of Stonehenge.**

The construction of megalithic dolmens such as this is common in Germany, Brittany and Great Britain. They are thought to be burial chambers.

> *c.* 3500 BC: The Sumerians develop the first urban civilization.

> *c.* 3000 BC: Candles are used for the first time in Egypt.

> From 3500 BC: The Egyptian glassblowers add potash, salt or soda to the quartz sand. This lowers the melting point of glass.

△ This prehistoric earthenware bowl was shaped by hand on a supporting slab, a crude yet elaborate technique that was slow and only allowed the production of a few pieces each day.

The potter's wheel: stimulating the production of earthenware

Mesopotamia

The potter's wheel is one of the prehistoric inventions that has had far-reaching consequences, immeasurably influencing everyday life throughout the centuries. With the bow-driven drill, the potter's wheel is acknowledged as the oldest mechanical craft tool developed by man.

The earliest ceramic objects date from the Paleolithic era, about 30,000 BC. These were not vessels but unfired clay figures and reliefs, usually associated with religious rituals and often representing the birds and animals that were hunted, deities, and people. Some of these objects probably fell accidentally into the fire, thus demonstrating how clay objects became stronger with the application of heat. This was the first step in the development of ceramics.

Ceramics were used not only for religious purposes but also for everyday objects such as pots, jugs, and dishes. The earliest earthenware vessels that have been discovered in Japan date from the 11th millennium BC. It was only 3,000 years later that earthenware vessels made their appearance in Mesopotamia. They were subsequently discovered in all other Stone Age civilizations. Potters made all these vessels by hand on a slab on the ground without using a potter's wheel. The earthenware object was then dried and fired. Some cultures still use this archaic method today, creating earthenware objects of remarkable quality. But the fundamental problem with this method is that earthenware objects can only be produced in small quantities and their production is extremely time-consuming.

In the middle of the 4th millennium BC potters finally discovered the tool that was to influence their craft well into the 19th century: the potter's wheel. This new technique consisted of placing the clay on a rotating disc, thus producing smooth, round vessels quickly and simply. The earliest archaeological evidence of earthenware vessels produced on a potter's wheel was discovered in Mesopotamia. The vessels date from the Uruk-Warka period (mid-4th millennium BC) and at first were produced using a combined technique of building up and turning. Later pots were produced entirely on a potter's wheel. This new technology soon spread from Mesopotamia via Crete to Greece and from there to the western Mediterranean. In Asia the earliest examples were found in China and date from the Longshan dynasty (*c.* 2700–1900 BC).

The potter's wheel as it is known today was at first a simple development of the non-centered disc or ground slab. It then developed into a primitive potter's wheel pivoting on a central pin before finally acquiring its present form. It was only when increasingly higher speeds required greater stability that a solid axis anchored to the floor was introduced. Among the motive power used to operate the early potter's wheels were the hands, belt drive, and shaft drive. In the latter case spoked wheels were frequently used instead of discs.

The potter's kick wheel driven by the foot is a Ptolemaic invention dating from the 1st century BC. This potter's wheel was used until the introduction of industrial mass production in the 19th century. The great advantages of the disc wheel were its quiet running and its momentum, which made it rotate more steadily.

The mass production of ceramics became possible with the invention of the potter's wheel that traveled from Mesopotamia via Crete to Greece.

The story of astronomy: Dreams and reality

Looking at the heavens

The starry sky has fascinated mankind since time immemorial and has always been a source of numerous questions. How far are the visible planets from the earth? How big is the universe? Where does the cosmos end? How was the earth created? The burning desire to grasp the incomprehensible was shared by scholars of the ancient cultures of Egypt, Babylon, and China 3,000 years before the birth of Christ. With impressive concentration they set about searching for the origin of the cosmos, which was shrouded in mystery. As they watched the heavens systematically and persistently, these early stargazers learned how to calculate when special events were to take place, such as eclipses of the sun or the moon, and the movements of the planets. However, astronomy served mainly for the determination of dates and marking the seasons, so that farmers, for instance, would know when the time for sowing or reaping had arrived.

The center of the universe

The essential question as to what point of the cosmos should be recognized as its center has changed radically through the ages. For a long time astronomers were convinced that the earth was the center of everything. In the distant past it was thought that the earth was flat, in the form of a disc, and that it rested on the ocean. However, astronomers in ancient times knew that it had the form of a globe and rotated on its own axis. In both cases, though, it was an unquestioned fact that the earth was the center of the cosmos. This geocentric world view was first challenged by Aristarchus of Samos (310–230 BC). The Greek astronomer suggested that it was in fact the sun and not the earth that was positioned at the center. However, this new (and correct) way of thinking failed to gain aceptance for almost another 2,000 years.

It was the Alexandrian scholar Claudius Ptolemy (*c.* 90–*c.* 160 BC) who reinforced the ancient view of the earth as the center of the universe. His theory of deferents and epicycles attempted to explain many of the anomalies observed in the movements of the planets.

It was only after the Middle Ages that the doctor and astronomer Nicolaus Copernicus (1473–1543) created an important milestone in the development of astronomy when he declared that the sun was at the center of the movement of the planets. This revolutionary idea caused intense turmoil in religious and philosophical circles, which continued to resist this view vehemently. Even one hundred years later the astronomer Giordano Bruno (1543–1600) was burnt at the stake for supporting the teachings of Copernicus.

Nikolaus Copernicus (1473–1543)

The sun takes center stage

With the invention of the refracting telescope in the early 17th century, new views of the heavens were finally possible. The astronomer Galileo Galilei (1564–1642) had heard of the invention and built one for himself. Using it, he discovered sunspots, the mountains on the moon, and the moons of Jupiter. The discovery of Jupiter's moons was a resounding sensation. Their mere existence shook the foundations of the belief in the earth's special position as the center of the universe. If all heavenly bodies circled the earth, how could Jupiter have moons revolving around it?

It still took a number of years until the heliocentric view of the world found general acceptance. This was because the inquisitors of the Catholic Church did not want to accept that the earth was not the center of the universe and they silenced Galileo. Under threat of torture they forced

Galileo Galilei (1564–1642)

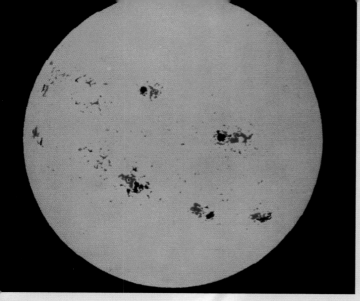

Galileo discovered sun spots while observing the sky with one of the first telescopes.

him to renounce his theories. It actually took until 1992 for him to be officially rehabilitated. However, although he had publicly renounced his belief, the astronomer had no doubt about the truth of his idea. It was clear to him that only the moon revolved round the earth, and that the earth itself revolved round the sun.

The scholar and contemporary of Galileo, Johannes Kepler (1571–1630), also made a key discovery that is still valid today. Kepler was the first to find out that the planets move round the sun in elliptical orbits rather than circular ones, as had been thought for thousands of years.

Soon after, Isaac Newton (1643–1727) established a further milestone in the history of astronomy when he discovered why the planets revolve around the sun. It was his realization that masses attract each other with the force of gravity that explained the phenomenon. The greater the mass of an object, the stronger the force of its gravity. The enormous mass of the sun and the corresponding strength

of its gravitational pull is why the sun governs the solar system. It is calculated that 99.87 percent of the total mass of the solar system is concentrated in the sun.

Isaac Newton
(1643-1727)

New worlds open up

With their telescopes, the astronomers of the 17th century had looked into other galaxies, without actually being aware that they were doing so. They discerned cloudy objects in the heavens that they could not identify more closely.

In the following century, the philosopher Immanuel Kant (1724 –1804) presented a possible explanation for these misty clouds. He assumed that there were countless other star systems in the universe, similar to the Milky Way, that were visible as bands of mist. Nevertheless, astronomers had to study the heavens for 300 years before it was possible to prove conclusively that the Milky Way galaxy is just one of many. This conclusion was reached when large reflecting telescopes became available to astronomers in the early 20th century. In 1917 it was possible to deduce that several nebulous formations in the universe were actually further galaxies.

How did the universe begin?

The American astronomer Edwin Powell Hubble (1889–1953) made a revolutionary discovery that was later to explain the origin of the whole universe. He laid the foundation for the big bang theory with his observation that the universe is not a static system but one that is constantly expanding. If this process is traced back to when it began, logically the point must be reached that reveals the spatial as well as the temporal origin of the universe. The idea of the big bang was born. An alternative cosmology, the steady state theory, assumed the continuous creation of matter, but this has been disproved.

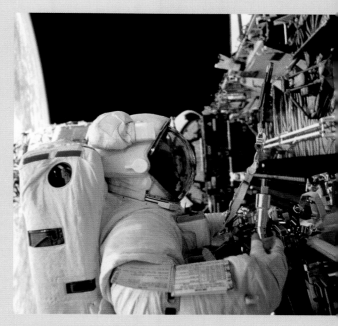

Special telescopes installed in space give today's astronomers views of the universe that were previously unimaginable.

The future

The astronomers of the 20th century have been able to make some astounding discoveries and man has even landed on the moon, the nearest heavenly body to earth. Nevertheless, this is only a tiny step towards the infinity of the universe. In comparison to the total size of the cosmos, the journey to the moon, about 250,000 miles, is infinitesimally short. Most of the other heavenly bodies that are seen as twinkling stars are so unbelievably far away that their light takes billions of years to reach the earth.

In exploring the universe, there is still a great gap between the desire of mankind to know everything about it, and the fact that this is impossible. Although astronomy is one of the oldest natural sciences, even after thousands of years the universe still has an infinite number of secrets to be discovered.

Paper: the basis of bureaucracy

Egypt

AROUND 3500 BC

> *c.* 3500 BC: The Meso-
potamians use nails to join
pieces of wood together.

> *c.* 3000 BC: The Egyptians
make mirrors from polished
copper.

> *c.* 3000 BC: The Nubians
begin mining copper and
gold.

A state can only be governed properly if it has established a bureaucracy, and a bureaucracy has to have written documents and records. This explains why the first material for writing on was invented in a large state with a busy administrative machinery. This state was ancient Egypt.

The direct predecessor of paper was papyrus, made of the reed *Cyperus papyrus* from about 3,500 BC. As this water reed grew only in the Nile delta, papyrus was made chiefly in Egypt. The soft core of the plant was cut into thin strips, soaked, and then rolled out flat.

Papyrus was used for writing on in Egypt from about 2700 BC In the 2nd century BC, King Eumenes II (197–159 BC) of Pergamon in Asia Minor developed the manufacture of parchment from the skins of calves, cattle or goats. This new material gradually took the place of papyrus and was used until well into the Middle Ages.

The cradle of modern paper manufacture, however, was in China. In about AD 105, the imperial administrator Tsai Lun from the province Hunan made a material for writing on by chopping up boiled bark from the mulberry tree, hemp, and old fishermen's nets. He then pounded this in water to make a pulp. He ladled out the fibers on bamboo mats and laid them on flat stones to dry. Thus he created the first sheets of "paper."

China guarded the art of papermaking as carefully as a state secret, which is why it took over 1,000 years for it to find its way from Asia to Europe. Spain was the first European country to manufacture paper in the year AD 1144. Italy followed in 1268 with the construction of a paper mill, and France started to make costly linen and hemp paper in about 1270. The first

German paper mill, the "Gleismühle," was built in Nuremberg by the merchant and town councilor Ulman Stromer in 1390.

Until the beginning of the 19th century, paper was made of rags, which were stored until they had begun to rot, then mashed with great hammers and dissolved in large vats of water. The pulp was then ladled off with shallow sieves and the matted fibers pressed to make the sheets of paper.

Technical progress soon reached the paper mills. In 1798 Nicolas-Louis Robert built a hand-operated machine with which a continuous reel of paper could be made for the first time. In 1840 while searching for new raw materials, the Saxon weaver Friedrich Gottlob Keller discovered a mechanical method of making wood pulp. Together with the paper maker Heinrich Voelter, he applied for a patent in 1846. By 1854 the chemical treatment to make cellulose from wood had been perfected. Wood pulp and cellulose revolutionized the papermaking industry.

However, without the discovery of papyrus by the Egyptians, the period from 3000 BC until well into the Middle Ages would have remained a blank period, unrecorded on the map of cultural history.

△ **The ancient art of paper-making is still practiced by a few enthusiasts.**

To make paper, rags were beaten and dissolved in a barrel full of water. The resulting pulp was then skimmed off, pressed and dried.

Bronze: the most important raw material of the period

Mesopotamia, Egypt, China

For over 2000 years bronze, an alloy of copper, served mankind as the most important material for making arms and armaments, craft appliances, jewelry, and, most importantly, tools. It was widespread in all early cultures and gave its name to a whole era of history, the Bronze Age.

3000 BC

AROUND 3000 BC

> *c.* 3000 BC: In Europe people are using copper to make tools.

> *c.* 3000 BC: Settlements spring up in northern Germany, Denmark and southern Scandinavia.

> *c.* 2750 BC: King Gilgamesh ascends the throne in the Mesopotamian city of Uruk.

Whether in the Mediterranean region, in India or in China, all early advanced civilizations used bronze as the most important material for a shorter or longer period of their history. Bronze is an alloy, a mixture of several metals, normally copper and tin. The Egyptians first used copper primarily for the production of weapons and tools. It is not known when and where it was first discovered that the soft metal copper could be melted with tin to form the harder and more resistant bronze metal. The oldest dated bronze objects date from the beginning of the 3rd millennium BC and they were found in the Middle East, on Crete, and in Egypt.

At that time it was not an easy matter to make bronze. The main problem lay in obtaining tin. Possible mining areas lay in Iran and on Cyprus. Only from 1600 BC, when the Egyptians became able to acquire sufficient quantities of tin for themselves, did bronze play a practical role for them. The craftsmen of the Indus culture, on the other hand, owned very productive deposits, and their bronze contained up to 15 percent tin.

The new bronze tools entirely revolutionized many crafts. Metal saws, chisels, and knives for woodcarving were used in the manufacture of furniture, as well as for building and in shipbuilding applications. By about the middle of the 2nd millennium BC the Chinese proved to be masters of bronze casting. Bells and complete carillons were superb examples of their metal-casting skills.

Weaponry also profited from the new material. The Greeks were masters of the manufacture of bronze weapons and armor, for example. Bronze helmets were already used in the Sumerian city of Ur in about 2500 BC. In Europe, where the helmet came into existence during the time of the Mycenean culture, that is at about 1300 BC, it was at first manufactured from leather. The earliest helmets of classical antiquity were normally made of bronze. A particularly elegantly shaped example was the Corinth helmet with its large cheek tabs and conspicuous nose guard, as is shown in many pictures on Greek vases.

Famous early bronze helmets of European culture range from the Etruscans as well as from Denmark. Cultural fame has been achieved by two bronze horn helmets that were found at Viksö in Denmark, which date from the 8th century BC.

The name "Bronze Age" was introduced in 1836 by the archaeologist Christian Jürgensen Thomsen (1788–1865). Today the Bronze Age in central Europe is understood to mean the period between 2200 and 800 BC but in the Middle East it covers the period between 3500 and 1600 BC. From about 1000 BC the copper-tin alloy was ousted by the harder iron, especially for weapons manufacture.

In ancient civilizations bronze was, with iron, the best material for making weapons and armor, as in this Viking shield back.

Hieroglyphs: holy signs for important words

Egypt

The desire to communicate by means of words and pictures is the characteristic that has always distinguished man from other living creatures. It is therefore not surprising that the early advanced civilizations of the Middle East were deeply involved in the lengthy cultural development of communication from the early cave-paintings to notches in clay tablets and finally to the scripts of today.

> *c.* 2950 BC: King Narmer unifies Lower and Upper Egypt, becoming the first pharaoh and the founder of the First Dynasty.

> *c.* 2750 BC: Egypt introduces a lunar calendar. The year is 365 days in length and begins with the appearance of Sirius in the night sky. This is July 19 in the modern calendar.

> *c.* 2500 BC: The first Egyptian mummies date from this period.

The complex cuneiform script had been developed in Southern Mesopotamia by the end of the 4th millennium BC. One of the oldest examples was the cuneiform script used by the Sumerians, who used a spatula-shaped tool to impress simplified pictographs representing words on clay tablets. Under the influence of other civilizations, the cuneiform script developed into a phonetic script with about 1,000 signs that were also understood by neighboring peoples, and were mainly used when exchanging commercial goods.

Hieroglyphs developed in Egypt in about 3000 BC, immediately after the union of Upper and Lower Egypt to form one large kingdom. The term is derived from the Greek words "hieroglyphikos grammata" meaning "holy signs." Because the Egyptians believed that the script had been invented by the god Thot, they also called hieroglyphs "words of god." Compared to the Roman alphabet of 26 characters, Egyptian hieroglyphs have 800 signs. One of the distinctive feature of hieroglyphs is the absence of vowels. By 2500 BC the Egyptians were using two types of scripts: hieroglyphs, which were engraved in stone or other durable material and were only used for formal texts, and the simpler, more fluent hieratic script, usually written in ink on papyrus.

The two scripts were based on the same principle, being divided into phonetic signs (phonograms), which are signs expressing meaning rather than sound (semograms), and determinatives, which are signs that explain the meaning of a word in a particular connection. The use of hieroglyphs was limited to an educated elite, the scribes, who held important positions in the administration and government of the country. The hieratic script was simplified in the 7th century BC, resulting in the development of the demotic script for everyday use.

In about 1200 BC the Phoenicians who lived in Asia Minor developed a completely new script: a consonant alphabet consisting of 22 characters. This first syllabary was gradually introduced into Greece by merchants. The Greek alphabet expanded the phonetic system to include vowels, thus making possible a complete, phonetically accurate reproduction of the written word.

The hieroglyphs that had been used for 3,500 years and then fallen into oblivion were eventually deciphered by Champollion in 1822. The key to this deciphering was the Rosetta Stone, a trilingual stone of polished black basalt that a soldier in Napoleon's army found in 1799 near Rosetta in the Nile delta. By studying and comparing the inscriptions saying the same thing in hieroglyphs, demotic, and Greek script, scholars were able to decipher the secret of the ancient scripts and thus discover important information about the early advanced civilizations of the ancient world.

The use of hieroglyphs, the "words of god," was limited to the intellectual elite in society.

Pure gold: pure luxury

Egypt and Nubia

Because gold is relatively soft, it was used only for precious vessels and jewelry, and never for tools and weapons. It has therefore always been considered a luxury good. Gold was much sought after by rulers because it symbolized power and authority; thus Midas, the legendary Phrygian king, wished that everything he touched would turn to gold.

3000 BC

AROUND 3000 BC

> *c.* 3000 BC: The Sumerian city states carry on a lively trade reaching into the Indus valley.

> *c.* 3000 BC: Cuneiform script evolves from the Mesopotamian pictographic writing system.

> *c.* 3000 BC: There are two kingdoms on the Nile: Lower Egypt in the Nile Delta and Upper Egypt on the upper reaches of the Nile.

△ The symbols of earthly power used to be artistically represented by delicate gold filigree work.

Metalwork originated in the Middle East. In the 4th millennium BC several civilizations in Asia Minor and north-east Persia had acquired the skills necessary to mine metals and melt them. This knowledge subsequently spread across the Aegean to Europe as well as to Africa and Asia. As early as 3000 BC Egyptian goldsmiths used gold from Nubia.

The prerequisites for metalwork were the availability of charcoal and the invention of the bellows in the 4th millennium. Bellows were used to increase the fire's temperature by supplying a greater volume of air and targeting it accurately. The skills that potters had acquired through their experience in using fire, their knowledge of kilns, and their skill in the regulation of temperature, were extremely useful to goldsmiths. The basic characteristics of metalwork hardly changed until the 18th century, when they were replaced by industrial processes.

Mining gold was a comparatively simple but labor-intensive operation. In alluvial deposits it could simply be separated from the earth by water, as in the technique of gold panning, or the auriferous ore could be mined and then crushed. Since gold only occurs in nature alloyed with silver, copper, and iron, the next operation consists of purifying it by melting it in a cupola, or by amalgamation with mercury. If the naturally occurring gold contains a high percentage of silver, it is known as electrum. In ancient times this was highly regarded as a metal in its own right.

In antiquity gold was found mainly in Egypt and in Nubia, whose name means "land of gold." In Greece gold was found on the islands and in Thrace, while the Romans opened up new mines in Spain and Dacia, the present-day Romania.

Because the demand for gold objects continued to rise, an increasing number of goldsmiths opened up workshops. The technical repetoire of these highly skilled craftsmen has hardly changed since the times of the Pharaohs. The most important techniques used by goldsmiths are filigree, granulation, drawing, casting, soldering, chasing, and engraving, as well as the gilding of objects made of other materials. The softness of gold meant that it could only be used for vessels, jewelry and other decorative objects; it was not hard enough for weapons or tools. Today gold jewelry is still one of the commonest ways of expressing personal wealth. While in the Bronze Age gold jewelry was exclusively reserved to the ruling classes, in classical Grecce and Rome it also became affordable for the middle classes.

Gold objects made for burial purposes in ancient Egypt included coffins, shrines, and death masks. These death masks were not always made from solid gold but were often covered with gold leaf. A superb example of the use of gold in burial is the gold treasure of the Egyptian Pharaoh Tutankhamun, who ruled 1358–1350 BC. His tomb was discovered by the archaeologist Howard Carter in 1923.

Pharaoh Tutankhamun's chair with its golden back embellished with filigree. Precious metal has always symbolized power and authority.

The wheel: accelerator of the course of history

Mesopotamia

△ **This medieval illustration of the wheel decorates an initial lettre from the Corbie psalter dating from the 8th century.**

Without the invention of the wheel, the cultural history of mankind would have been quite different. Mass migration, military campaigns or the conquest of new regions would all have been more laborious without wheeled transport. Wagons were essential for carrying heavy materials for the building of houses or places of worship. In many cultures the endless movement of the wheel also symbolized the divine infinite.

Even when people settle in a certain place, they still need a certain amount of mobility, be it to go hunting or to explore the region. The relevant concerns of early peoples were to visit as many places as they could in one day to collect food such as wild herbs and plants, or to hunt, then to transport this food home again as quickly and easily as possible. On foot this was arduous and slow. Later the need for greater supplies and more building materials for houses grew proportionately with the size of settlements. The population needed greater quantities of wood for fuel and building. A large part of this strenuous transport work was carried out by horses and oxen.

The idea of the wheel eventually grew out of the method of laying tree trunks together to form rollers. In the 3rd millennium BC, the Mesopotamians sawed massive slices off the trunks, connected them to axles and attached them to wagons. The oldest known illustration shows such wagons as vehicles of war: the "Mosaic Banner of Ur" (*c.* 2,600 BC) depicts a procession of soldiers with horse-drawn chariots.

Soon, however, it was apparent that solid wooden wheels could not support very heavy loads. In order to spread the pressure more evenly, the wheelwrights constructed a disc made of several segments of a circle. The axle was either fixed or movable. Shortly after this the technological advances led to a disc wheel with an inserted hub that was also interchangeable. The wheel gauge of all known prehistoric wheeled vehicles was about 4 ft. The wheels that came later with half-moon shaped holes in them were lighter than solid ones, but vulnerable to a stick getting caught in the holes. From 2000 BC the Mesopotamians started to manufacture lighter, more maneuverable wheels with spokes. These were less sturdy than the others and broke more easily, so they were only suitable for carrying light loads. War chariots carrying one person were usually fitted with spoked wheels. Normally only the ruler would drive such a chariot on a military campaign. This type of vehicle needed suitable horses, light-footed and specially bred for this purpose.

North of the Alps, wheeled vehicles were used less than in the Mediterranean area because of the damper conditions underfoot. Here it was not until the expansion of the road network under the Roman empire that the transport of goods and traveling in wagons became commonplace. During the Bronze Age, spoked wheels cast from metal finally superseded wooden wheels.

Having neither a beginning nor an end, the wheel played a role in religion. The ancient Greeks thought that the sun was pulled across the sky by a wheeled chariot, and sun gods such as Helios, Phaeton or the sea god Poseidon all drove chariots. Thus the infinite turning of the wheel come to symbolize the power of fate.

The oldest representations of the wheel show them fitted to chariots, as on this Greek vase dating from the 8th or 7th century BC

The pyramids: mysterious monuments for god-kings

Pharaoh Djoser (c. 2644-2623 BC)

The fascination exercised by the monumental graves of the pharaohs of ancient Egypt continues unbroken. 4,500 years after they were built, these last remaining wonders of the ancient world are still the most mysterious constructions of mankind.

With the step pyramid in Saqqâra the pharaoh Djoser and his architect and doctor Imhotep introduced a new era in the art of building. Until this time the kings of Egypt had been buried in mastabas, tombs with sloping sides and flat roofs. These were underground grave chambers, the upper part of which consisted of rooms for religious purposes and chambers for the burial objects. The Djoser burial complex, the first monumental stone construction built by the Egyptians, was a structure with six mastabas constructed one above the other, reaching a height of 200 ft. The temple area, the pyramid itself, was for honoring the dead king.

The actual inventor of pyramid construction is regarded as the pharaoh Snefru (2575–2551 BC). He had several such structures built, among them the step pyramid in Meidum and the monument known as the red pyramid in Dahshur, where he himself was buried. This pyramid made of blocks of red limestone, with sides 720 ft long and 345 ft high, had an ingenious burial chamber system. The most spectacular of the Egyptian burial monuments is the pyramid complex built on the stone plateau at Giza, 8 miles west of Cairo. These monuments were built by the pharaohs Cheops, Chephren, and Mykerinus.

The Cheops pyramid is the largest pyramid in the world. It covers an area of 13 acres and was originally 482 ft high. The four sides squarely face the four points of the compass and are 365.24 "pyramid meters" long, the number of days in a year. A "pyramid meter" is about 2 feet, which is one ten-millionth part of the polar radius of the Earth. Some of the corridors are also placed in precise relation to the stars, for instance the North Star. Were the pyramids therefore astronomical observatories? The astronomical features are not to be denied, and it is quite likely that the Egyptians had a profound knowledge of astronomy. Their builders must also have been skilled in mathematics. The circumference of the area of a pyramid is almost identical to the circumference of a circle whose radius equals the height of the pyramid. So if the circumference of the pyramids is divided by twice the height, the result is 3.14. Were the ancient Egyptians perhaps familiar with the factor pi?

The tomb consists of about 2.5 million blocks of limestone that are laid on top of each other in 105 steps. According to the latest calculations, almost 36,000 stonelayers, engineers and laborers worked on the construction. A further 10,000 stonemasons were occupied in the underground quarries of Tura on the east banks of the Nile, quarrying the white stone used for covering the pyramid. Since Cheops only reigned for 23 years, 800 tons of stone must have been quarried, transported, dressed and laid daily. It is not known how this was achieved.

The period of the great Egyptian pyramids only lasted about 100 years (2551–2472 BC), just a moment in time compared to the years they have endured. As yet their secrets have not been revealed.

△ The mastaba or step pyramid of Saqqâra heralded the age of the Egyptian pyramids.

Pyramids. These surviving "wonders of the world" from antiquity still conceal many mysteries today.

△ Representation of a comet dating from 1532.

Comets: the first record of a comet's appearance

China

Reports of comets survive from every ancient culture, from Greece and Egypt to Babylonia and particularly China. From earliest times these heavenly appearances spread fear and terror, although the actual impact of a comet seldom caused much damage.

Chinese astronomers in the Stone Age were already carefully observing the heavens. It was recognized that many stars had constant positions in the heavens and ran on regular courses across the firmament. Astronomers inferred from this that the gods had created the heaven as invariable. They divided it into "moon houses" or constellations, groups of neighboring stars. By the second half of the 3rd century BC, Chinese astronomers had recorded 283 constellations with a total of 1,464 individual stars in 28 moon houses. In 550 BC they built the first armillary sphere, a three-dimensional model of the heavens, with whose help they could recognize the position of the heavenly bodies. The earliest Chinese book on astronomy dates from the 4th century BC and contains a record of the equatorial coordinates of 115 stars and 28 moon houses.

If phenomena that deviated from the norm appeared in the sky, people reacted to it with fear and insecurity. Priests of the Shang dynasty, 1500–1000 BC, carved records of solar and lunar eclipses on tortoiseshell and bones. Comets in particular were associated with disaster. These shooting stars with tails did not fit into the usual heavenly picture: they vanished as suddenly as they had appeared, and they looked quite different from "normal" stars. At that time the course of a comet could not be forecast and it cut across the orbits of other planets.

Chinese priest-astronomers were probably the first to observe these unusual heavenly bodies in the year 2296 BC. These astronomers were closely associated with the imperial house and its rule, discussing the prevailing political and religious questions of the time. Their observations mainly served the immediate practical application of government business and they were not interested in developing an independent astronomical theory.

From the 11th century BC written records of comets and meteorite swarms increased. Halley's comet for example appeared a total of 31 times over China in the course of the centuries. In AD 635 Chinese astronomers recognized that the direction of the comet's tail was always turned away from the sun. The earliest illustration of a comet was found in a book with silken sides that was discovered in a grave in 168 BC. A total of 250 drawings depict comets, clouds, rainbows and constellations of stars. However, this book was probably illustrating a range of possible appearances of heavenly bodies rather than representing comets that had actually been sighted.

In that comets had spread fear and terror throughout the world for thousands of years, their true nature seemed almost prosaic when it was discovered. A comet originates from a core of ice that mainly contains water and cosmic dust. When it approaches the sun, its tail is partially transformed into a gaseous state. The comet scientist Fred Whipple once aptly compared its appearance to a "dirty snowball."

A comet falling on earth rarely caused much damage, yet these celestial phenomena have always aroused fear and terror among the population.

Weights, measures, and scales: sound rules for trading

Egypt and Mesopotamia

Uniform measures and weights regulate the exchange of wares and therefore the social structure in a society. Their standardization is necessary for the normal functioning of daily life.

2130 BC

AROUND 2130 BC

> 2650 BC: The Egyptians finally manage to unify Upper and Lower Egypt. They establish a central administration and expand their trade relationships with Asia Minor. A few years later the pharaohs make Memphis their permanent seat of residence.

> 2630 BC: The first pyramid is built near Saqqâra in Egypt.

> In neighboring Mesopotamia the Sumerians govern the land between the Tigris and the Euphrates. They are divided into several city states with the city of Ur at their head.

> Further east, on the Indus and on the Yellow River (*Huanghe*) in China, conditions are ripe for the rise of two other great civilizations.

△ Scales symbolized truth and justice in Egyptian culture.

The rise of the early advanced civilizations in the Middle East, Egypt, and Mesopotamia led to a rapid growth in trade between the sometimes far-flung settlements. Only with weights and measures that could be compared with one another was a smoothly functioning exchange of goods possible.

The problem of standardizing weights and measures lay in choosing suitable units. For length, humans had been using the measures of their own bodies for 5,000 years. For example, a "hand's width," a "cubit" (the length of the forearm, from Latin *cubitum* = elbow), or a "foot" were the original measures, the use of which can be traced back to about 3200 BC. From the early part of the 3rd millennium BC, the Egyptians used the cubit for measuring wood and fabrics. For longer lengths, such as those used in surveying, they used a knotted rope of 100 cubits.

Varied trading activities and a complicated system of taxes obliged the Egyptians to develop accurate methods of weighing and measuring. Until Ptolemaic times (323–282 BC) coins were unknown to the Egyptians, the price of wares being expressed in corn or pieces of copper. These amounts were not uniformly weighed, but gauged using hollow measures, the most widely used one being about 1 gallon. The only thing weighed by the Egyptians with simple beam scales was metal. As a unit they used the "gold standard," which corresponded to a weight of ½ oz. They also used scales with weights for weighing medicine.

Above all, however, the Egyptians saw scales as a symbol of truth and justice. According to Egyptian mythology, in order to be able to enter the realm of beyond, the heart of the deceased was "weighed" by the gods to test the dead person's honesty and justice. Their attendants usually assured the gods, as the palace attendant Hunefer did in 1300 BC, that they had "never reduced the measure of corn" or "pressed on the balance beam," meaning that they had never cheated others.

It appears that the manipulation of weights and measures in order to increase a merchant's own profit was no rarity even in those ancient days. For this reason, the Sumerians had their stone or bronze weights engraved with royal inscriptions, which showed that the weights had been "calibrated." Later proper precision scales were made by the Romans. These Roman *statera* consisted of a weighing dish and a sliding weight that hung from a balance beam with arms of different length and a scale engraved on it. However, these did not solve the problem of the absence of a universal unit of measurement.

Until the 19th century there existed an enormous variety of confusing weights and measures. The metric system sought to replace them by a single standard. On March 30, 1791, the French National Convention decided on the 40-millionth part of the circumference of the Earth as the official unit of length, the original Paris meter.

Since 1875, scientific measurements for length, mass and time have been standardized by the Système International d'Unités (SI units).

The creation of standard weights and measures is one of the most important conditions for the development of advanced civilizations.

Iron: a step along the road to progress

Hittites

> 1715 BC: The Assyrians establish the city of Nineveh.

> 1500 BC: The Minoan palace of Knossos is destroyed by a volcanic eruption. The decline of Minoan rule in the Mediterranean follows.

> 1450 BC: In Egypt the use of bellows in furnaces is discovered. This facilitates the melting of metal.

"Not there, where golden Ceres smiles" said Friedrich Schiller, waxing lyrical, but "where the iron grows in the mountain wilds, there spring lords from the Earth." Indeed iron, the brittle material that the Hittites learned to work before all other peoples, was a guarantee of military and economic power for over two thousand years.

Iron, a silvery-white metal, is the fourth most abundant element on earth and it is regarded as the most important of the heavy metals. Technically, usable iron ore contains between 25 and 70 percent iron. Whereas "pig iron" is not malleable because of its high silicon, phosphorous, and sulfur content, in technical terminology "wrought iron" is used to describe any malleable iron.

In very ancient cultures iron often played only a minimal role. The oldest example of melted and forged iron is a dagger from the middle of the 3rd millennium BC that was found in the ruins of Alaca Hüyük in northern Anatolia in Turkey. About 800 years later, the Hittites, an Indo-Germanic people that populated the eastern part of Asia Minor in 2000 BC, started using the new material instead of copper and bronze. They produced a kind of iron that still contained many impurities and therefore had to be forged, that is, heated till it was red hot and hammered repeatedly. At first the new metal was more elastic than copper but no harder than bronze, and therefore not suitable for all uses. In 1400 BC, Armenian smiths from the southern Caucasus discovered a method of working the metal that started the success story of iron: they hardened, or "steeled," a piece of forged iron by heating it to red heat in a charcoal fire and then plunging it in water.

From 1000 BC, iron accompanied the rise of the great empires of classical antiquity. The Greeks used it for making weapons from the 6th century BC, while in the Alps and Danube region, the Celts proved themselves to be ingenious smiths in the making of hardened steel swords. The Romans set up their first forge for weapons on the island of Elba, where Etruscan blacksmiths hammered at the anvils. The might of the Roman Empire leaned heavily on the new, "steeled" weapons and equipment. Damascene steel, made by combining different kinds of iron and steel together, was the epitome of the art of working iron and steel in late antiquity. As iron ore was found in large quantities, unlike copper or tin, its use spread more and more rapidly. As early as the beginning of the 2nd century BC, daily life could no longer be imagined without iron. In the Celtic town of Oppidum on the Danube, known today as Manching, weapons and tools of all kinds have been found: axes, pincers, scissors, files, wheel tires, nails and needles. The product spectrum of the Roman smithies of the time was no less impressive.

The first blast furnaces for smelting iron ore were built in the 14th century, but blast furnaces were not used on a grand scale until the blasting technique was improved in 1760. The production of iron then sky-rocketed. In the 18th century, iron and steel works produced iron by the pound or kilogram, while by the end of the 19th century they were producing it by the ton. Like steel fortresses, iron works loomed over the industrial landscapes of the 19th and 20th centuries and marked the beginning of the modern age, as did the railroad with its forged iron rails.

Iron, a gift from the gods. For thousands of years military power depended on weapons made of iron.

The compass:
an invaluable guide for travelers

China

AROUND 1200 BC

> **1250 BC:** The Egyptian pharaoh Ramses II builds the Temple of Abu Simbel and his mortuary temple at Thebes.

> *c.* **1250 BC:** The royal scribe Hunnefer writes the Egyptian *Book of the Dead*. It forms the basis for the belief that the dead come before a judge to justify their deeds while they were alive.

> *c.* **1230 BC:** Moses leads the Israelites out of Egypt and back to Canaan.

Before the compass helped them to find their way, humans oriented themselves by the path of the sun, the stars, or by seeking conspicuous landmarks. Only with the compass could they determine directions precisely. Without the compass, Columbus would probably not have dared to search for the sea route to India, Vasco da Gama would not have sailed around Africa, and Magellan would not have circumnavigated the globe.

A precursor of the compass was developed by the Chinese to demonstrate the Earth's magnetic field. A figure stood on a differential gear mounted on the "South Pointing Carriage." This equalized the difference in the number of revolutions between the inner and the outer wheel of the carriage when driving round a corner. The figure was therefore not influenced by the change of direction, but remained stable, the pointing arm always pointing south without fail.

The compass is the oldest instrument for determining direction. It functions on the principle of magnetism. Humans cannot feel magnetic fields with their senses, but the phenomenon was observed in the 5th century BC. The first magnets were discovered when it was noticed that a certain kind of stone, magnetite, attracted small pieces of metal, which collected at the poles of the stone. That the earth also possessed such a magnetic pole was unknown at this time. The earth's magnetic pole is in almost the same place as the north geographic pole. A freely swinging magnetic needle, for instance a needle that has been rubbed on a piece of magnetite, will always swing to lie in the direction of the magnetic pole. Sometimes a large deposit of iron under the surface will cause the needle to deviate slightly, but the overall direction is always correct. The prototype compass consists of a disc, the compass card, marked with the points of the compass, and a magnetic needle that is mounted in the center. From the Sung dynasty (AD 420–479) onwards, scholars of feng shui who were seeking the most auspicious place for a house or a grave used this instrument as one of their tools. The locations they were seeking had to be in complete accord with nature and the cosmic principles of yin and yang. Also in the 3rd century BC, the "sinan" was used. This too was a magnetic pointer with a north-south orientation and was only used for religious purposes. In the year AD 83, the invention of the "south-pointing spoon" followed, a magnetite stone in the form of a Chinese soup spoon lying on a plate of bronze.

The first description of a magnet comes from Shen Kuo and was written about AD 1080. In 1135, Shi Lin Kuang Shi described two special forms of the compass. One was in the form of a wooden fish floating on water with magnetite in its "stomach," and the other was a rotatable wooden tortoise attached to a bamboo pole.

It was also Chinese sailors who first used a compass for navigating on the ocean on their way to India and East Africa. The use of compasses in shipping heralded a new era for trade in the 12th and 13th centuries.

From 1200 onwards, European sailors began to use this practical "navigation system." Subsequently the compass proved invaluable on the great voyages of discovery.

Early Chinese compass. The prototype of this instrument consists of a disc showing the cardinal points.

The spinning wheel: catalyst of textile production

China and India

The rapid development of the loom created a demand for a machine that could produce thread very quickly. The ordinary hand-operated spindle was replaced by the spinning wheel. Together the inventions of the loom and the spinning wheel revolutionized the entire textile industry.

1000 BC

AROUND 1000 BC

> 1100 BC: The Assyrians conquer Babylon.

> 1100 BC: The Ethiopian kingdom arises in Africa.

> 1000 BC: David becomes king of Israel after the death of Saul.

The precise date of the invention of the spinning wheel is unknown. While simple precursors of the spinning wheel were used and mentioned in China and India in 1000 BC, the more sophisticated European version appeared well over 2,000 years later in the 11th century. Before the spinning wheel was invented, people used a very simple method to produce thread, a spindle that was operated by hand. Spinning was one of mankind's basic skills, developed in early civilizations, and it consisted simply of twisting many short fibers into a continuous long one. But in order to achieve this, people had first to recognize the principle of uninterrupted rotary movement in the same direction. The spindle was therefore the most important invention in early textiles.

The earliest evidence of the existence of the spinning wharve (the wooden disc on the spindle serving as a pulley) in all Neolithic civilization dates from 5000 BC. The other element of the spindle was the distaff, on which the fibers waiting to be spun were placed. The spinner would pluck small amounts of fibers from the mass of fibers stored on the distaff and twist them with her fingers to make a continuous thread that she wrapped round the spindle as she kept it rotating with the other hand.

With the further development of the loom and the desire for increasingly colorful fabrics with ever more complicated patterns, the requirement for threads of different qualities rose considerably. The simple hand-operated spindle could no longer meet this growing demand.

Because the wheel as such had already been known for long time, the obvious solution appeared to be to simplify the spinning and bobbin work by using the rotary movement of the wheel. So in the 5th millennium BC it is thought that spinning wheels began to be used in China to produce silk threads. But archaeologically this can only be inferred from the dramatic disappearance of spinning wharves on archaeological sites, which may be ascribed to the introduction of this new production method.

In prehistory and antiquity spinning, like weaving, was women's work; in fact it was considered the responsibility and symbol of the dutiful wife. Ancient tombs were frequently decorated with representations of women spinning while a spindle and distaff are often found inside the tombs of women at various periods of history.

However important the invention of the spindle and spinning wheel may appear, they did not have a deep impact on the everyday life of the population as a whole. They did however ease the everyday work of women, who usually had to make clothes for the whole family as part of the housework.

In the 18th century in England the invention of the spinning jenny, a multiple spinning machine that was used in spinning mills, proved to be a revolutionary innovation. This industrial revolution separated the home and the work place, thus introducing a completely new way of life.

Like weaving, spinning was mainly women's work.

Solar eclipse: the first recorded eclipse of the sun

Assyrian astronomers

People travel all over the world to watch the phenomenon of the sun darkening during an eclipse, a breathtaking natural phenomenon that in antiquity used to alarm people considerably. In ancient civilizations this event was seen a threat and a bad omen for the people and their ruler. Only prayers and expiatory sacrifices could ward off the evil that threatened.

> 753 BC: According to legend, the city of Rome is founded.

> c. 750 BC: The Celts settle the British Isles.

> c. 650 BC: In the Assyrian city Nineveh, a central state archive is established. Decrees, letters and documents inscribed on clay tablets are collected here.

The phenomenon of the solar eclipse occurs when the moon slides between the sun and the earth, partially or completely throwing its shadow onto the earth. The course of the moon round the earth is in the opposite direction of that of the earth around the sun, the ecliptic, but with an inclination of about 5 degrees. Only when the moon is on the point of intersection with the ecliptic is a solar eclipse possible, and this only occurs at the time of a new moon.

For a long time the phenomenon of the solar eclipse was interpreted as a message from a supernatural power and a threat to human civilization. The darkened sun caused panic and seemed to be a sign that the end of the world was near. Solar eclipses were also believed to be responsible for events such as the birth of deformed children. In order to ward off such misfortunes astronomers had to learn to forecast these cosmic phenomena and warn people of their impending occurrence.

Rulers in Mesopotamia paid particular attention to solar eclipses. Asarhaddon and Assourbanipal built numerous observatories during the 7th century, and in the capital Nineveh they set up a central archive, like a ministry of astronomy, that gathered all the information and assessed its value and importance. The archive recorded a total of ten solar eclipses in the course of its 30-year existence (679–648 BC).

The records of the Assyrian astronomers still surprise scientists today with their accuracy.

They recorded for instance the time of a solar eclipse and the place where it could be seen. It was extremely important for the king to know the day of this spectacular natural phenomenon, since a solar eclipse had severe political consequences; it indicated that god was displeased with the earthly ruler and that he was expressing his displeasure by plunging the world into darkness. Frequently this resulted in the death sentence for the ruler. In order to avoid this terrible fate, the ruler usually abdicated shortly before a solar eclipse, choosing a "substitute king" to represent him who then died in the real king's place. The curse was lifted and the king could resume his usual business again.

In the 5th century BC Greek scientists came to realize that solar and lunar eclipses were caused by the relative positions of the celestial bodies in space. As a result Thales of Miletus was able to calculate and thus forecast the solar eclipse of May 28, 585 BC. Independently of one another, Empedocles and Anaxagoras later developed a new concept of the cosmos and the planets. They saw the sky as a sphere with the stars moving along an orbit within it.

In spite of the progress of science, people are still moved by the mystical effect of a solar eclipse, so that when one is expected thousands of people gather to watch the darkening of the sun.

Even today solar eclipses are considered one of the most spectacular celestial phenomena. In pre-Christian times the rulers of Mesopotamia built observatories to observe and record them.

The first aqueduct: supplier of irrigation

Eupalinus of Megara (6th century BC)

A constant water supply played a significant role in the rise of the first great cultures. Without a predictable water supply the farmers could not cultivate their fields and the population would not have had enough to drink. But how could this precious element be obtained in sufficient quantity?

530 BC

AROUND 530 BC

> *c.* 550 BC: Rome introduces the lunar calendar. To begin with, the year is made up of ten months.

> 530 BC: Pythagoras of Samos develops his formula for the lengths of the sides of a right-angled triangle.

> 525 BC: The Persians conquer Egypt and incorporate it into their empire.

△ Drawing dating from AD 52 depicting the Aqua Claudia built by the emperor Claudius.

There were water supply mechanisms in place in ancient Mesopotamia but the architectural achievement of the time is the antique tunnel built by Eupalinus of Megara. This is the central part of a system for conveying water built in 530 BC to supply the Greek city of Samos. The underground pipe ran 1,000 yards to the north face of the mountain Ampelos, traveled under the mountain ridge through a tunnel 1,130 in length, and then for another 550 yards to a covered well. The source was a spring in the village of Aigades, which has now been built over.

When building the tunnel, the workers dug through the rock from both sides. In order to achieve the meeting of the two tunnels, which did not align exactly, a curved section was dug. For the first section the workers had to dig through about 16,000 cu ft of solid rock, for the tunnel with the canal about 54,000 cu ft, and for the city pipe another 5,400 cu ft. As their only tools were hammers and chisels, construction probably took about ten years. The upkeep of the tunnel was almost more trouble than the necessary stabilizing measures that had to be taken. Alluvial loam was constantly being deposited through damaged parts of the clay pipes, of which there were about 4,000.

How could this problem be solved? The Romans built the most sophisticated systems in the antique world for conveying water. The man-made stone aqueducts (from the Latin *aqua* = water and *ducere* = to lead) were made of covered or open channels and were usually carried over arches supported by tall columns. Water from the mountains flowed to the cities along these channels at a slight incline. These long aqueducts supplied households and thermal baths with fresh water and also transported dirty water away from the city.

The first water pipe leading to Rome, the Aqua Appia 10 miles long, was built in 312 BC under Appius Claudius Caecus. Until then people had drawn their supply of the precious element from the Tiber as well as from springs and wells. The first aqueduct to carry water above the earth was the Aqua Marcia built by the order of Marcius Rex in 144 BC. The most spectacular was the Aqua Claudia, begun in AD 38 by the emperor Caligula and completed by Claudius in AD 52. The aqueduct was 43 miles long in all, and the last 6 miles before reaching Rome were built over arches. The most conspicuous part of this construction was the monumental double arch known as the Porta Maggiore. Without a doubt, Rome had the best water supply of all the cities of antiquity. However, it was the Greek Eupalinus who achieved the masterly engineering feat of building a water pipe that supplied about 20,000 people with fresh drinking water for 1,000 years.

Water is a vital commodity. In antiquity water was carried across long distances to where it was needed. Some of the constructions built to achieve this, such as the Pont du Gard near Nîmes shown here, have survived several thousands of years.

Man and writing:
Without letters there is no culture

From pictures to characters

Passing on the knowledge accumulated in the course of time is one of the oldest traditions of human beings. But oral transmission alone would not preserve a cultural heritage forever. Wall paintings and notches cut in sticks provided a way of making information more durable. These lifelike representations and vivid graphic symbols were the precursors of written communication. The fact that they have survived clearly shows that writing is one of the best ways of preserving a cultural heritage.

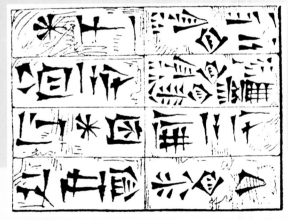

One of the earliest scripts was the cuneiform script that originated in Mesopotamia.

The early pictorial scripts were a representational rendering of events. The oldest remains of such a script were discovered in Mesopotamia and date back to 3000 BC. As time went by, symbols became more abstract and simplified, thus leading to the development of the cuneiform script. At first the characters were related to pictures, then single words, and finally symbols. The characters were made by a stylus in soft clay, and the name "cuneiform" ("wedge-shaped") describes their appearance. Clay was a particularly suitable writing material because it was readily available everywhere, unlike wood, stone, or metal. Small tablets were shaped from soft clay, written on while still pliable, and then left to dry in the air. When the texts were particularly important, the clay tablets were fired to make them even more durable.

The Egyptians on the other hand mainly used papyrus to write on, using hieroglyphs composed of abstract pictorial symbols. As well as being another form in the development of script in 3000 BC, hieroglyphs are particularly important because they are also an essential source of information about Egyptian civilization and everyday life along the Nile.

Even today a script survives that has developed from a pictorial to a word script while retaining its original form. Chinese script is 4,000 years old and is the oldest written language still in use today. Because word scripts are not closely linked to pronunciation, its invention in China with its many languages and dialects provided a new uniformity. The subsequent adoption of the Chinese script by the Japanese and Koreans further contributed to its strength and importance, and showed the cultural power of a common script. Last but not least, the great respect for tradition and sense of responsibility towards their culture that is charateristic of these Asian countries is probably rooted in this common script.

Words become letters

But how did the western alphabet start? Unlike all the scripts mentioned above, the alphabet used letters from the very beginning. The characters no longer represented a partialur meaning, word or syllable, but specific sounds. These alphabets are particularly simple and easy to use, as a simple comparison shows: while most alphabets have an average of 30 characters, a word script such as modern Chinese needs between 6,000 and 8,000 characters merely for ordinary, everyday use. A scientific or technical text can easily increase the number of characters needed tenfold.

All alphabets have a common origin: the North Semitic character script that can be traced back to about 1500 BC. This consisted only of consonants. When the Greeks adapted it later they added vowels and created their own alphabet, which dates from the 8th century B.C. The word "alphabet" comes from the first two letters of the Greek alphabet, alpha and beta. The Greek alphabet played a major part in the cultural development of Europe. The Latin alphabet used in the

The invention of book printing in 1445 enabled scholars to study scientific works and literature.

western world today was derived from the Greek one and became the official script of universal communication .

Writing becomes faster

For centuries writing was a matter of personal handwriting, whether using a stylus or a goose quill. Professional clerks or copyists often spent their entire lives copying only a few books because of the length of time it took. This is why the invention of movable metal type by Gutenberg in 1445 was such an important revolution. The new printing technology considerably speeded up the multiplication of books. It was also more objective than handwritten copied works, and less prone to the mistakes that arose

in copying. It was possible to print as many copies of a book as were wanted, and in addition to ecclesiastical books, classic works of literature and popular writings were now printed. In 1609 the first regularly published newspapers appeared in Wolfenbüttel and Strasbourg, and the expanding range of periodical publications opened up a new type of readership. The invention and spread of printing undoubtedly contributed enormously to the general education of the population.

The importance of documents also increased in many areas of life. For instance, in the world of trade, communicating by writing had become increasingly important because the traveling merchants of the Middle Ages had changed their habits and settled in one place. But even simple correspondence was very expensive because it involved first a draft, then the actual letter, and finally a copy for the merchant's own file, each of which had to be written separately with a quill pen and ink. Therefore the invention of double or multiple quills in the 17th–18th century was great progress. They made it possible to produce two or more copies of a document at the same time by using a wooden holder that linked two quill pens together to produce parallel writing.

In the Middle Ages books were copied by monks by hand and ornamented with superb illuminations. Most of them were religious works.

A number of mechanical devices to facilitate writing were developed during the 18th century, including several ingenious "writing machines" of strange appearance. In 1714 Henry Mill patented a machine that could be described as a typewriter so far as its function was concerned although the concept itself was only put into effect in 1832. Many variations of this new writing machine were developed in order to make writing quicker, easier, and visually more pleasing.

It was not only commerce that benefited from these developments. The author Mark Twain was the first writer to send his publisher a manuscript while keeping a copy, because in 1874 he had bought himself a typewriter for $125. In the next hundred years the development and universal spread of the typewriter led to an enormous increase of text processing in every field.

The computer

The extraordinarily rapid development of micro-electronics displaced the typewriter towards the end of the 20th century, replacing it with computer technology. It has never been easier to work with words than it is today, when software programs enable anyone to carry out complex word processing on a home computer. In this age of "virtuality," writing seems almost to have become dematerialized, no longer dependent on a writing medium and therefore almost invisible. On the other hand, as a result of the ubiquitous multimedia, it has also become prominent. The content may often quickly become obsolete, but writing itself remains one of the most important carriers of information and culture.

> 510 BC: The end of Etruscan rule marks the beginning of the Roman republic. Two consuls govern the city.

> c. 500 BC: Siddhartha Gautama, also called Buddha, the Enlightened, founds the Buddhist faith.

> c. 500 BC: Confucius writes the *Book of Sayings* in which he teaches patience, devotion, strictness towards oneself, and morality.

△ For many centuries the abacus remained an important instrument in the business world. Here it is seen in use in a 16th-century German shop.

The abacus: never was calculating so easy

Egypt, Babylon, Greece, Rome

Even in ancient times, an important requirement for economic activity was that buyers and traders could count the quantity and value of goods accurately. But when dealing with large quantities it was easy for the participants to lose track. To solve this the resourceful mathematicians in the Far East developed a calculating device, the abacus.

Before the Middle Ages when the decimal system became generally accepted in cultures that used Arabic numerals, people represented numerical values as columns of marks. The Babylonians or the Egyptians for example carved large sums in clay or stone in this way. For small quantities it was simple and quick to total the sum on the ten fingers. But with trading and paying for merchandise or the calculation of duties, this method quickly reached its limits. To represent large quantities, the dealers therefore used twigs, grains of corn or stones, each symbolizing a particular number of items of fruit, livestock or sacks of grain.

The Egyptians and the Babylonians arranged the value of goods in groups of ten, after the number of fingers on both hands, while the Romans used groups of five. But they also wanted to add the groups or divide them up without losing track. Following the example of mathematicians who inscribed their geometrical diagrams on drawing boards sprinkled with sand, the traders traced a grid of longitudinal and cross lines in the sand. Each little counting stone had a value assigned to it. The longitudinal columns represented the decimal system in rising sequence from right to left. The units column was followed by the tens column, then the hundreds, and so on. Nine stones lay in each column, each being added from the bottom upwards in the course of counting. When all stones of a column were in the upper part, a new group of ten would be marked by the first stone in the next column. The nine stones of the counting column were moved back to the starting point again. An area in the upper part of the board was divided up crosswise into sections in which the traders noted the respective place values of the stones and the unit or currency. Later the bottom and the side were divided in the same way. This system enabled the four basic arithmetical operations to be carried out.

Soon, devices made of wood, metal or stone replaced the procedure of writing the calculation in the sand. The name for this calculating device, the "abacus," came either from the Greek *abax, abakos*, meaning drawing board, or from a Hebrew word for dust, *abhaq*. The abacus quickly traveled by the trade routes from Babylon and Egypt to Greece and Rome. The respectd profession of arithmetic teachers made people familiar with the abacus, which was a real help in calculation. The Roman government stipulated the use of the abacus for state cashiers' offices and schools. The Romans also developed a transportable version of the device. This hand abacus consisted of a bronze plate the size of a postcard, with eight vertical grooves in which the counter stones were moved up and down. Calculations were made using the base 5 number system.

Even mechanical or electronic calculating machines did not oust the abacus completely. Abacuses are still in use today in China (*suan-pan*), Japan (*soroban*), India, and Eastern Europe (*stschoty*).

The abacus: a calculating aid that is still used today in many parts of the world for carrying out the four basic arithmetical operations.

From magic to modern medicine

Hippocrates of Cos (*c.* 460-370 BC)

Hippocrates of Cos, recognized as the father of medicine, was introduced to the healing arts by his father while still a child. The collection of works published under his name, the *Corpus Hippocraticum*, is still used as the key to understanding the healing methods of antiquity.

Hippocrates, who journeyed through Greece and Asia Minor as a traveling doctor, was renowned in his lifetime as a physician and was an exemplar for many healers. He was responsible for a whole new way of thinking in medicine and his new approach made his work seem almost modern. He tried to recognize the natural causes of illness by objective scientific examination of the patient.

To understand what was so innovative about the medicine of Hippocrates, it must be compared with the healing methods of the pre-classical age. At that time, the healer was influenced by irrational magical and religious thinking. It is true that wounds or illnesses were treated with herbs, but the most important role was played by charms and spells.

Hippocrates radically turned away from magic. The basis of his work was to observe the human body closely and take all influencing factors into account. Apart from the personal constitution of the patient, it was particularly the way of life and nutrition that he noted, as well as the climate in which the patient lived. For the first time it was possible to speak of a "holistic" view of the human being as an individual.

Hippocrates also established the theory of the "four cardinal humors." It held that in the human body there should be an equal balance of the four bodily fluids: blood, phlegm, and two kinds of bile, light and dark. Hippocrates interpreted an imbalance of these fluids as a disease, and the doctor's job was to restore the normal condition. No longer was sickness regarded as a scourge sent by the gods, but it was assumed to be the result of natural causes that could be treated by natural remedies.

The *Corpus Hippocraticum* clearly presented these new views of Hippocrates. However, not all of its texts can be ascribed to him alone since at least 20 different doctors worked as contributors. The work contains medical histories, case studies, notes, and theorems. There is also the famous Hippocratic oath that is regarded as the expression of a self-confident and ancient medical profession that was dedicated to the ideals of ethics and purity and, above all, to the good of the patient:

"I will give my advice and prescriptions to heal the sick to the best of my knowledge and ability. In doing so I shall protect my patients from everything that could damage them or do them harm. Never will I administer a deadly substance or recommend taking such a substance even if I am asked to do so. Never will I help a woman to have an abortion."

Today, although doctors no longer take an official Hippocratic oath, the demand that the life of the patient is to be set above all other considerations is still seen as the basic principle of the ethics of the medical professional. Conflicts arise particularly in the case of abortion, euthanasia, and the use of life-sustaining measures in terminal illnesses.

The work of Hippocrates is vital to the understanding of the ancient art of healing.

HIPPOKRATES

Botany: all about plants

Theophrastus of Eresus (371-287 BC)

Theophrastus of Eresus, a student and successor of Aristotle, was one of the most versatile natural scientists of antiquity. He studied physics, chemistry, medicine and philosophy. His two botanical works were still decisive authorities almost 1,800 years later. He laid the cornerstone of modern botany three centuries before the birth of Christ.

300 BC

AROUND 300 BC

> 333 BC: Alexander the Great defeats the Persians under Darius III in the Battle of Issus. Following this he conquers the whole of Asia Minor.

> 323 BC: After the death of Alexander the Great, his successors, the Diadochi, share out his empire.

> 322 BC: The philosopher Aristotle dies in Chalcis.

Theophrastus came originally from the island of Lesbos. Even as a child, nature held an irresistible fascination for him and he started a large natural science collection. As an adult he went to Athens to join the Peripatetic School of Aristotle (384–322). (*Peripatos* was ancient Greek for "lobby" or"foyer.") After the death of his teacher, Theophrastus was asked to take over the management of the school.

Theophrastus's knowledge of plants was soon to become of enormous value to Aristotle. Alexander the Great (356–323 BC), the Macedonian king and former pupil of Aristotle, undertook countless campaigns between 334 and 324 BC that took him as far away as India. Taking advantage of the opportunities, he turned them into scientific expeditions as well. Alexander ordered many ethnological and scientific observations to be made of the customs of the peoples, the geography of the countries he was passing through, and the plants, animals, and minerals that he found. Theophrastus was then able to evaluate the botanical specimens of Alexander's campaigns.

Aristotle had already given zoology a sound scientific base. Now his student Theophrastus wanted to do the same for botany. Up to this time, plants had been regarded solely with an eye to their potential use. Theophrastus on the contrary, in the spirit of his famous teacher, studied their "nature," categorizing them between inanimate things and animals. He is even supposed to have planted a botanical garden in Athens to aid him in his studies.

In about 300 BC he wrote his botanical works, which still represent the foundation of modern botany. In his *Historia plantarum* ("Natural history of plants"), this meticulous researcher described the external formation of plants with their flowers, leaves, and fruits, and divided them into four groups: trees, shrubs, perennials, and herbs. Even then, Theophrastus recognized the important influence that geographical surroundings and climate conditions have on the growth and characteristics of plants, and he was, therefore, the creator of an early botanical geography. The specimens and observations from Alexander's campaigns in countries in different climate zones were of particular help to him in this. In his second work *Causae plantarum* ("On the causes of plant growth"), he described how plants develop, grow and multiply themselves.

Theophrastus was not acclaimed for these works during his lifetime. In his *Natural History*, Pliny the Elder (23–79 BC) regarded plants simply as useful or not. It was not until the 15th century that the works of Theophrastus turned up in central Europe where they were used for a long time as the definitive work in the teaching and practice of botany. Using his works as a foundation, the "Fathers of Botany," Leonhart Fuchs (1501–66), Hieronymus Bock (1498–1554) and Otto Brunfels (c. 1488–1534) built up the modern study of botany. The extraordinary plant expert from antiquity was eventually recognized when a species of primrose, *Primula theophrastus*, was named after him.

The foundations of botany formulated by Theophrastus in antiquity were further developed in the modern era by Leonhart Fuchs.

Violaten allerley.
Von dem Nammen.

Linius spricht / das die Violblům / nach B
der Roßen vnd Gilgen / etwan vor zeyten bey den Römeren die gröste eere vnnd
preyß habe gehebt vor allen blůmlin / vnnd sey darumb im Kryechischen ion genant. das zů der zeyt als Jupiter (nach poëtischer deütung) die iungkfraw Jo/
in ein ků verwädelt / dz erdtrich auß erber mid diße blůmlin zům ersten hat lassen
wachßen ir zů einer speiß. Deßhalb auch in latin Viola / quasi Vitula genant.

Geschlecht vnd art.

Violaten werden vff fyererley erzelet vom Dioscor. als braune / gelbe / weis-
se / vnd hymmelfarb. Die braunen seind die gemeynen Violaten / die Gelben
Gelb Violaten genant. Die anderen seind so wir Negelblůmen nennen / Ga-
ryophylli zů latin.

Gestalt der braunen / oder purpur
Violaten.

Die braun Violat hat ein blatt dem Ephew gleich / doch minder / zärter /
schwärtzer / vñ vß der wurtzelē gond kleine styclin / an welchen wachßen die blůmlin. reücht wol / wie dañ yederman wol bewißt. Dißes kraut hat keinen stengel
wie andere kreüter / har auch kein öst / bleibet grün winter vnnd summer wo man
es weyß zůhalten / zů aller zeyt dyenstlich der artzeney.

The foundation of geometry

Euclid (*c.* 300 BC)

Around 300 BC, the Greek mathematician Euclid created a system of theories of geometry that was to determine the basis of this science for 2,200 years. Mathematicians of all eras have brooded over his parallel axiom. In the 19th century it became the starting point for modern non-Euclidean geometries.

> From 300 BC onwards: Buddhism spreads across India.

> 298 BC: In the third Samnite War, Rome conquers the Samnites, Umbrians, Etruscans, Sabines, and Lucanians, consolidating its power over all middle and lower Italy.

> 285 BC: An enormous statue of the sun god Helios is erected in the harbor of Rhodes. The Colossus of Rhodes is one of the seven wonders of the ancient world.

Mathematics has always had the most prominent place among the Greek sciences. Thales of Miletus (*c.* 650–560 BC), the oldest known Greek natural scientist, was also the first mathematician. The most famous theorem of Greek geometry was formulated by Pythagoras (*c.* 570–480 BC): "In a right-angled triangle, the square on the hypotenuse is equal to the sum of the squares on the other two sides." It was not just their mathematical skills that differentiated the Greeks from their predecessors in Egypt and Mesopotamia, but rather their striving to give logical proof of the natural laws that they had discovered.

This is what Euclid succeeded in doing. He lived and worked in Alexandria in the Nile delta, the city built by Alexander the Great (356–323 BC) that was the cultural center of the ancient world. His main work, the *Elements*, consisted of a 13-volume compendium containing the complete mathematical knowledge of his day. This treatise turned out to be the most influential mathematical textbook of all time. Alongside a systematic illustration of geometrical fundamentals, Euclid also formulated the "fundamental theorem of arithmetic." This stated that every natural number that is larger than 1 is either a prime number (one that can only be divided by itself), or a product of other prime numbers.

In geometry, Euclid first defined the basic elements: "A point is something with no part" or "a line is length without breadth." Then the famous postulates and axioms followed, basic rules or simple sentences that can be traced back to even more simple ideas. One of his postulates

was "Given two points there is an interval (a straight line) between them," and "All right angles are equal."

Euclid's parallel axiom had particular significance from the beginning. This stated that straight lines or planes always remain at a constant distance from one another, no matter how far they are prolonged.

However, Euclid's direct successors found this axiom somewhat less evident than his other theorems. About 2,200 years later the mathematician Nikolai Lobachevsky (1792–1856) doubted its validity and founded non-Euclidean geometry in protest. According to this, at least two parallels can intersect a point on a given plane. A further difference between the axiomatic theories of today and Euclid's geometry is the belief that no significance as regards content can be given to the basic concepts (the point, the line, and so on).

Further geometries followed that were not based on Euclid's ideas. For instance, the mathematician Bernhard Riemann (1826–66) created a non-Euclidean geometry, giving the example of two ships on a meridian that would meet at the pole. Non-Euclidean geometries found physical application at the beginning of the 20th century in the theory of relativity of Albert Einstein (1879–1955).

The origin and earliest application of geometry (from the Greek "measuring the earth") was the measuring of land.

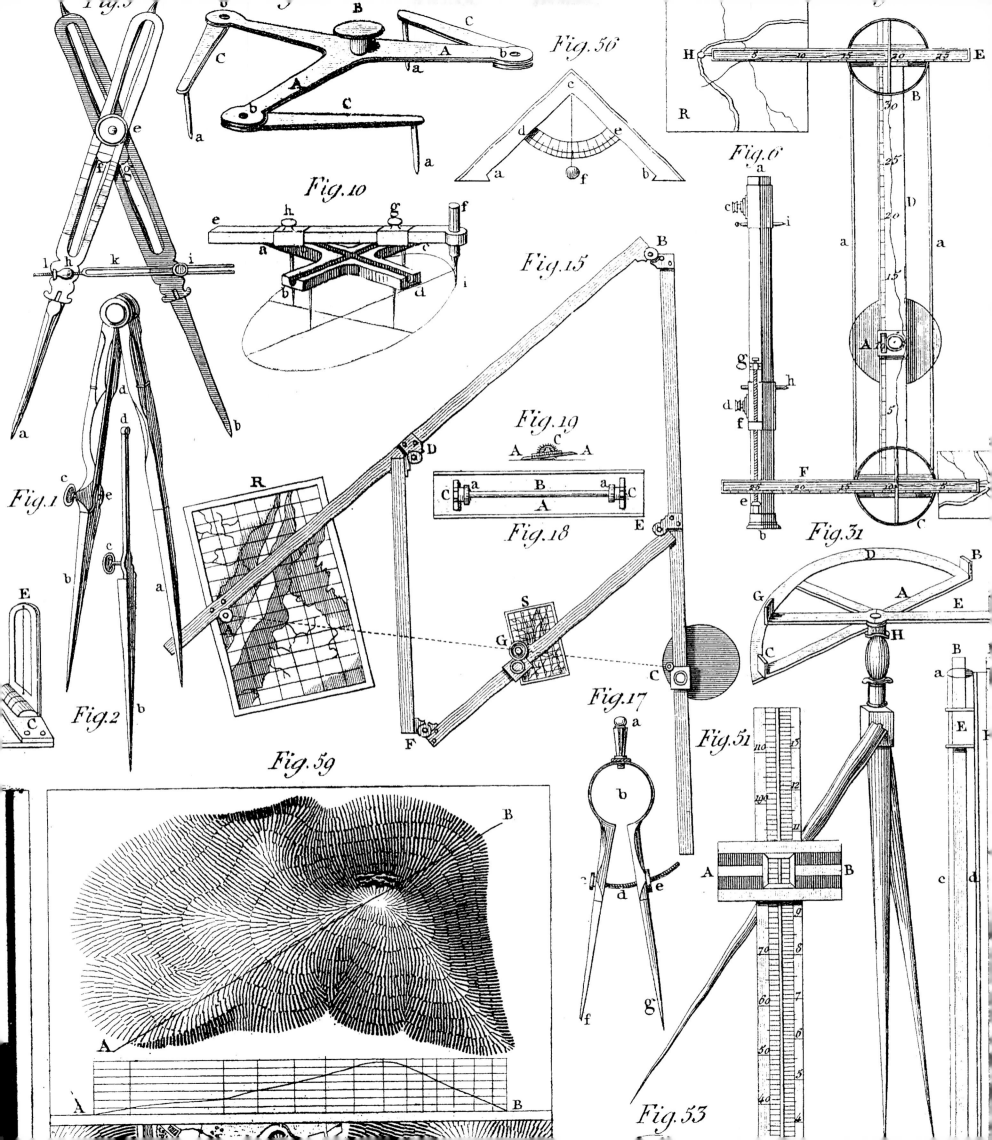

Fig.5

Fig.56

Fig.6

Fig.10

Fig.15

Fig.19

Fig.18

Fig.31

Fig.1

Fig.2

Fig.17

Fig.51

Fig.59

Fig.53

Pi: squaring the circle

Archimedes (285-212 BC), Liu Hui (3rd century AD)

Since time immemorial the circle had been considered the ultimate symbol of perfection. However, the calculation of the area of a circle presented mathematicians with a difficult problem, since it is not a straightforward matter. The calculation of the area of a circle involves the ratio of the circumference to the diameter, the constant known as "pi," which is an irrational number with an infinite number of digits after the decimal point. The mathematician who tackled this problem geometrically with a ruler and compasses to arrive at the first approximate value of pi was a genius.

> *c.* 300 BC: In the Ohio Valley in North America the Hopewell culture comes into being. The Hopewell people build temple mounds and make valuable jewelry that they bury with their dead.

> 300 BC: Rome first allows plebeians to hold public office.

> 270 BC: The first schools for gladiators are established in Rome.

It was already known in the 5th century BC that the surface area of a circle was always in proportion the square of its radius. What was still missing, however, was the mathematical basis on which to calculate this ratio known as "pi," the name of the Greek letter "π" that represents it.

The Greek mathematician Archimedes was the first person to tackle the problem systematically in about 250 BC, and his thought process was as simple as it was brilliant. If one polygon is drawn outside a circle and another with the same number of sides is drawn inside the circle, then the area of the circle will be half the sum of the areas of the two polygons. The larger the number of angles in the polygon, the more accurate the resulting figure for pi.

Archimedes started first with two hexagons – one inside the circle and one outside the circle. By constantly increasing the number of sides he eventually raised the number of angles to 96, and with each increase the polygon became closer to a circle. For the ratio of the circumference to the diameter he arrived at a value of between 3 10/70 and 3 10/71, which made Pi accurate to two decimal places (3.14). This was the first major step on the difficult road towards mastering the circle.

But it was not only in Greece that the circle tested the minds of mathematicians. In China too, albeit later, the mathematician Liu Hui had also developed the "Archimedian" approach of the geometric technique of approximation. He took the process much further than Archimedes and in AD 263 he was able to calculate the correct value of pi to the fifth decimal place (3.14159) by increasing the number of angles of the polygon to 3,072. This made it possible to calculate the surface area of a circle with great accuracy. But one problem still remained.

As well as introducing the concept of infinity into mathematics, the number pi also highlighted the inevitably of approximation and the limits of the exact calculation of the world in figures, since a number that continues endlessly cannot be recorded arithmetically in its entirety. Such a number is known as an irrational number, one that cannot be expressed as the exact ratio of two whole numbers.

It is true that today supercomputers can calculate the value of pi to millions of decimal places, but even these calculations remain incomplete. The fact is that the squaring of the circle would occupy a mathematician for an infinity of lifetimes.

The number pi shows the limitation of the numerical measurement of the world because it cannot be completely recorded arithmetically. Even the long number shown here is incomplete.

3.1415926535 8979323846 2643383279 5028841971 6939937510 5820974944 5923078164 0628620899 8628034825 3421170679
8214808651 3282306647 0938446095 5058223172 5359408128 4811174502 8410270193 8521105559 6446229489 5493038196
4428810975 6659334461 2847564823 3786783165 2712019091 4564856692 3460348610 4543266482 1339360726 0249141273
7245870066 0631558817 4881520920 9628292540 9171536436 7892590360 0113305305 4882046652 1384146951 9415116094
3305727036 5759591953 0921861173 8193261179 3105118548 0744623799 6274956735 1885752724 8912279381 8301194912

9833673362 4406566430 8602139494 6395224737 1907021798 6094370277 0539217176 2931767523 8467481846 7669405132
0005681271 4526356082 7785771342 7577896091 7363717872 1468440901 2249534301 4654958537 1050792279 6892589235
4201995611 2129021960 8640344181 5981362977 4771309960 5187072113 4999999837 2978049951 0597317328 1609631859
5024459455 3469083026 4252230825 3344685035 2619311881 7101000313 7838752886 5875332083 8142061717 7669147303
5982534904 2875546873 1159562863 8823537875 9375195778 1857780532 1712268066 1300192787 6611195909 2164201989

3809525720 1065485863 2788659361 5338182796 8230301952 0353018529 6899577362 2599413891 2497217752 8347913151
5574857242 4541506959 5082953311 6861727855 8890750983 8175463746 4939319255 0604009277 0167113900 9848824012
8583616035 6370766010 4710181942 9555961989 4676783744 9448255379 7747268471 0404753464 6208046684 2590694912
9331367702 8989152104 7521620569 6602405803 8150193511 2533824300 3558764024 7496473263 9141992726 0426992279
6782354781 6360093417 2164121992 4586315030 2861829745 5570674983 8505494588 5869269956 9092721079 7509302955

3211653449 8720275596 0236480665 4991198818 3479775356 6369807426 5425278625 5181841757 4672890977 7727938000
8164706001 6145249192 1732172147 7235014144 1973568548 1613611573 5255213347 5741849468 4385233239 0739414333
4547762416 8625189835 6948556209 9219222184 2725502542 5688767179 0494601653 4668049886 2723279178 6085784383
8279679766 8145410095 3883786360 9506800642 2512520511 7392984896 0841284886 2694560424 1965285022 2106611863
0674427862 2039194945 0471237137 86960955   389 0865832645 9958133904 7802759009

9465764078 9512694683 9835259570 98   476 9909026401 3639443745 5305068203
4962524517 4939965143 1429809190 6   509372 2   46151 570   87 4105978859 5977297549 8930161753 9284681382
6868386894 2774155991 8559252459   95943104 9 24680 845   36 4469584865 3836736222 6260991246 0805124388
4390451244 1365497627 8079771569 435997700 1 60894 416   55 5848406353 4220722258 2848864815 8456028506
0168427394 5226746767 8895252138 5225499546 6   782398 64   16 3548862305 7745649803 5593634568 1743241125

1507606947 9451096596 0940252288 7971089314   136867 22   405 6010150330 8617928680 9208747609 1782493858
9009714909 6759852613 6554978189 3129784821   989487 22   485 7564014270 4775551323 7964145152 3746234364
5428584447 9526586782 1051141354 7357395231   716610 21   536 2314429524 8493718711 0145765403 5902799344
0374200731 0578539062 1983874478 0847848968   445713 86   435 0643021845 3191048481 0053706146 8067491927
8191197939 9520614196 6342875444 0643745 1   921799 9 591 9561814675 1426912397 4894090718 6494231961

5679452080 9514655022 5231603881 93014   3785595 6   87 08303 697 9207734672 2182562599 6615014215
0306803844 7734549202 6054146659 2520   50732518 6   3408 9071 0486331734 6496514539 0579626856
1005508106 6587969981 6357473638 405   028970641 40   9039 7595156771 5770042033 7869936007
2305587631 7635942187 3125147120 532   618612586 732   488291 6447060957 5270695722 0917567116
7229109816 9091528017 3506712748 5832   8 3520935396 57251   791513698 8209144421 0067510334 6711031412

6711136990 8658516398 3150197016 5151168517 1437657618 3515565088 4909989859 9823873455 2833163550 7647918535
8932261854 8963213293 3089857064 2046752590 7091548141 6549859461 6371802709 8199430992 4488957571 2828905923
2332609729 9712084433 5732654893 8239119325 9746366730 5836041428 1388303203 8249037589 8524374417 0291327656
1809377344 4030707469 2112019130 2033038019 7621101100 4492932151 6084244485 9637669838 9522868478 3123552658
2131449576 8572624334 4189303968 6426243410 7732269780 2807318915 4411010446 8232527162 0105265227 2111660396

6655730925 4711055785 3763466820 6531098965 2691862056 4769312570 5863566201 8558100729 3606598764 8611791045
3348850346 1136576867 5324944166 8039626579 7877185560 8455296541 2665408530 6143444318 5867697514 5661406800
7002378776 5913440171 2749470420 5622305389 9456131407 1127000407 8547332699 3908145466 4645880797 2708266830
6343285878 5698305235 8089330657 5740679545 7163775254 2021149557 6158140025 0126228594 1302164715 5097925923
0990796547 3761255176 5675135751 7829666454 7791745011 2996148903 0463994713 2962107340 4375189573 5961458901

9389713111 7904297828 5647503203 1986915140 2870808599 0480109412 1472213179 4764777262 2414254854 5403321571
8530614228 8137585043 0633217518 2979866223 7172159160 7716692547 4873898665 4949450114 6540628433 6639379003
9769265672 1463853067 3609657120 9180763832 7166416274 8888007869 2560290228 4721040317 2118608204 1900042296
6171196377 9213375751 1495950156 6049631862 9472654736 4252308177 0367515906 7350235072 8354056704 0386743513
6222247715 8915049530 9844489333 0963408780 7693259939 7805419341 4473774418 4263129860 3099888687 4132604721

5695162396 5864573021 6315981931 9516735381 2974167729 4786724229 2465436680 0980676928 2382806899 6400482435
4037014195 1496589794 0924323789 6907069779 4223625082 2168895738 3798623001 5937764716 5122893578 6015881617
5578297352 3344604281 5126272037 3431465319 7777416031 9906655418 7639792933 4419521541 3418994854 4473456738
3162499341 9131814809 2777710386 3877343177 2075456545 3220777092 1201905166 0962804909 2636019759 8828161332
3166636528 6193266863 3606273567 6303544776 2803504507 7723554710 5859548702 7908143562 4014517180 6246436267

9456127531 8134078330 3362542327 8394497538 2437205835 3114771199 2606381334 6776879695 9703098339 1307710987
0408591337 4641442822 7726346594 7047458784 7787201927 7152807317 6790770715 7213444730 6057007334 9243693113
8350493163 1284042512 1925651798 0694113528 0131470130 4781643788 5185290928 5452011658 3934196562 1349143415

The heliocentric view of the world: the sun takes center place

Aristarchus of Samos (c. 310-230 BC)

The sun does not rotate around the earth but the earth rotates around the sun, the center of the cosmos. Formulated by the astronomer Aristarchus of Samos in 280 BC, this "heliocentric" view of the world was a revolutionary opinion that science and the Church did not accept for several centuries.

The astronomer Aristarchus of Samos was the first person to demonstrate that the earth rotates around the sun, and that it is the sun that is the center of a spatially limited cosmos. Aristotle, 384–322 BC, an authority in the field of the natural history, had already suggested this theory. He had proved that the earth is round, for example, basing this theory on the fact that the earth's shadow on the moon is always round. He solved other astronomical and physical problems that were consistent with the state of knowledge as it then was. His opinion was therefore respected.

Nevertheless, this view of the world yielded some incongruities; for instance the orbits of some of the planets seemed to wander to-and-fro in their orbits instead of rotating smoothly round the earth. However the scientists ignored these puzzles, or they tried to explain them by an older theory that postulated a "central fire," around which the sun itself, the earth, and the planets moved in concentric circles.

In his works that are unfortunately only preserved as fragments, Aristarchus explained very precisely that the sun was the immovable center in the universe, while the earth and all the other planets moved round it. Aristarchus also recognized that the earth rotated once round its own axis in the course of a day, while the sun and the fixed stars remained immovable.

But how had the scientist arrived at these astonishing conclusions? Aristarchus based his heliocentric theory on his calculations of the distances between the earth, moon, and sun, and their relative sizes. According to him, the sun was 20 times further away from the earth than the moon and seven times larger than the earth. It therefore seemed more logical to him that the sun, which was considerably larger than the earth, should be regarded as the center of the universe. By the knowledge of today, these values were admittedly low estimates, but compared to earlier statements, they were revolutionary, as were his conclusions. His contemporaries therefore accused him of disregarding religious laws.

In the years that followed, scientists heatedly discussed the new "heliocentric" philosophy. The astronomer Ptolemy (c. 100–160 BC), for example, knew of the theory of Aristarchus, but with his Ptolemaic system he consciously decided on the geocentric universe.

Nicholas Copernicus (1473–1543) was able to refute this incorrect assumption scientifically in about 1500. He recognized that the heliocentric theory solved many astronomical problems with one stroke. From fear of the Inquisition Copernicus did not publish his results for a long time, and when they finally appeared they were immediately banned by the Catholic Church. Only in the year 1996 did Pope John Paul II accept the teachings of the Copernicus and consequently those of the Aristarchus.

Aristarchus of Samos placed the sun at the center of the planetary system three centuries before the birth of Christ. It was only 1,800 years later that science and the Church finally accepted his views.

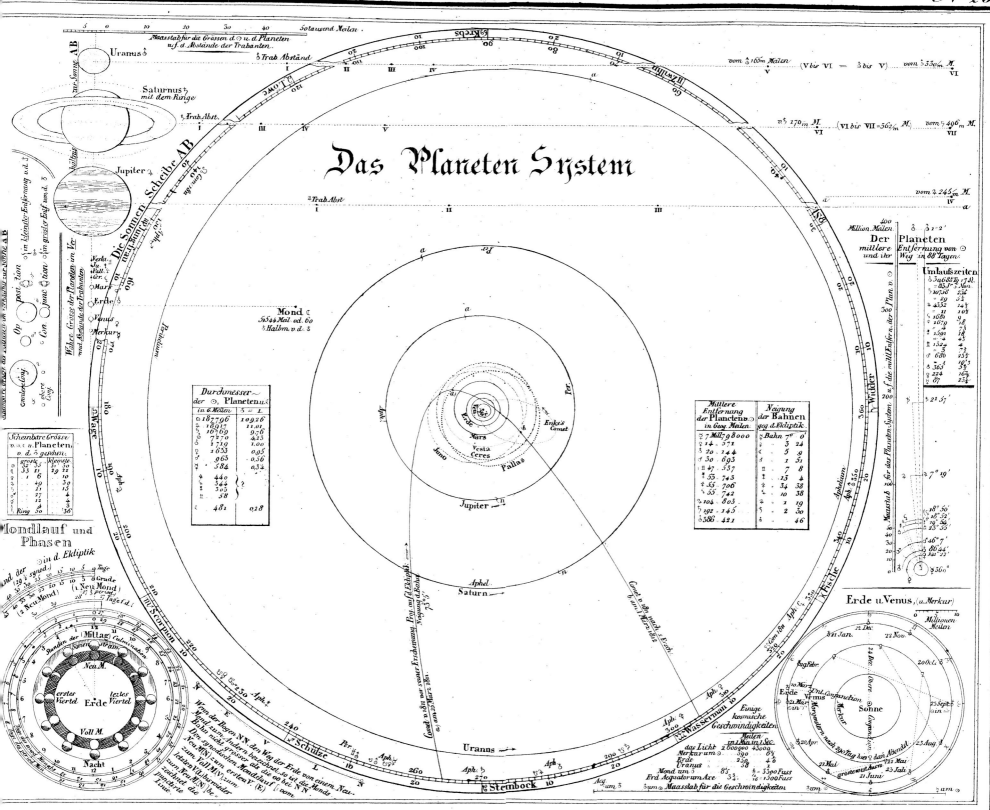

Das Planeten System

Porcelain: white gold from China

China

Today fine porcelain is no longer the exclusive preserve of kings. Invented in China in the distant past, it was admired and highly sought-after in Europe. Now it can be found in most homes, thanks to the experiments of the alchemist Johann Friedrich Böttger (1682–1719).

The term porcelain is derived from the Italian *porcellana* meaning "pearl oyster," whose color it resembles. Porcelain is considered the finest example of ceramic production. It is made from a mixture of kaolin (soft, malleable clay), quartz, and feldspar (a colorless mineral) that solidifies when fired. The firing temperature can reach 1,800 to 2,600° F.

This precious porcelain originally came from China, which had a long tradition of pottery and ceramic work. Objects surviving from the Western Chou dynasty (1122–770 BC) confirm that pottery existed at least 2,500 years ago. The Chinese gradually refined the manufacturing techniques of china and were already using white fired glazes in the Tang dynasty (AD 618–907). Experts date the invention of porcelain to AD 618. Because of its white, shimmering, almost transparent appearance, porcelain was sometimes known as "white gold." During the Sung dynasty (960–1279) Chinese craftsmen created elegant china objects decorated with colored glazes such as ivory, pale green and pale blue, reddish brown, and black. The most important objects had a greenish glaze. Porcelain experienced a remarkable revival during the Ming dynasty (16th–17th century). The center of this amazing renaissance was the town of Ching-tê-chên, which had more than 3,000 kilns.

The first reports on "white gold" were brought to Europe in the 14th century. Towards the end of the Ming dynasty, in the first half of the 17th century, this precious merchandise was imported into Europe, first by Portuguese and Dutch traders, and later by British merchants.

Porcelain was particularly sought after by the royal houses in Europe.

The Chinese guarded the art of making porcelain like a state secret, and European attempts to emulate the Chinese merely resulted in softer, cruder faience and earthenware ceramics. The decisive breakthrough took place at the court of August III of Saxony, who entrusted the alchemist Johann Friedrich Böttger (1682–1719) with the task of discovering the secret. Together with the physicist and mathematician Ehrenfried Walther von Tschirnhaus (1651–1708), Böttger first succeeded in producing an extremely hard, red ceramic, Böttger stoneware. He produced pure white porcelain for the first time in 1708, when he used pure kaolin from Schneeberg instead of the ferruginous colored clay.

Böttger is therefore recognized as the inventor of European hard paste porcelain, and two years later a porcelain factory was founded in the vicinity of Meissen. Other porcelain factories were subsequently set up in Vienna and Venice once craftsmen from the Meissen factory had divulged the secret. In the second half of the 18th century many more porcelain factories were established in Germany under royal patronage. The most important were Nymphenburg, Fürstenberg, Frankenthal, and Berlin. The delicate nature of china seemed to complement the artistic sensitivity of the rococo extremely well. The love of *chinoiserie* that marked this period also expressed itself in the design and decoration of porcelain pieces.

Johann Böttger was the inventor of European hard paste porcelain. This example was made by the Meissen factory.

Zero: a numeric symbol

Babylonia and India

The idea of zero as a number in its own right has not always been a self-evident fact. Originally it was only used as an empty sign and as a reading aid without any value, like the comma. It was only in the 9th century AD that this radically changed, enabling mathematics to reach a new level of understanding.

One, two, three – the zero is dropped as soon as one starts counting. The same was true in early civilizations. In practice there is no intrinsic requirement for a number without a value. The zero began its career through the back door, when it became apparent that written figures required a sign was that would clearly express the value of individual digits in their numeric context. People looked for a neutral place indicator and it was found in the sign known as "zero," which has no value.

The first known case of a zero being used was in Babylon in about 300 BC. Unlike the Greeks, for instance, the Babylonians already used a system of place values, that is, a numerical writing system in which the value of a digit is expressed by its position. In the number 781, for instance, the 7 is placed in the hundreds column, the 8 in the tens and the 1 in the units.

But what is to be done if one of these places remains empty, for instance, 7 1 instead of 781? A gap-filler is needed to distinguish it from 71 by separating the 7 and the 1. The Babylonian solution was the sign of a slanting double wedge that joined the two numbers, which meant that each digit could be placed unambiguously in its correct place value in a numerical sequence. This invention was a decisive moment in the promotion of accuracy.

In the Americas, a similar approach is found in the land of the Mayans. They too used the sophisticated place value system and like the Babylonians they became aware of the need for a zero. While the Babylonian zero was represented by a double wedge, the Mayans used a glyph, that is a pictorial character. But in both cases the zero was a symbol, an optical sign without magnitude or quantity of its own.

It was only much later that zero became a number with mathematical properties, an independent number that not only filled a place but also defined its own value.

Alexander the Great introduced Babylonian ideas to the East, and the zero eventually acquired its decisive status in India. Here mathematics had developed considerably since the 2nd century AD, concentrating on arithmetic, geometry and increasingly algebra. In about AD 500 the Indians introduced the decimal system with a perfect place value system. They calculated with nine numbers (from which our own numerals developed) and finally gave the zero its usual position, between –1 and 1 in the numerical sequence. In the 7th century AD the mathematician Brahmagupta was including negative numerical values in his work. It was in AD 876 that the symbol "0" representing zero appeared in a temple inscription in Gwalior.

The creation of zero as a numerical value that is included in calculations, in an abstract and operative capacity, gave a new dimension for mathematics and it was a pioneering development for the discipline as a whole.

The symbol zero opened up a completely new dimension in the understanding of mathematics.

Windmills: grinding corn more easily

Persia

Around AD 900 windmills began to be used to grind cereals. This was an enormous step forward that made life much easier for many, because until then grinding cereal had always been an activity that was laboriously carried out by hand.

AROUND THE YEAR 900

> Arabic scholars build the first camera obscura, to observe the course of the sun and other heavenly bodies.

> The Vikings discover Greenland.

> Louis the Younger becomes king of Francia Orientalis empire under the guardianship of the archbishop Hatto. He is the last Carolingian king.

> Benedictine monks establish a school for medicine in Salerno, Italy. The students are taught in the teachings of the Hippocrates and Galen.

> In present-day Mexico the Toltecs establish the city of Tula. A step pyramid, temple ruins, and gigantic stone figures survive today.

△ Sails fitted to the outside of the windmill were rotated by the wind and turned the grinding mechanism.

Cereal has been a basic food for mankind for about 10,000 years. In the 3rd millennium BC people began using simple corn mills to grind cereals. The corn was placed in a hollowed-out stone while a smaller stone was moved to and fro on top of it to crush the corn. Later mills were rotated by a handle and had a built-in funnel in the upper millstone for filling while the stone continued to be turned.

In the 1st century AD draught animals harnessed to shafts rotated cone-shaped millstone. Another step forward was the watermill, first used in 85 BC. The flowing water of a stream caused the waterwheel to rotate, which in turn operated the millstone.

The Persians, a seafaring people, began the search for a new concept for the mill. They reflected that if the power of the wind could move very large ships, it could also be harnessed to move wheels. The first corn mill driven by wind power dates from AD 915 and was built in the then Persian province of Seistan. In a single-story, tower-like building, a horizontal mill wheel, originally still positioned below the millstone, rotated a vertical axle shaft. This shaft was connected to the upper, rotating millstone through a hole in the lower, fixed millstone. Sails outside of the building were driven round by the wind and activated the grinding process.

At the end of the 12th century there were windmills in England, Normandy, and Flanders, and a little later also in Germany. By the late 16th century the sails – four large sails, usually mounted on a rotating wooden structure – reached a diameter of 50 to 80 ft. They were slightly tilted so as to present a better angle of attack to the wind. The milling equipment and grain were inside the tower-like structure that was a mobile timber-frame construction. The reason for this arrangement was so that the upper part of the mill could be turned to face the direction of the wind. The millstone was rotated by a rod and later also by a small crank. The sails were connected to the upper millstone by wooden miter gears that engaged with each other at right-angles and transferred the power.

In the 14th century windmills were no longer built on a mobile base but fixed to the ground because this provided more space. However, the part carrying the sails had to remain movable so as to face the direction of the wind. This was achieved by building a rotating cap and roof that could be turned in the appropriate direction. These are called cap windmills.

With the arrival of the steam engine the windmill lost much of its importance. The first steam-driven mill came into operation in England in 1784.

However, having almost disappeared completely, wind power has recently made a come-back. It is now used for the environmentally-friendly production of electricity.

A windmill in Holland. Its technical principles were originally developed in Persia in the 10th century.

Optics: about seeing and what is seen

Ibn al-Haitham (c. 965 to 1039)

Optics is the science of vision and light. Research in this field includes physical aspects – the generation, nature, and propagation of light – and also physiological aspects, how the eye itself operates. The discoveries made by the Islamic scholar Ibn al-Haitham (Latin name "Alhazen") in the field of optics influenced scientists well into the 17th century.

AROUND THE YEAR 1010

> *c.* 1000: The Vikings under Leif Eriksson reach Labrador on the North American coast.

> *c.* 1000: The culture of the Iroquois originates in northeastern North America.

> 1008: The Swedish king Olaf Skötkonung is baptized. So begins the Christianization of Sweden under the control of north German bishops.

> 1010: The allied city-states Pisa and Genoa attack the Arabic-controlled island of Sardinia, conquering it in 1016.

> 1012: The oldest synagogue in Germany is built in Cologne.

In antiquity and later in the Middle Ages the science of optics was mainly concentrated on two areas: how light spread, and how eyesight worked. The latter was particularly important in the treatment of diseases of the eye. In antiquity two contradictory theories of vision were current. The "emission theory" assumed that the human eye sent out "sight rays." These then collided with visible objects whose image they brought back to the eye. The "receiving theory," on the other hand, held that an unknown phenomenon was produced by the object that then stimulated the eye to perceive the image. Apart from these two theories there were combinations of both, as well as other theories that were rooted in various disciplines such as medicine, physics, philosophy, and mathematics.

Optics was a science of particular interest to the scholar Abu Ali al-Hasan ibn al-Hasan ibn al-Haitham who came from Basra in the country that is now Iraq. His studies concentrated especially on the works of ancient natural scientists whose works had only been translated into Arabic a century earlier. His main aim was to discover the truth in a rational rather than a religious way and he soon became famous for his knowledge of science. As a result, the caliph Al-Hakim, who ruled from 996 till 1021, summoned him to Cairo and supported him. Alhazen was to remain in Egypt until his death in 1039.

Alhazen's work lived on long after his death. He was a versatile author and scientist who wrote over 90 works. He wrote commentaries on the texts of famous classical scientists such as Aristotle, Euclid, and Ptolemy, and he was interested in a wide range of subjects including optics, medicine, mathematics, physics, astronomy, cosmology, and even theology.

In the field of optics Alhazen analyzed all the theories, combined or altered them according to his opinion, and then published his own theory in the *Kitab-al-Manazir* ("Treasury of Optics"). In it he described the anatomy of the eye that consisted of the following: four outer coats of the eyeball and three fluids (aqueous humor, lens, and vitreous body). According to Alhazen, two hollow optic nerves led from the front part of the brain to the eyes. Unlike his predecessors, Alhazen did not believe in a one-sided emission of rays. He based the process of vision on the reflection of the light by objects. The reflected light then returned uninterruptedly to the eye. Light also caused changes in the eye, for instance temporary "blindness" after looking at a strong light. Ahazen was particularly interested in the phenomena of reflection and refraction. He was the first to suggest the use of polished lenses to enlarge objects, thus giving birth to the idea of the magnifying glass.

The invention of spectacles in the Middle Ages would have been impossible without Alhazen's preliminary work. In the West his works influenced famous scientists such as Roger Bacon, John Pecham, Galileo Galilei, and Descartes. It was in the 17th century that Johan Kepler developed the modern theory of sight.

Alhazen described the anatomy of the eye in about 1000, thus becoming a founder of the science of optics.

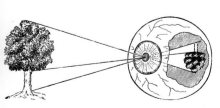

△ **Alhazen believed that sight was based on the reflection of light by the objects in view.**

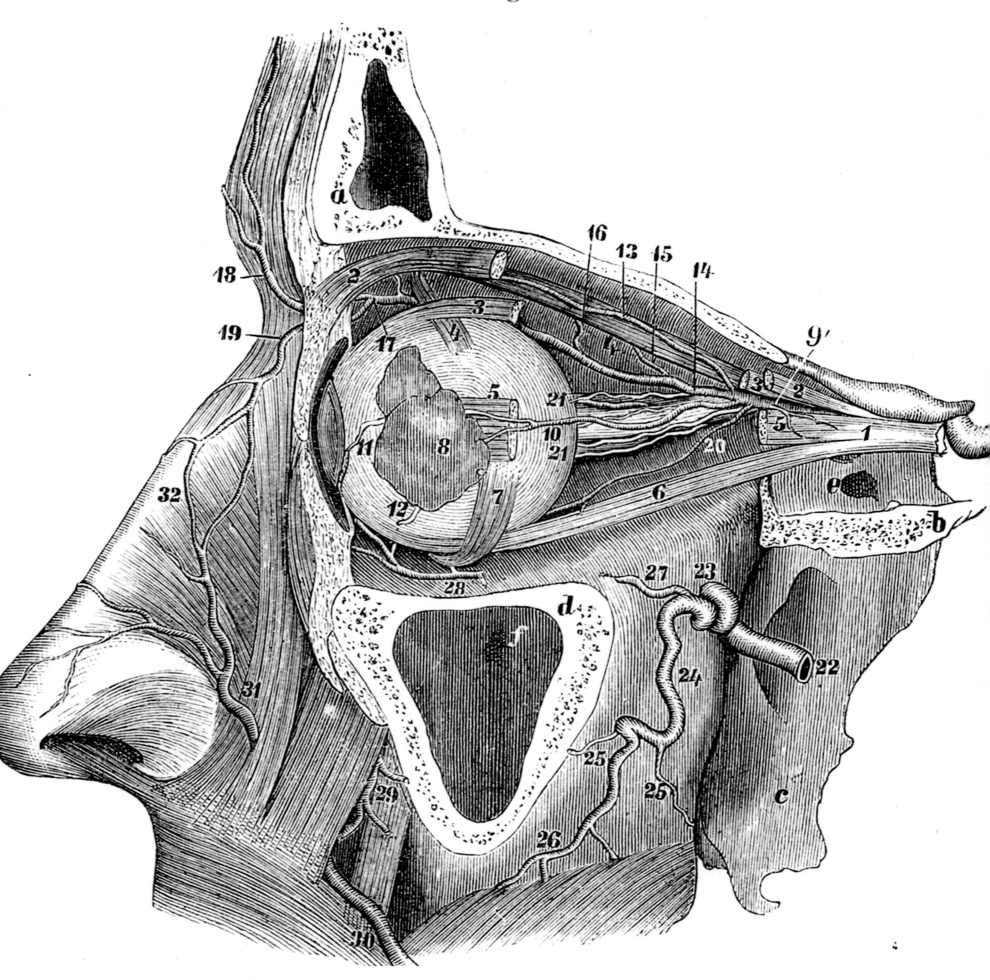

Fig. 86.

Mineralogy: in the realm of crystals

Avicenna (980-1037)

Mineral raw materials are the basis of any modern economy. Almost 1,000 years ago, the Arab doctor Avicenna laid the foundations of modern mineralogy, the study of the composition of stones and minerals, and how they were deposited.

1020

AROUND THE YEAR 1020

> **1022:** Henry II subjugates the Byzantines in southern Italy and thus widens the German sphere of influence in the country.

> **1024:** The death of Henry II marks the end of the Saxonian dynasty of the Holy Roman Empire. The reign of the Salian dynasty begins with Conrad II, who reigns until 1125.

> **1024:** The first recorded paper money is printed in China.

> **1025:** The Arab scholar al-Biruni calculates the formula for the sum of a geometrical progression of numbers, in which each number is double the value of the previous one. The final figure is extremely large, but calculable.

Minerals and gem stones were the first materials used by mankind. From them tools, weapons, and jewelry were manufactured. Their possession signified riches and power and they were also often the cause of armed conflict. The first person who melted metal from ore must have recognized the secret of its chemical composition. The craftsmen who, in the middle of the 3rd millennium BC, made glass by burning certain types of sand and soda or plant ash, were also on the track of this secret.

From the beginning of the Middle Kingdom, about 2,040 BC, the Egyptians were making sumptuous necklaces and armbands from precious stones such as chalcedony, turquoise, and lapis lazuli. Egyptian amulets in the form of scarabs made of opal or jasper testify to the healing properties or protection from evil spirits with which people invested precious stones. The most comprehensive medical work of antiquity, written by the Greek physician Pedanius Dioscorides (1st century AD) in 60 AD also dealt with minerals. It described the pharmaceutical uses of about 100 mineral products.

In about 300 BC, the Greek natural scientist Theophrastus of Eresus (c. 371–287 BC) wrote an influential work on minerals. In this book, which has sadly been lost, he categorized inorganic materials according to their chemical properties as "flammable" and "inflammable," "meltable" and "water-soluble." He named a number of precious stones with the names they still have today, for example emerald, jasper, and amethyst. He also demonstrated chemical-technical knowledge when he explained glass-making, lime-burning, and the process for obtaining mercury. A work on minerals and stones by an unknown author was circulating in Islamic countries about AD 850. It differentiated between precious stones, sulfur and arsenic compounds, salts, metals, and also three groups of stones with magical properties.

In 1020, the Arab physician Avicenna laid the foundations of modern mineralogy. In his *Book of Healing* he deals with the creation and classification of minerals including the creation of mountains, and his *Canon of Medicine* deals with the pharmaceutical use of minerals. Avicenna divided minerals into four groups: the water-soluble "salts," the flammable "sulfur types," the "stones" that undergo no change in water or fire, and the meltable ores and metals. This system remained valid for almost 800 years.

In the 12th century, the abbess and mystic Hildegard of Bingen (1098–1179) further developed the medicinal use of stones. It was not until the 17th and 18th centuries that scientists began to study minerals from a less "esoteric" aspect. Mineralogy, which includes crystallography and petrography among other disciplines, devotes itself to scientific research into the form, structure and formation of stones. However, the French abbot René-Just Haüy (1743–1822), who laid the foundations of modern crystallography, was still classifying minerals in 1809 according to the plan of the great Arabian doctor Avicenna.

The amethyst was given its present name by the Greek naturalist Theophrastus of Eresos in the 3rd century BC.

The astrolabe: the stars in the sky show the way at night

Arab astronomers

Few astronomical instruments fascinated people in the Middle Ages and the Renaissance so much as the astrolabe. It enabled the position of the stars to be measured, even at night when the sundial could not function. Both secular and ecclesiastical rulers were enthusiastic about this strange device.

In the 8th century Arab astronomers developed a revolving star map made of metal, inspired by examples from classical Greece and late antiquity. In this round device different discs could be placed, on which the various constellations of the sun and stars were engraved. By pointing the instrument towards the sun it was possible to identify constellations and establish the time. In this way in the past astronomers were able to work out various celestial and horizontal coordinates and use the astrolabe as a viewing instrument for measuring zenithal distances. In the first astrolabes the image of the earth was fixed, representing the geocentric conception of the universe, while in later instruments the representation of the sky was fixed and the earth's reference lines, the horizon, great circle and azimuth, rotated around it.

Such an instrument was used by Hipparchus of Nicaea (c. 160 BC), the inventor of the spatial projection that was of fundamental importance in a two-dimensional representation of the sky. In his writings Ptolemy (c. 100–160 BC) also described a precursor of the astrolabe, the *horoscopium*. But Ptolemy used the term *astrolabos* to describe the armillary sphere, a three-dimensional model of the sky.

The final development of the astrolabe took place in Byzantium. It was from there that knowledge of such a measuring instrument finally reached Arab scholars in the 8th century. Barely a century later the Arabs had become masters of the construction of astrolabes and used it in many fields, such as navigation. As well as having a general interest in the sciences of antiquity, the enthusiasm of the Arabs for this apparatus also had a religious foundation, since with it Muslims could determine the direction of Mecca anywhere in the world, and also establish the times of prayer and the date of Ramadan, the month of fasting. In the Arab world mastery of the astrolabe later became a symbol of education, as in a story in *The Arabian Nights* where a princess has to prove how clever she is by showing that she could use such an instrument.

In the 10th century the astrolabe made its appearance in western Europe as a result of the Moorish occupation of Spain. Monasteries in particular were very interested in this fascinating new instrument because of their work in astronomy. It was a monk, Hermann von Reichenau, who produced the first generally comprehensible introduction to the construction of an astrolabe. In the mid-11th century Wilhelm von Hirsau made such an instrument, inspired by the Arab astrolabe but with local coordinates.

As a precursor of the theodolite and the sextant that became so important in navigation, the astrolabe was of fundamental importance in medieval astronomy and without it many of the astronomical discoveries known today would not have been possible.

The astrolabe shown here in a 16th century painting of an ambassador was an indispensable instrument for establishing time and position.

The fork: a blasphemous invention for eating?

Byzantium

> 1072: King Malcom III Canmore of Scotland is conquered by the English king William I. The reign of the Scottish clans ends.

> 1073: Gregory VII is elected pope in Rome. His Gregorian reforms prohibit the marriage of priests and the trade in offices.

> 1077: In the investiture controversy concerning the appointment of bishops, the German king Henry IV receives absolution from Pope Gregory VII at Canossa.

Until well into the Middle Ages people in western civilizations ate with their fingers. At the beginning of the 11th century, the attempt on the part of a Byzantine princess to introduce the use of forks at the court of Venice failed. The church even temporarily forbade the use of forks, declaring that copying the human hand in such a way was blasphemy. Only 600 years later did the fork finally make its way into European gastronomic culture.

After the knife and the spoon, the fork is the youngest member of the "eating irons." One of its predecessors is doubtless the roasting spit, which was used by the ancient Greeks and Romans as well as European peoples. With a spit, a piece of meat could be roasted over the fire and the hot morsel brought to the mouth without burning the fingers. The development to the modern fork progressed from this single-pronged roasting spit to the two-pronged meat and cake fork, and further by way of the carving and serving forks used by servants at court to offer roast meats to the guests.

Excavations have proved, however, that the Babylonians already had knowledge of forks, although other sources show that they normally used their fingers when eating. Forks were used in early Byzantine culture by the noble families. It was a Byzantine princess who brought the fork to Italy in 1071. When she married Domenico Silvio, a descendant of the Doge of Venice, she brought with her as part of her dowry two golden two-pronged forks that she commenced using at the table. However, her efforts to convince the people and the Church of the practical value of this utensil were of no avail.

The Church in particular regarded the fork with great suspicion, in that it copied the God-given form of the human hand and therefore came dangerously close to blasphemy. The fork was even temporarily forbidden for this reason. The first mention of a fork as a utensil at table was in 1032, at Montecassino in Italy. However, it was used mainly for serving meat.

This remained the state of affairs for quite some time. It was only gradually that the cultivated manner of eating with a fork was established, and it did not reach France and the Burgundian court until the end of the Middle Ages. It took another 100 years until its use became established in other European countries. In 1518, Martin Luther was vehemently against its use: "God save me from little forks!"

In the 17th century, after having been derided for many years as a "foreign fashion fad," the fork began to change its shape. It lost the straight, rigid form, behind which the original spit was still recognizable, and became more rounded, like the spoon. In contrast with the twin-tined carving fork, there were now usually three or four tines. The shape, somewhat similar to a shovel, made its change of function more obvious. Instead of always being spiked by the fork, with the help of the knife, food could also be "forked" up in the manner that it is used today.

△ Eating with a fork spread very slowly.

People in western civilizations ate with their fingers well into the Middle Ages.

Hours, days, and years: The story of time measurement

The rhythm of nature

No one can resist the merciless passing of time, but the speed at which time appears to be flying past today seems to be faster then ever. The seasons, the phases of the moon, and the unremitting alternation of day and night made people aware of the existence of a cyclical rhythm in nature and gave them an understanding of time. Being part of this natural cycle, people lived according to the laws of nature and cosmos. In fact, the first time-measuring instrument was conceived on the basis of observations of nature with the object of recording the passage of time in a large "register," the calendar.

It was probably in the 3rd millennium BC. that the Sumerians and Babylonians developed the first calendar that was based on moon phases. But when the unit of measurement was the period taken by the sun in its apparent revolution round the earth—the solar day—there was a discrepancy, since the year does not consist exactly of a whole number of days. Years therefore had to be lengthened because otherwise time was left over that did not fit into the system. Calendar systems were constantly altered and corrected during subsequent millennia in order to resolve this problem. It was Pope Gregory XIII who gave the calendar its present form. In 1582 he introduced a new leap year system that brought astronomical and

This historic engraving shows hourglasses being made.

religious dates back in line. This calendar, named the Gregorian calendar after its author, is still used today.

Nevertheless, people were more interested in the immediate present and future than they were in years, months, and weeks. The sun helped in assessing the time of the day, but only when the connection of the length of the shadow with time was recognized did it become possible to measure time at all accurately. The first sundials to show the time of day were simply poles stuck perpendicularly into the ground.

But naturally this only worked in good weather when the sun was shining.

Sundials were therefore only one of the forms of timekeeping used in ancient civilizations. The burning of a graduated candle, and the flow of a carefully calculated quantity of sand or water through a restriction, were all used to make candle clocks, sand clocks, and water clocks. In addition astronomers also used various instruments for measuring angles to calculate the time.

The mechanical clock

The need for more accurate timekeeping only arose in Europe in the 13th century with the development of towns as busy trading and production centers. The organization of community life made the mechanical clock a necessity long before industrialization. A mechanism consisting of gear wheels driven by a weight and controlled by a foliot escapement was developed to indicate the regular passing of time. Gear wheels were already known in antiquity, so it was the invention of the escapement that was the revolutionary feature. Such clocks indicated the time by striking a bell. The subsequent replacement of the foliot by a pendulum considerably improved the accuracy of timekeeping, and at the same time clocks began to indicate hours and minutes (and in some cases seconds) on a dial.

Over the years clocks became smaller and also more accessible to people. At first there was only one clock in the town,

This Chinese clock-tower dating from 1088 A.D. worked on the principle of the water-clock.

perhaps the church clock. But with the development of longcase clocks, wall clocks and table clocks, timepieces began to invade the homes of the more prosperous citizens. Eventually pendant and pocket watches brought portable timekeeping to individuals.

But mechanical clocks were still not particularly accurate. They became so with the development of more accurate pendulum escapements. Now it became possible to regulate people's working life more precisely and science too was able to take advantage of more accurate timekeeping.

In the 19th century the invention of electricity also led to many changes in the measurement of time. As well as providing the electric drive for the pendulum by various means, electricity also made it possible to synchronize a number of clocks at the same time. Thus a central master clock would convey impulses at intervals to other slave clocks, so that they all moved their hands together. Standard time could now be distributed over a large areas, and many towns and cities installed such systems of public clocks. Electricity resulted in artificial lighting that emphasized the fundamental aspect of time measurement: the difference between day and night.

The first wristwatches appeared towards the end of the century but their use only became widespread during World War I.

Wristwatches also had to fulfill different requirements from clocks because they were more directly exposed to dirt and shocks.

After about 700 years the era of the mechanical clock and watch inevitably began to come to an end. The quartz clock that used the constant oscillation of a quartz crystal was invented in New York in 1929 by W. A. Marrison. But even quartz clocks were not absolutely accurate. The introduction of atomic clocks in the 1950s was a considerable step in the direction of absolute precision. It was based on the oscillation of cesium atoms. This principle provided the basis for a new definition of time: since 1967 the official definition of a second has been 9,192,631,770 oscillations of the cesium atom. Until then it had been defined as one 86,400th part of the mean solar day.

Relative and "inner time"

To Newton, time was an absolute quantity but Einstein disproved this. It is extremely hard for ordinary individuals to understand the relativity of time because it goes against everything that is know in everyday life. Unimpressed by physics, time remains a reliable standard even though people usually experience it differently. Everyone is familiar with the paradox of time whereby it seems to go much faster when one is busy than when one has little to do. But in retrospect, an amusing time appears to have lasted longer than it did, while a boring time

seems to have lasted less long. An explanation for the phenomenon is that the brain has to process an amount of information during a certain period of time, so the more information, the longer the time will appear to have lasted.

It is also evident that many bodily functions are ruled by a "body clock" whose rhythm is likely to be familiar to all, through mid-morning hunger pangs for instance. Physiological processes are subjected to precise, measurable, regularly reoccurring high and low points. Body temperature, hormone levels, nerve cell activity, sleep patterns, and depth of attention follow their own rhythm, subject to individual deviations. Readings also vary according to whether the individual is a morning or an evening type.

People are influenced by the external rhythms of society, such as work timetables, background noises, and public clocks. But even in sound-proof, air-conditioned and artificially lit rooms screened from all external stimuli, people still follow a certain rhythm, thus proving the existence of an inner clock.

The coordination of the internal body clock with the requirements of modern working life is nowadays often quite difficult.

The cannon: a bombshell in the history of warfare

Chinese alchemists

1250

AROUND THE YEAR 1250

> *c.* 1250: The culture of the Inca in Cuzco, present-day Peru, achieves its finest flowering.

> 1260: The English naturalist Roger Bacon establishes that a fire can burn only with a supply of air.

> 1270: The French king Louis IX succumbs to an epidemic on his second crusade to Tunis.

> *c.* 1280: King Rama Khamhaeng establishes the first Siamese empire in present-day Thailand.

> 1291: In Switzerland, the cantons Schwyz, Unterwalden and Uri form the "Everlasting League" to protect themselves against attacks by the Habsburgs.

> *c.* 1300: The foot loom comes in use.

One of the most revolutionary inventions of the Middle Ages took place in China and was later introduced with dramatic effect into Europe. This invention was the discovery of gunpowder and the development of firearms and cannons. It had a much greater social political impact in Europe than it had had in its country of origin, since it helped bring about the end of the age of chivalry.

△ **Gunpowder reached Europe in the 13th century and firearms such as cannons followed in its wake.**

Chinese warriors had long been interested in weapons that would make close combat unnecessary. Described by the Chinese as the "fire drug" ("huo yao"), gunpowder consists of a mixture of saltpeter (calcium nitrate), sulfur, and charcoal. In the 9th century Chinese alchemists discovered that a mixture of these substances in a particular proportion had explosive qualities. The discovery was first mentioned in documents dating from 1044.

By the early 10th century many Chinese warlords were already using incendiary projectiles, described as "flying fire." These were followed by smoke shells and explosive shells as well as flame-throwing bamboo tubes, the so-called "fire-spears." Handguns made their first appearance in the mid-12th century, and these were the precursors of the muskets and cannons that were invented in the 13th century.

It was in the 13th century that gunpowder arrived in Moorish Spain before making its way to the rest of Europe. The first written "recipe" for gunpowder was mentioned by Roger Bacon (1265) in England and Albertus Magnus (1275) in Cologne.

Gunpowder for artillery was first mentioned in Europe in reports on the Hundred Years War (1337–1453). Later the artificial production of saltpeter became a lucrative business, even when the manufacturing of gunpowder and cannons carried the death penalty. The alchemist and scientist Berthold Schwarz, born near Freiburg, built the first working cannons in Europe in 1370. Denounced by the Inquisition, he hid in a convent where he lived as a monk, but he was discovered and executed in 1388.

The social and political impact of the invention of gunpowder and cannons was much more significant in the west than it had been in China. The Middle Ages in Europe were a period distinguished by turmoil and far-reaching changes. In contrast, the feudal empire of China underwent no social changes for 500 years. There, gunpowder merely complemented the range of weapons that already existed, while in Europe it made traditional weapons and fighting techniques obsolete. Thus it also heralded the end of the age of chivalry.

In Europe cannons replaced traditional weapons and fighting techniques, resulting in the rapid disappearance of the medieval knights.

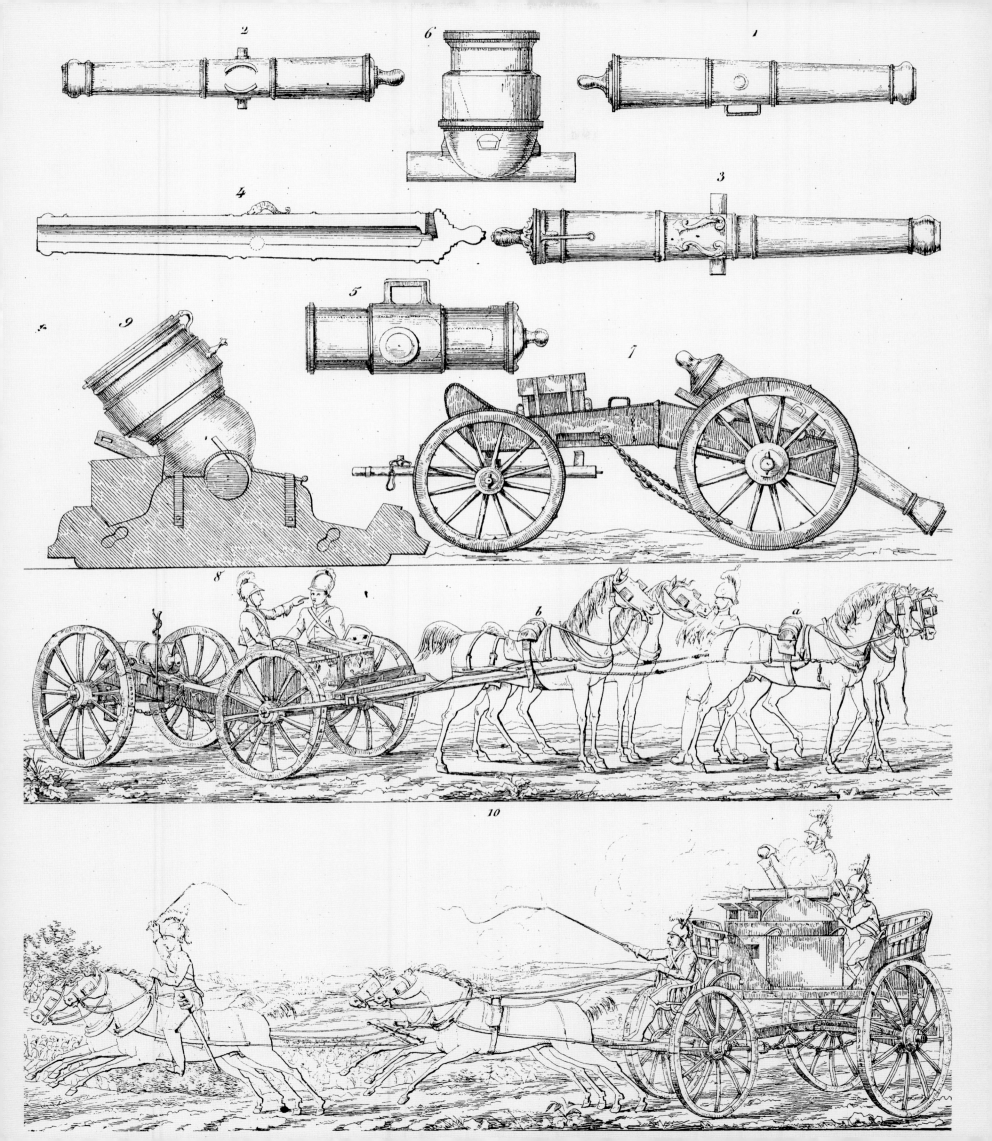

The mechanical clock creates a new sense of time

Europe

At the end of the 13th century, large clocks began to be placed in the towers of churches and town halls. Their striking mechanisms tolled the hours for all to hear. From then on, mankind's everyday life and working time was increasingly determined by the clock.

1290

AROUND THE YEAR 1290

> 1290: The English king Edward I has all Jews who are active in financial transactions expelled.

> From 1291: The crusaders bring new kinds of cereals, seasonings, vegetables, and fruits to Europe, including rice, buckwheat, peppers, lemons, and apricots.

> 1292: The Castilian king Sancho IV conquers the straits of Gibraltar.

> 1292: The German electors appoint Adolf of Nassau as their king.

> 1295: Edward I appoints the "Model Parliament," which immediately discusses new taxes.

Before the introduction of clocks, people used special instruments to measure time. Early timepieces made use of the position of the sun or the moon, while others measured time by the length of an event; for instance, the hourglass measured how long it took for sand to run through a narrow opening. Monasteries in particular believed that an ordered daily round was important. The eight offices of prayer were a symbol of the divine order and they could not be missed. Therefore, the signal for each assembly was given as soon as a water-vessel had dripped empty, or a candle had burnt down to the next mark.

A predecessor of the mechanical clockwork was built by the priest Pacificus in the middle of the 9th century but it was not very accurate. In the 13th century a clockwork mechanism was developed that was more regular. This new mechanism had a horizontal beam, the foliot, that swung back and forth horizontally on a vertical shaft with two metal leaves that engaged with a weight-driven cogwheel. An adjustable weight was attached to each end of the beam to adjust the period of its oscillation. Each time the beam swung backwards or forwards, one of the leaves engaged with the cogwheel and released one of the cogs. The movement of this wheel through a chain of wheels rotated a clock face past a stationary hour hand, or, more commonly, caused a striking mechanism to strike a bell.

From 1290 on, this type of clock spread throughout Europe. The oldest public example was made in 1386 for Salisbury Cathedral and is still telling the time. The elegant and ingenious mechanism inspired Dante Alighieri (1265–1321) to compare clockwork to a round dance. From the mid-14th century town hall clocks developed into objects of prestige. They did not just tell the time, they delighted the citizens with musical mechanisms and moving figures.

Clockmakers were continuously improving the clockwork mechanism. With the use of a spiral spring for power instead of weights, clocks became smaller and smaller. Peter Heinlein's (1480–1542) "onion" clocks fitted into a jacket pocket and ran for 40 hours without having to be wound. In 1609, Galileo Galiliei (1564–1642) introduced the pendulum, whose regular swing made timepieces much more accurate. In 1657, Chistiaan Huygens (1629–1695) received a patent for his further development of the pendulum clock. However, a real sensation was caused by the ship's chronometer, built by John Harrison (1693–1776) in 1728. Even on a ship that was pitching to and fro, his spring-driven clock kept time sufficiently accurate to calculate the exact longitude within 0.5 degrees, a distance of 30 miles.

The mechanical clock made people less dependent on the rhythms of nature but at the same time made them slaves of the clock. Clocks began to dictate the beginning and end of the working day, and they also provided a measure for the value of work. As a mechanical measuring instrument, the clockwork mechanism was a pioneering development for science and technology.

The invention of reliable timekeepers meant that time became increasingly important in people's everyday lives.

Glasses: better vision for those with poor sight

Alexassandro di Spina (d. 1313)

In 1299, the technically experienced Dominican monk Alessandro di Spina fascinated his contemporaries with an unusual invention. He mounted two glass lenses and linked them together in a frame, creating a device that enabled the older monks to read manuscripts clearly again.

1299

AROUND THE YEAR 1299

> 1288: Westminster Hall in London has the first striking clock in the world.

> 1298: At a meeting in Mainz the seven German electors depose Adolf of Nassau and appoint Albert I, a Habsburg as the new king.

> 1298: The rebellion of the Scottish aristocracy under leadership of William Wallace is crushed by England at the battle of Falkirk.

> 1300: In Mayapán in present-day Mexico the Cocom and Toltec peoples become dominant.

> 1300: In Rome Pope Boniface VIII declares the first Holy Year.

> 1301: Sultan Osman I establishes the Ottoman empire.

The eyesight of many people decreases from the age of 45 onwards. The eye's lens loses the ability to contract in order to focus, so that it becomes harder to see close objects clearly. Cicero (106–43 BC) complained about this problem in a letter and found no solution, other than having a slave read to him. Scholars, writers, and craftsmen in particular were seriously hampered in the pursuit of their profession by failing eyesight. A large pool of ability and knowledge remained untapped because no solution could be found to the problem of eyesight getting worse with increasing age.

It was the Arab scientist and naturalist Abu Ali al-Hasan Ibn al-Haitham (known as "Alhazen," AD 996–1038) who produced the first serious theories on understanding sight and the role of glass lenses and mirrors in relation to beams of light. Among other things, Ibn al-Haitham noticed that looking at an object through the segment of a glass sphere made it appear larger. He was encouraged by this observation to use glass lenses with curved surfaces as aids to vision. In about 1240 Ezam Golek Vitello (1220–80) translated the writings of Ibn al-Haitham into Latin, making them more widely accessible.

At about the same time, certain clear minerals were used as aids to vision. Segments of a sphere cut from polished quartz (rock crystal) or beryl were ground flat on one side and outwardly curved on the other side. Placing the flat side on the letters of a manuscript, the letters were seen enlarged on the rounded side. The effect was comparable to seeing the structure of a leaf through a drop of water. Later this "gem stone" was set in a metal frame with a wooden or horn handle like a magnifying glass, thus making it easier to use. In time this "eyeglass" became increasingly flat, and curved on both sides.

It is not known for certain who first developed spectacles from two joined eyeglasses. In the late 13th century Alessandro di Spina, a Dominican monk from Pisa, picked up the idea and joined two eyeglasses by riveting together the handles of their frames. They were held in front of the eyes or clamped onto the nose and, being convex lenses, they strengthened the refractive power of the eyes.

Alessandro's construction soon spread across Italy. This new aid to vision enabled the pool of human knowledge and creativity to be tapped for a larger proportion of each person's lifetime. It is probably no coincidence that spectacles became widespread at the same time as the Renaissance, the new era of great ideas and inventions.

△ Glass lenses were already being used as aids to vision before the invention of spectacles.

Scholars, writers, and craftsmen suffered particularly from their failing eyesight. As a result Alessandro di Spina's invention soon spread throughout Europe.

Sulfuric acid: the alchemist's dream

Djabir Ibn Haijjan (*c.* 721–*c.* 815)

"Sulfuric acid is to the chemist what iron is to the engineer." This is how chemists in the mid-1800s described the significance of their most essential element; after all, sulfuric acid is the most important mineral acid. Using it with other substances enables all the other acids, such as hydrochloric acid or phosphoric acid, to be produced. The Islamic alchemist Djabir Ibn Haijjan was the first to obtain this valuable substance.

△ The workshops of medieval alchemists were the foundation of the modern chemical industry.

Sulfuric acid is one of the most important inorganic acids. It is obtained from sulfur, which, because of its unpleasant smell and according to the legend, was thought to accompany appearances of the devil. Sulfuric acid itself has no discernible odor, but the alchemists who discovered it had always had a tendency to religious mysticism. Because of this, and the importance of handing down skills and craftsmanship, alchemy occupied a position of honor in the Islamic world. One of the undisputed authorities of the chemical and alchemical arts was Djabir Ibn Haijjan. Known in the west by the name of Geber, this scholar lived at the time of the caliph Harun-al-Rashid (766–809) in Kufah near Baghdad. Geber indeed wrote many treatises, but it is doubtful that all the 3,000 chemical and alchemical tracts attributed to him came from his pen.

One of these tracts describes the manufacture of sulfuric acid, or H_2SO_4 as the substance was later known. Alchemists produced sulfuric acid by treating various colored, transparent and glass-like minerals, the vitriols (Latin *vitreus* = made of glass). Today, blue, green, and white vitriols are known as copper, iron, and zinc sulfate respectively; sulfates are the salts in sulfuric acid. Another raw material used for obtaining sulfuric acid was the mineral alum, which also contains sulfate. Because of its colorless, odorless and oily appearance, the strongly corrosive H_2SO_4 was also known as oil of vitriol.

Yet another method of producing sulfuric acid is by burning sulfur. Pyrotechnists make gunpowder and fireworks from the highly explosive mixture of sulfur and potassium nitrate. The description of such an ignition can be found in a "Fireworks book" written in 1420. In 1750, in Birmingham, England, the lead chamber process was a further development of this procedure, producing sulfuric acid by burning sulfur while adding saltpetre and moist air.

By the mid-17th century, oil of vitriol was used to etch glass. In 1794, the French chemist Armand Séguin (1767–1835) introduced sulfuric acid treatment to the tanning industry. As acid has a dehydrating effect, the drying time of the leather was reduced considerably. By the 19th century, scientists were using sulfuric acid either directly or indirectly for the manufacture of almost all chemical products; for instance, to produce nitro-glycerin, the raw material in dynamite, or as the basis for paints. From 1875 onwards, improved technical conditions made possible the mass production of sulfuric acid. By 1892, German industry alone was producing about 500,000 tons of sulfuric acid each year. Today, more than half of the sulfuric acid produced worldwide is used in the manufacture of fertilizer.

Natural sulfur deposits along the edge of the volcano on the island of Vulcano, one of the Aeolian Islands. According to legend, the evil smell of sulfur accompanied the appearance of the devil.

The mystery of the rainbow

Dietrich von Freiberg (*c.* 1250–after 1310), René Descartes (1596–1650)

Already in ancient Greece, natural philosophers sought to explain the phenomenon of the rainbow. It was the Dominican monk Dietrich von Freiberg who lived in the Middle Ages who found the explanation that is still valid today for this iridescent and colorful apparition in the sky.

Sunshine follows a thunderstorm, and sometimes a rainbow too. According to the natural philosopher Anaximenes (*c.* 580–520 BC), this colored arc across the heavens was caused by a ray of sunshine falling upon compressed masses of air. However Aristotle (384–322 BC) believed that it was some sort of optical effect caused by the reflection and refraction of the sun's rays.

Islamic scholars worked further on meteorological optics and passed on their knowledge to the western world. The Polish natural scientist Witelo (*c.* 1230–*c.* 1275) came quite close to the full explanation of how a rainbow originates, saying that when the sun shines through a drop of water, the light is refracted on the surface of the drop. This means that when the light leaves one medium, air, and enters another, water, it changes direction. The different wavelengths of the light are refracted differently with the result that light is broken down into its spectral colors. The sequence of color is always the same: from violet through indigo, blue, green, yellow, and orange to red. According to Witelo, the curved outer surface on the other side of the drop of water, or rain, reflects the colors back to the observer. However, it was not until 1304 in his work *De iride* (Greek *iris* = rainbow) that the Dominican monk Dietrich von Freiburg completed the explanation with a second important aspect: the reflection of light inside each individual drop of rainwater.

In the 17th century, the French philosopher and mathematician René Descartes substantiated this theory and solved the question of why a rainbow is only to be seen from certain viewpoints. His explanation was supported by the principle of the linear dispersion of light and the law of the refraction of light rays that had recently been discovered. From his experiments with single drops of water of varying sizes, Descartes drew conclusions concerning the reaction of an infinite number of drops and their relation to one another in space. A rainbow originates when the sun shines on a wall of mist or rain. A bundle of parallel light rays falls on a curved raindrop, the surface of which reflects some of the rays. The other rays are refracted at the junction between water and air, enter the raindrop, and reach the rear surface of the drop where again, some are reflected while some are refracted and leave the drop. To see the phenomenon, an observer must stand between the sun and the wall of rain, facing the drops of water. Rays that exit the rear of the drop do not reach the eye of the observer. The only rays that are visible are those that have entered the drop of water, are then reflected from the rear of the drop, refracted at the junction and then leave the drop.

In the 19th century, the British mathematician and astronomer George Airy (1801–92) was of the opinion that, according to this theory, every rainbow must be identical. In actual fact, however, the bands of color are of different widths or the colors are of different intensities. This, said Airy, was due to the wave character of light and the different size of the drops. Today, the observation of the refraction of quantums of light on molecules of water allows more accurate insights into this phenomenon.

The Dominican monk Dietrich von Freiburg explained the phenomenon of the rainbow as being the result of the reflection of light inside water drops.

Perspective: a perfect illusion

Leon Battista Alberti (1404-1472)

How is it that the viewer has a real three-dimensional impression of Christ and the apostles when looking at *The Last Supper* painted by Leonardo da Vinci? These amazing perspective creations by Renaissance artists exist because of the work of two men, Leon Battista Alberti and Filippo Brunelleschi. Alberti was the first to write down the rules of linear perspective, thus completely changing the course of the history of art.

The term "perspective" (from the Latin *perspicere* = to see through) describes the representation of three-dimensional images on a flat surface in a way that corresponds to the visual conditions in space. Linear perspective represents bodies or objects in space in proportion to their distance from the plane of the picture. The transfer of the picture onto the picture plane is achieved with the aid of a framework of "imaginary" lines meeting at a "vanishing point." Leon Battista Alberti discovered this method of perspective, thus heralding the modern era of art. Alberti was a *uomo universale* ("universal man"), knowledgeable about philology and literature, archaeology and the history of art, mathematics and architecture. He learned to paint as a way of relaxing after a nervous breakdown.

The discovery of perspective came after thousands of years of artistic creations by man. The late Paleolithic cave paintings in Spain and southern France (dating from c. 17,000 BC) are a perfect example of such early works of art. They represented mainly hunting scenes in which the animals were of different sizes in order to suggest the distance between them and the hunter.

It was only many thousands of years later that the frescoes discovered in the pyramids of ancient Egypt in the 3rd millennium revealed a primitive version of perspective, that of parallel shift. Here the figures and objects were positioned diagonally behind each other across the picture plane. Because the figures, mostly shown in profile and of similar size, were also almost on top of each other, these representations were still relatively flat. Foreshortening and diagonal views made their first appearance in ancient Greece during the classical and Hellenistic period. Few such paintings have been preserved, but ancient writings mention them. Most of these perspective paintings were conceived as stage sets for the theatre plays that were so popular in antiquity. The Romans later adopted this method of painting that had been developed by the ancient Greeks and perfected it in the frescoes of Pompeii and Herculaneum.

In the Middle Ages painters mainly used size to indicate perspective. The "important" figures in a painting such as Christ and the saints were much larger than less important characters such as the patron, for instance. But the Gothic frescoes of Giotto di Bondone (*c.* 1267–1337) already show the first signs of linear perspective. The Renaissance fascination with antiquity led to the rediscovery of perspective painting. It was in about 1425 that the first painting with linear perspective was created within Brunelleschi's circle. This was the fresco of the Trinity in the church of Santa Maria Novella in Florence by Masaccio (1401–28). In 1435, Alberti set down certain rules to be applied in painting on the basis of a mirror experiment by Brunelleschi, immortalizing them in his book *On Painting*. Alberti's ideal was the art of ancient Rome, and also their ethical and moral representations.

The Romans had perfected the use of perspective in painting, as is shown by the frescoes at Herculaneum, but their knowledge became lost.

Book printing: man enters the modern age

Johannes Gutenberg (c. 1397-1468)

The invention of printing with movable metal type marks the beginning of the modern era. Until then education had been a privilege enjoyed only by the aristocracy and the Church. Only when it became possible to produce books rapidly, in large numbers, and at a relatively low cost did the knowledge hidden behind the walls of monasteries become more accessible.

1445

AROUND THE YEAR 1445

> **1441:** The University of Bordeaux is established.

> **1441:** Xiu's rebellion destroys the city of Mayapán, the cultural center of the Toltec rulers.

> **1445:** The Portuguese seafarer Diego Gomes sails round Cape Verde on the west coast of Africa. He also discovers the Cape Verde Islands.

> **1449:** A new outbreak of the plague occurs in Germany.

> **1450:** After France's victory under King Charles VII, England is forced to withdraw from Normandy.

△ Gutenberg's invention that used movable lead characters completely revolutionized book printing.

The ability to pass on knowledge to the next generation is essential for the survival of a civilization, and the existence of a form of writing is a fundamental prerequisite. The oldest known writing was the cuneiform script developed in southern Mesopotamia towards the end of the 4th millennium BC. Carved in stone, these characters were longlasting but hard to transport. With the invention of papyrus in Egypt in about 3500 BC, people were able to send written messages. In the 2nd century BC King Eumenes II (197–159 BC) discovered parchment, a new material for writing made from animal skin that was much stronger than papyrus.

Printing became possible with another important invention, paper. This had been used in China since AD 105 but it remained a well-kept secret for over 1000 years. The technique reached Europe in the 12th century. It involved making a pulp of crushed rag fibers that were "scooped up" on bamboo mats, forming sheets when they dried. It was much less costly than parchment and very suitable for printing.

The technique of printing on paper with inked stamps or engraved blocks already existed before Gutenberg's time. At that time documents were either handwritten, or printed from woodcuts, a process in which a panel of wood was engraved with the letters for printing a single page. This was how the so-called "block books" were produced. This technique enabled many copies to be made from a single block, but preparing the wood block in the first place was a difficult and lengthy process.

In 1445 Johannes Gutenberg of Mainz revolutionized book printing with his invention of movable lead type. These were individual characters that were arranged to form a block of words and sentences from which printed impressions could be taken. The durable, reusable lead characters cast in standard sizes made possible the unlimited, and more importantly, speedier production of books. Between 1452 and 1454 Gutenberg printed the celebrated "42-line" or "Gutenberg" Bible in an edition of 180 copies, 30 of them on parchment. Gutenberg's revolutionary achievement was not the production of his famous Bible but the substantial acceleration of the production of copies. With books, the teaching in the new universities made knowledge available that had hitherto been the preserve of monasteries. Nevertheless it was not until 1800 that as much as 80 percent of the population of industrial countries could read.

The basic principles of Gutenberg's printing process survived well into the 20th century. In the 19th century the hand press was replaced by the mechanical rotary press with enormous reels of paper and high printing speeds. Mechanical typesetting machines were succeeded from 1946 by the technique of filmsetting. Since the 1980s, computerized typesetting and printing systems have almost completely replaced the old methods. Nevertheless Gutenberg's outstanding achievement remains undiminished, because it enabled mankind to move from the Middle Ages into the modern era.

Gutenberg's printing technique using movable characters greatly accelerated the multiplication of books.

Der Buchdrucker.

Ich bin geschicket mit der preß
So ich aufftrag den Firniß reß/
So bald mein dienr den bengel zuckt/
So ist ein bogn papyrs gedruckt.
Da durch kombt manche Kunst an tag/
Die man leichtlich bekommen mag.
Vor zeiten hat man die bücher gschribn/
Zu Meintz die Kunst ward erstlich triebn.

Der Buchbinder.

Ich bind allerley Bücher ein/
Geistlich vnd Weltlich/groß vnd klein/
In Perment oder Bretter nur
Vnd beschlags mit guter Clausur
Vnd Spangen/vnd stempff sie zur zier/
Ich sie auch im anfang planier/
Etlich vergüld ich auff dem schnitt/
Da verdien ich viel geldes mit.

A mistake in the calendar leads to a new view of the world

Nicolaus Copernicus (1473-1543)

All Nicolaus Copernicus really wanted to do was to improve the calculations of the calendar and restore the philosophical principles of ancient astronomy. What he actually did was to revolutionize science with his heliocentric view of the world, thus ousting mankind from its position at the center of the universe.

△ It was the astronomer Copernicus who developed the theory of a heliocentric world.

Nicolaus Copernicus was born in Poland. After the death of his father, he was educated by his uncle Lukas Watzelrode (died 1512), who was a bishop in Ermland in eastern Prussia. From 1496, Copernicus studied law at the University of Bologna in Italy. After his return he worked at the observatory in Frauenburg in East Prussia. While there, he was able to observe that the moon was covering the star Aldebaran. This discovery made him doubt the theory that stated that the planets moved around the Earth. In 1501, Copernicus returned to Italy to study medicine and in 1510 he was appointed canon of the Cathedral in Frauenburg. Based on his continuing astronomical observations, he devised a system that was to mark the beginning of a new era.

In the time of Copernicus, astronomy was still firmly based on the foundations laid by Ptolemy (AD *c.* 100–*c.*160), who was an advocate of the geocentric system, holding that the earth stood at the center of the universe. All other planets, as well as the sun, moved around it. On this basis Ptolemy developed a mathematical model of the movements of the planets. At first it was not the positions of the earth and sun that bothered Copernicus, but the fact that the calendars calculated from this model were faulty, a question that also occupied many other astronomers. As the length given for a year was wrong, the astronomical start of Spring had moved from March 21 to March 11. Copernicus also thought that Ptolemy's model did not take into account the theory of the Greek philosopher Plato (427–*c.*348 BC), which stated that the heavenly bodies could only move

in circular orbits at a constant speed. While searching for an alternative view to that of Ptolemy, Copernicus unearthed the hypothesis of the Greek astronomer Aristarchus of Samos (320–*c.* 250 BC), propounding a heliocentric system. The idea that the sun stood at the center of the universe helped to explain many of the inconsistencies that had arisen when calculating the orbits of the planets. Stimulated by this theory, Copernicus stated that the earth and other planets revolve around the sun, and secondly, that the Earth rotates on its own axis once a day. This was the cause of the apparent daily rotation of the fixed stars.

Copernicus' main work, *De Revolutionibus Orbium Coelestium* ("On the Revolution of the Celestial Spheres"), did not appear in print until 1543, the year of his death. In astronomical circles, however, a small book was in circulation from 1510 onwards that described the essentials of his system. The new teaching of Copernicus revolutionized astronomy and posed questions for all the scientists who were to follow, including the physicist Galileo Galilei (1564–1642). They now had to explain why the double rotation of the Earth could not be perceived. Theologians had to accept that mankind, created in the "image of God" and master of the earth, did not stand at the center of things. Only modern physics was able to "relativize" the Copernican System, for in the physics of relativity it is quite immaterial whether the earth or the sun is at the center of the universe.

Copernicus claimed that the earth and other planets moved in orbits round the sun.

Fossils: a new concept of the history of the world

Girolamo Fracastoro (c. 1483-1553)

For a long time even natural scientists regarded fossils as "games" or Nature's experimenting with creating forms similar to living creatures. Girolamo Fracastoro was the first to recognize them as the remains of living creatures. Today, fossils are regarded as the most important pages in the book of the Earth's history.

1517

AROUND THE YEAR 1517

> **1516:** Thomas More publishes his work *Utopia*: in an ideal state private property would no longer exist.

> **1517:** Martin Luther publishes his 95 theses, in which he protests against the sale of indulgences, since God alone could free the human being from his or her sins. The result was the Reformation.

> **1519:** Ferdinand Magellan sets out on the first circumnavigation of the globe. Commissioned by the Spanish crown, this expedition was intended to prove that the world was round.

> **1519:** Hernándo Cortés invades the Aztec capital Tenochtitlán. The natives receive him hospitably because they believe that the light-skinned conquerors are visitors from their gods.

The remains of plants or animals embedded in stone awoke the curiosity of people in ancient times. The Greek natural philosopher Xenophon (570–c. 470 BC) believed that they might have been washed by floods to the places they were found. Aristotle (c. 384–322) thought fossils proved his theory that all life originated in mud and soil, and that these were creatures that had not awakened to full life, thus remaining hidden in the earth. In Chinese culture, fossils were described from about 500 AD In 770, Chinese historians associated them with their mythological ideas of land and sea.

Amazingly enough, it was mainly the early Christian church historians who accepted Xenophon's ancient hypothesis. They interpreted the creatures turned to stone as victims of the Biblical flood. Tertullian (150-225 AD), a theologian from Carthage, explained that water had originally covered the earth and pointed to the mussel shells found in the mountains as proof of this. Bishop Eusebius of Caesarea (c. AD 260–340) in Palestine deduced the height of the waters during the flood from the heights at which the shells were found.

This was in contrast to the views of the Arab physician and natural scientist Avicenna (980–1037), who created the basis of mineralogy in 1020. He declared that fossils were the products of a *vis lapidificativa*, a "petrifying power." Although he did not deny the possibility that they might be of organic origin, his hypothesis, combined with that of Aristotle, influenced the belief that later reigned in Europe that fossils were created by a *vis plastica*, a "forming power."

The Veronese doctor and philosopher Girolamo Fracastoro was the first to examine the beliefs that had been handed down with a more critical eye. When fossilized mussel shells were found embedded in stone near Verona in 1517, he was unwilling to ascribe them either to the Biblical flood or to the *vis plastica*. He also rejected the idea that they could have been swept there by any other floods. Rather, he was of the opinion that the finds demonstrated that mussels had once existed near Verona, because the area had been covered by sea at the time.

Fracastoro's theory fell on deaf ears and the explanation ascribing the fossils to the myth of the flood held firm. As late as 1746, the author Voltaire (Francois-Marie Arouet, 1694–1778), known as a philosopher of the Enlightenment, discounted the organic origin of fossils. He said that the fossils found in the Alps had been left there by travelers. Not until the last part of the 18th century Fracastoro's theory on the true nature of fossils accepted by scholars such as Professor Johann Freidrich Blumenbach from Göttingen (1752–1840). The collecting of evidence for the history of the world, including paleontology, the science of fossils, began on a grand scale in the 19th century with the publication of Darwin's theory of evolution.

Girolamo Fracastoro recognized fossilized mussels as remains of earlier living creatures.

Anatomy: the structure of the human body

Andreas Vesalius (1514-1564)

The word "anatomy" is derived from the Greek word *anatemnein* meaning "to cut open." In this field many of the teachings of Galen, a physician of ancient Greece, are still valid, but his efforts to bring "light into the darkness" also led to many inaccuracies and misconceptions. Vesalius replaced it with a more accurate view based on dissection.

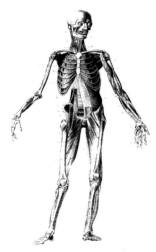

△ The term anatomy is derived from the Greek *anatemnein* meaning "to cut open."

The science of anatomy, the physical structure of the human body and its organs, is the oldest discipline in medicine. Herophilus of Chalcedon and Erasistratus of Cos carried out the first dissections of corpses in the 3rd century BC. The 100 or so publications by Galen, the ancient world's most famous physician after Hippocrates, remained a valid foundation until the 17th century, not least because the dissection of corpses became forbidden on religious grounds in the 2nd century AD. It was only in 1302 that the dissection of a corpse was carried out in Bologna in order to determine the cause of an unexplained death.

The physician and surgeon Andreas Vesalius, who was born in Brussels, was one of the first to reject some of Galen's discoveries. Vesalius had mainly examined dead animals and he drew conclusions from these observations that he applied to the human body. He preferred to rely on what he saw with his own eyes rather than on ancient writings, and in doing so he formed the foundation of modern anatomy.

Andreas Vesalius published *Tabulae anatomicae sex* ("Six anatomical tables") in 1538 with three diagrams of heart, veins, and arteries, and three drawings of skeletons. As professor of surgery in Padua, he began dissecting the corpses of those executed in the city from 1539 onwards, and in 1540 he began to carry out anatomical analyses in public. In 1543 Vesalius published his life's work on anatomy, *De humani corporis fabrica libri septem* ("Seven books on the structure of the human body"), a work that formed the theoretical foundation for the development of this discipline of medicine. With sarcasm he highlighted over 200 mistakes in anatomy as it was known at the time, especially those of Galen, such as the five-lobed liver, the seven-segmented breast bone, and the lower jaw in two parts. The illustrations, probably from Titian's studio, also contributed to the lasting fame of this work.

While the results of Vesalius's research met with excited approval from his students and progressive professors, there was great resistance from Galen's supporters. Vesalius's own teacher, Jacques Dubois, gave him the nickname *Vesanus* ("the madman"). In order to explain Galen's mistakes, Dubois claimed that the human body had changed since antiquity.

Vesalius suffered so much from his colleagues' contempt that he gave up his research and became court physician and surgeon at the Spanish court.

In no other field of medicine were developments so important as the discoveries made by Vesalius in anatomy. All the most important discoveries in medicine owe a debt to Vesalius, who changed the face of medicine as it had been since antiquity by placing man firmly at its center.

The erroneous interpretations of parts of the human anatomy by the ancient scholars were rejected by the scientists of the Renaissance.

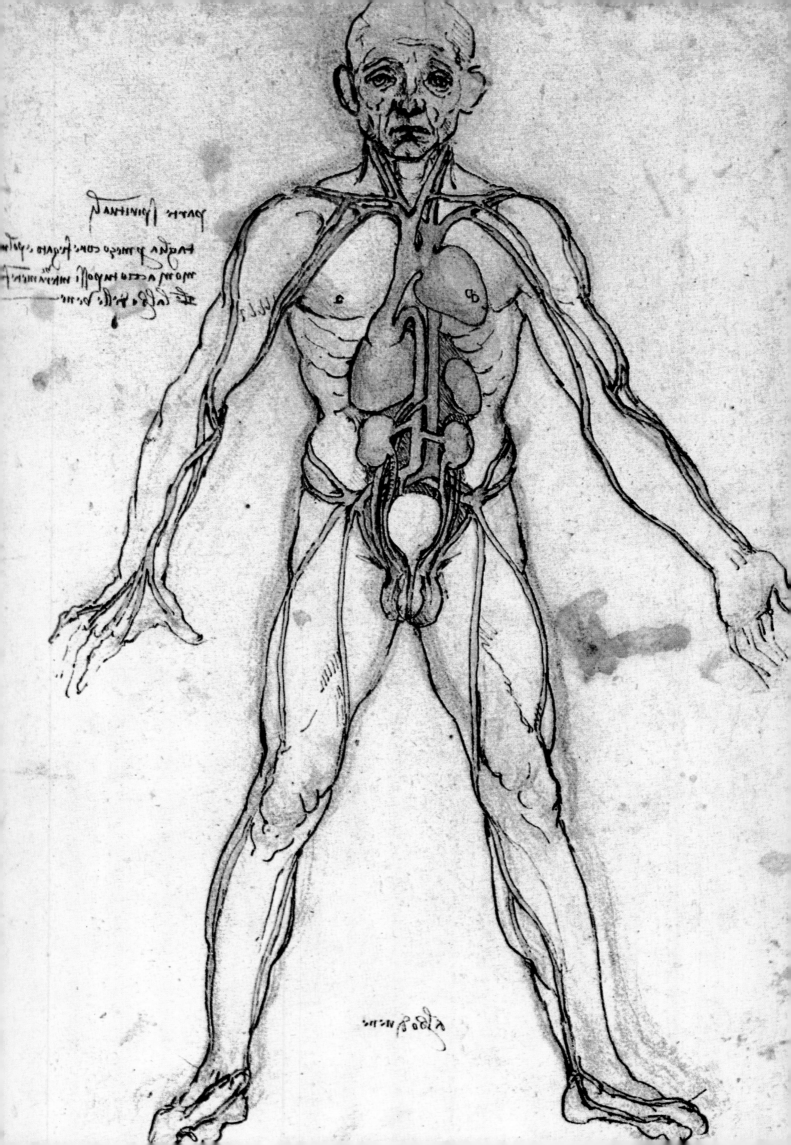

The pendulum and gravity: verticality reveals its secrets

Galileo Galilei (1564-1642)

In itself, falling is a very earthly phenomenon. If gravity is not resisted, it will inexorably bring every freely moving object promptly back to earth. Galileo Galilei systematically investigated the process of falling for the first time and discovered that bodies all fall with the same acceleration, regardless of their mass.

△ Legend has it that Galileo experimentally dropped objects from the leaning tower of Pisa.

The belief of Aristotle (384–322 BC) that a body falls faster the heavier it is, meaning that the acceleration in the speed at which it falls is proportional to its mass, was eventually proved to be false. However, the error was maintained for hundreds of years. Aristotelian physics were the valid measure of all things throughout ancient times, and it was not until the end of the 16th century that Aristotle's theory of gravitation was disproved.

In 1596, the Dutch mathematician Simon Stevin (1548–1620) was the first to devote himself to the practical investigation of the laws of gravity. In one experiment he dropped two balls of different weights and sizes from the same height. He then repeated the experiment using balls of the same size but with different weights. In both cases the balls hit the ground at the same time. The mass and form of a body were therefore unrelated to its acceleration. This observation was sensational in that it overturned the theory of Aristotle, but Stevin depended only on his sense of hearing. He was convinced that he had heard the sound of both balls hitting the ground simultaneously, but he never offered systematic proof.

So it was left to Galileo Galilei to take up the case in the year 1609. His theory was that the speed of falling was influenced by the period over which it took place. This meant that a body would fall faster the longer it fell. His problem was to prove this theory in a way that could be measured. Since falling vertically was not easy to measure because of the rapid gain in speed, Galileo moved his experiments onto an inclined plane, down which he rolled balls of various sizes, weights and densities. This helped to decrease speed enough for the results to be measured by the water clocks of the day – this was his first ingenious step. Nevertheless, his supposed experiments at the leaning tower of Pisa have proved the stuff of legend.

If the angle of inclination is raised to 90 degrees, the vertical, the condition of free fall has been reached. Galileo still had this experiment to carry out. He needed to prove that the final speed of objects falling at different angles of inclination would be the same. He managed to achieve this with the aid of a pendulum. In 1581 Galileo had realized, supposedly while watching the swinging of a candelabrum in Pisa Cathedral, that the length of a pendulum determines its period of swing. Now he also saw that the period of a pendulum's oscillation was independent of the weight of the pendulum or the extent of the swing, a fact that finally proved the laws of gravity. In summary, neither the acceleration of gravity nor its force vary with the mass or shape of an object. Leaving out the effect of air resistance, all objects fall at the same speed.

The Aristotelian spell was broken. Galileo had smoothed the path for the methodology of modern physics by proving that experiment and measurement must complement mathematics and reflection.

Galileo developed the law of the pendulum. Here he is shown watching the swinging of the candelabrum in the cathedral of Pisa that is said to have given him the idea.

The microscope: the invisible becomes visible

Hans and Zacharias Janssen (1580-*c.* 1638), Antonie van Leeuwenhoek (1632-1723)

Even as a child Zacharias Janssen helped his father Hans, a spectacles maker, in his experiments using various lenses to magnify small objects. The pioneering result of their work came in 1590 with an apparatus consisting of two lenses and three tubes sliding inside each other, the first compound microscope. Perceived at first as simply a curious optical gadget, this invention would later revolutionize the world of medicine and science.

△ **The discoveries made using the microscope revolutionized medicine and the natural sciences.**

The optical effects of shaped and polished glass were already known in the 16th century. Its magnifying effect was used in magnifying glasses and spectacles, and experiments were made combining one lens with another. Based in Middleburg, Holland, the maker of spectacles Johannes (Hans) Janssen and his son Zacharias noticed during their experiments that the magnifying effect of a concave lens was multiplied by the addition of a second lens. In about 1590 they built the first known microscope. It consisted of three tubes sliding into each other, the two inner tubes being extendable from the outer tube. At the end of one tube they mounted a converging lens that served as the objective and was placed close to the object to be examined. At the other end was another lens, the eyepiece, that further magnified the object being examined. The user looked through the eyepiece as if through a magnifying glass. Unextended, the microscope magnified an object three times, and if both tubes were extended it magnified the object ten times.

The human eye can see insects as small as fleas, but through the microscope it can also clearly distinguish the legs and sucking bristles of these tiny insects. Suddenly a whole unknown world opened up beyond the human eye's limit of vision. In turn this mysterious world aroused the curiosity of naturalists who recorded their observations in detailed drawings. The most important among them was Antonie van Leeuwenhoek (1632–1723), a self-taught amateur scientist from Delft who had a great influence on science and the development of microscopy itself. The compound microscopes made at that time produced a poor image with troublesome chromatic aberrations and distortions. A further disadvantage was that the kind of microscope invented by Janssen could only magnify between 50 and 150 times. By contrast, Leeuwenhoek made simple microscopes with a single lens. He built about 500 microscopes, making the lenses himself. They were of such quality that he achieved a magnification of 300 times. Leeuwenhoek made spectacular discoveries with these instruments, which brought him fame and in 1680 he was elected a fellow of the Royal Society of England. In 1674 he discovered that a drop of stagnant rainwater contained a mass of swarming micro-organisms with bizarre shapes and colors.

Since these early beginnings, scientific research has conquered increasingly small worlds with the constant improvement of microscopes and scientific progress in all fields. Today scientists are even able to examine the structure of atoms with electron microscopes with a resolution of less than 0.2 nanometers, two billionths of a meter.

After further technical developments the microscope eventually acquired the definitive shape as it is known today.

From Pythagoras to Adam Riese: The development of mathematics

"Check please!"

Science has always been a question of the fundamental perspectives of human thought and action. This is why mathematics in particular owes its origins to an essential change in focus in mankind's view of the world. What does this mean? "Check please!" may inspire one person to write out and add up the cost of meal, and another to look carefully at the surroundings and to ponder upon nature. On the one hand is the practical application, on the other the principle of observation. It is within the latter area that today's mathematics has its origins.

Gottfried Wilhelm Leibniz (1646–1716)

Mathematics as a practical, essential discipline was developed by the Egyptians, the Babylonians, and the Mayans in successive stages. In the main it was used for astronomical purposes (calendar determination), and for surveying land, that is, for practical purposes only. It was not until the time of the Greek scholars that knowledge was sought for its own sake. So it was only then that the science of mathematics, in the sense in which it is understood today, had its beginnings.

With ruler and compass

When philosophy dawned in Greece, it placed the essence of things at the center of attention and thereby opened up space for abstract thought. Within this framework it was Pythagoras (c. 550 BC) and his pupils who first shone illumination on pure mathematics. Taking their philosophical idea that "the essence of all things is number" as their starting point, they occupied themselves particularly with theories of numbers and proportions. First elementary proofs were forthcoming mainly in geometry—Pythagoras' theorem is still world famous. In 300 BC, Euclid began to propound axioms, the formulation of self-evident logical theories, which was an early contribution towards the systematic building up of mathematical rules. Along with the Bible, Euclid's *Elements* became one of the most widely read books in the world.

However, whatever the names of the pioneers, whether Pythagoras, Euclid or Archimedes, a particular characteristic of the beginnings of mathematics was that it was based exclusively in the field of geometry. Whether the problem concerned arithmetic (calculating with numbers), algebra (dealing with equations), trigonometry (solving angle functions), or analysis (the investigation of limits), the Greeks would solve it with geometry. Not for nothing did the inscription over the portal of Plato's Academy read "Do not enter, those who are unacquainted with geometry."

Souvenirs of a journey

By no means unacquainted with geometry, Indian mathematics, which had begun about 1000 BC, started to develop the "algebrization" of mathematics in the 5th century AD. The most significant achievement of Indian arithmetic was the introduction of zero as a number. This enabled the whole decimal place value system to be used, which not only made the illustration of numbers very much easier, but also their implementation in calculations. Following this, it was chiefly the Arabs who took mathematics further. They used the same numbers and place values as the Indians. From this they created an algebra building on the Greek and Babylonian body of thought. The name "algebra" itself is taken from the title of a book by the Arab

René Descartes (1596–1650)

scholar Al-Khwarizmi, from whose name "algorithm" can also be traced.

East meets west

During the Middle Ages in Europe, science ground more or less to a halt. The apocalyptic atmosphere of early Christendom was not conducive to innovative impulses. Then the body of thought introduced by the Arabs re-invigorated the scene decisively, and not only in mathematics. In 1200, for instance, Leonardo of Pisa (Fibonacci) set up the first European memorial to the new Arabic numerals in his *Liber abaci*.

However, it was not until the transition to modern times that real progress was made. As trade started to increase in Italy the practical mastery of problems of calculation became of central importance. Problems had to be solved and, since the algorithms for the four basic arithmetical operations (addition, subtraction, multiplication and division) had been available since the 15th century, this was fairly successful. Masters of arithmetic were soon publishing comprehensive books on elementary mathematics. Among the most popular were the works on arithmetic by Adam Riese (1492–1559), whose books led to the popular saying "according to Adam Riese."

The practical application of mathematics for specific purposes has always been as important as the advance in theoretical knowledge. It is an important tool for use in business for instance to help achieve successful results.

Formulas of emancipation

Now Europe entered the field. New achievements in mathematics came thick and fast after 1550 and the decimal system had also become established. Of great importance to mathematics was the development of the use of symbols, along with the process of standardization. This meant that, as well as writing numbers in the normal way, amounts could also be expressed in a "shorthand" form as letters.

In addition, the discovery of logarithms and the introduction of tables of logarithms were a great help. They facilitated multiplication and division of numbers by enabling these operations to be carried out by addition and subtraction respectively. These advances increased the capabilities of mathematics. Then in the 17th century the creation of analytical geometry enabled geometrical problems to be solved by algebraic operations. This was the achievement of Fermat and Descartes.

Coordinates of infinity

During the years of the Enlightenment, the waves of mathematics broke on further unknown shores. The tidal wave of

Mathematics have played a decisive part in the further development of many professions and sciences.

Calculating machine dating from 1632.

knowledge arose chiefly with Newton and Leibniz. Probably independently of each other, they discovered differential and integral calculus, that is, the mathematical concept of a limit becoming infinitely smaller, which had its beginnings in the Renaissance.

With differential and integral calculus, the first great hour of analysis struck. Infinity, in which abstract functions could travel endlessly, could suddenly be grasped mathematically. This was an even more important breakthrough. In the 18th century it was mainly Euler who took up this development with great enthusiasm. For the first time he explored angle functions, exponential functions, and logarithms purely analytically—that is, completely without geometry—and thereby decisively assisted the progress of mathematical analysis.

Consistently logical

It is surprising, that at this time there was no formal outline in the strictest scientific sense for the already formalized mathematical way of thought. However, the mathematicians of the 19th century began to rectify this in a surprising way. Arising from the necessity of having to classify the laws of mathematical conclusions in a systematic way, mathematically formulated logic was developed. A basic motif of mathematics, still current today, became apparent as a trend towards the logical securing of knowledge and its transposition into a systematic design. At the same time, mathematics was developing into countless new subsidiary disciplines, for instance into set theory or stochastics, based on probability calculus. With the final outline of a foundation, however, the fundamental development was essentially complete.

Merely addition and subtraction?

The most obvious trend in the development of mathematics has been the increasing separation from geometry, following which the disciplines of arithmetic, algebra, and analysis have each evolved as an independent discipline. It is also noteworthy that, in spite of the great increase in the possibilities for the application of mathematics, the original credo of the ancient Greeks has stood the test of time: Mathematics is more than just addition and subtraction.

The invention of the computer has brought about radical changes in mathematics.

The thermometer: heat and cold can now be measured

Galileo Galilei (1564-1642)

The modern world cannot be imagined without devices for measuring and controlling temperatures. They regulate the temperature in living and working spaces, keep food from spoiling, and give an indication of a person's health. The first "thermometer" was made by Galileo Galilei in 1597.

1597

AROUND THE YEAR 1597

> 1593: Catholic Northern Ireland rebels against English rule. It seeks assistance from Catholic Spain.

> 1594: Canada becomes French property.

> 1598: The Edict of Nantes by the French king Henri IV guarantees equality for the Huguenots.

> 1597: The Dutch polar-researcher Willem Barents dies of scurvy in the polar sea while searching for the north-west passage to China.

> 1599: The East India Company is established in London with a monopoly on trading with the colonies.

The scientists of the ancient world and the Middle Ages questioned the "quality" of things, that is, their characteristics. Aristotle (384–322 BC), the most significant of the Greek natural scientists, regarded "warmth" and "cold" as characteristics that were inherent in a thing or not. "Warmth" belonged to living creatures and "cold" to metals and stones. The founders of modern natural science sought to measure these characteristics and to express them in numbers.

The basic principle of measuring temperature has been known since antiquity. Certain substances such as hydrogen, nitrogen, oxygen, and fluids expand when they are heated. From the pressure and volume of an accurately measured amount of a substance, its temperature can be calculated. In 220 BC, the Greek engineer Philon of Bazanz described a "warmth perceptor." Water heated or cooled in a tube rose or sank respectively. In the 16th century, various medical or natural philosophical works mentioned the idea of dividing heat or cold into degrees.

The first "thermoscope" ("warmth observer") or "thermometer" ("warmth measurer") was constructed by the physicist Galileo Galilei in Padua between 1593 and 1597. The instrument was based on the law of thermal expansion of air. Galileo used a glass tube, the closed upper end of which bellied out into a globe. The lower, open end was dipped into colored water. When the globe was heated, the warmed air pressed the water in the tube downwards, while when it was cooled, the compressed air sucked the water higher into the tube.

The doctor Santorio Santorio (1561–1636) fitted Galileo's apparatus with a scale divided into four parts and used it as a measuring instrument for medical purposes. In one of Santorio's works, *Medicina statica* (1614), the name "*instrumento temperamentorum*" is mentioned for the first time. A later *Commentary on Galen* by Santorio actually describes several thermometers, which could determine the blood warmth of humans and measure a high body temperature. An illustration in the book shows a patient with a thermometer in his mouth connected to a small vessel by means of a flexible tube that was to determine the warmth of the breath. In spite of rather imprecise results, the thermometer spread rapidly through medical practice in the 17th century. In 1718 the glass blower Daniel Gabriel Fahrenheit (1686–1736) made the first thermometer that was calibrated with the "Fahrenheit" scale, the scale still used in the United States. As calibration points he used the freezing point and boiling point of water. In 1742, the natural scientist Anders Celsius (1701–44) developed Fahrenheit's thermometer, using a calibration based on the barometer at sea level. He introduced the Celsius scale divided into 100 degrees.

Today doctors measure body temperature with a mercury thermometer or with a digital measuring instrument. In the latter case, the sensor consists of a heat conductor connected by a flexible tube to an electronic apparatus in which the evaluation of the temperature takes place.

Man's attempts at measuring temperature goes back a long time. This is the historic air thermometer developed by Otto von Guericke in 1672.

MOBILE PERPETUUM

MOBILE PERPETUUM

Fig. I.

Fig. II.

Magnus
frigus

Aer fri-
gidus

Aer sub-
frigidus

Aer tem-
peratus

Aer sub-
calidus

Aer calidus

Magnus
calor

Embryology: all life has its origins in an egg

Hieronymus Fabricius ab Aquapendente (1537-1619)

How the development of a human being proceeds from fertilization to birth presented a puzzle to the naturalists of antiquity. Their theories survived almost until the beginning of the 17th century. What actually happened during the nine months of a pregnancy in the womb was first observed and described by the Italian anatomist Hieronymus Fabricius.

1600

AROUND THE YEAR 1600

> 1600: Origination of the baroque style in the Catholic countries of Europe, characterized by opulent, magnificent forms.

> 1600: The Swiss mathematician Jost Bürgi is the first to calculate using decimals.

> 1601: Portuguese seamen reach Australia. This first discovery was kept secret, which is why James Cook, who discovers the fifth continent in 1770, is regarded as its official discoverer.

> 1602: The rebellion of the Northern Irish Catholics against England is crushed.

With a few exceptions, ancient teaching about reproduction concentrated only on the male. It was thought that his seed also created the soul of a human being; the role of the mother in the formation of life amounted only to the supply of organic construction materials. Writings by the Greek doctor Hippocrates (c. 460–375 BC) form the basis of the "preformation theory." This assumed that all the characteristics of the future creature were already modeled in the male seed and that the embryo had only to grow in the mother's womb. Aristotle, 384–322 BC, formulated a new hypothesis, that the embryo must develop from the seed, but this theory received hardly any attention. The theory of postformation or epigenesis was first confirmed in the 19th century.

Until the early 16th century, science was content to follow the writings of antiquity. The dogma of the church prevented any biological research into the development of human life. These religious restrictions were first loosened during the Reformation.

Doctor Hieronymus Fabricius, named "Fabricius of Aquapendente," used this opportunity to study embryonic development in more detail. As research objects, he used chickens' eggs in particular. The recently invented microscope was of incalculable value to him in his research. It revealed to him the previously unseen development of the fetus. With the aid of this instrument, Fabricius was able to transform embryology into a serious science.

In 1600 Fabricius published his first great work on embryonic development, *De formatu foetu*, "On the formation of the fetus." In it he recorded the role of the placenta for the first time and described the sustenance of the embryo in the womb through the umbilical cord. *De formatu ovis et pulli*, "On the development of the egg and chicken" appeared in 1621, after his death. In it Fabricius gave the results of his examinations in more detail. His works also contained the first illustrations of human and animal embryos, internal views of the pregnant uterus, and illustrations of the placenta, which were revolutionary at that time.

The pioneering results of Fabricius inspired other scientists to comparable experiments. His most important successor in the area of the embryology was the Englishman William Harvey (1578-1657). He was the first to observe the development of the inner organs of the fetus. In this way, he refuted the preformation theory propagated since antiquity. His famous remark "*Omne vivum ex ovo*" ("All life originates from an egg") also corrected the "supporting role" until then ascribed to the female egg. In 1651 Harvey published his work *De generatione animalium*, "On the formation of animals," in which he described the growth of animal embryos.

Many of the discoveries of Fabricius and his successors paved the way for the modern theory of evolution.

It was only in the 17th century that scientists discovered how a baby developed before birth.

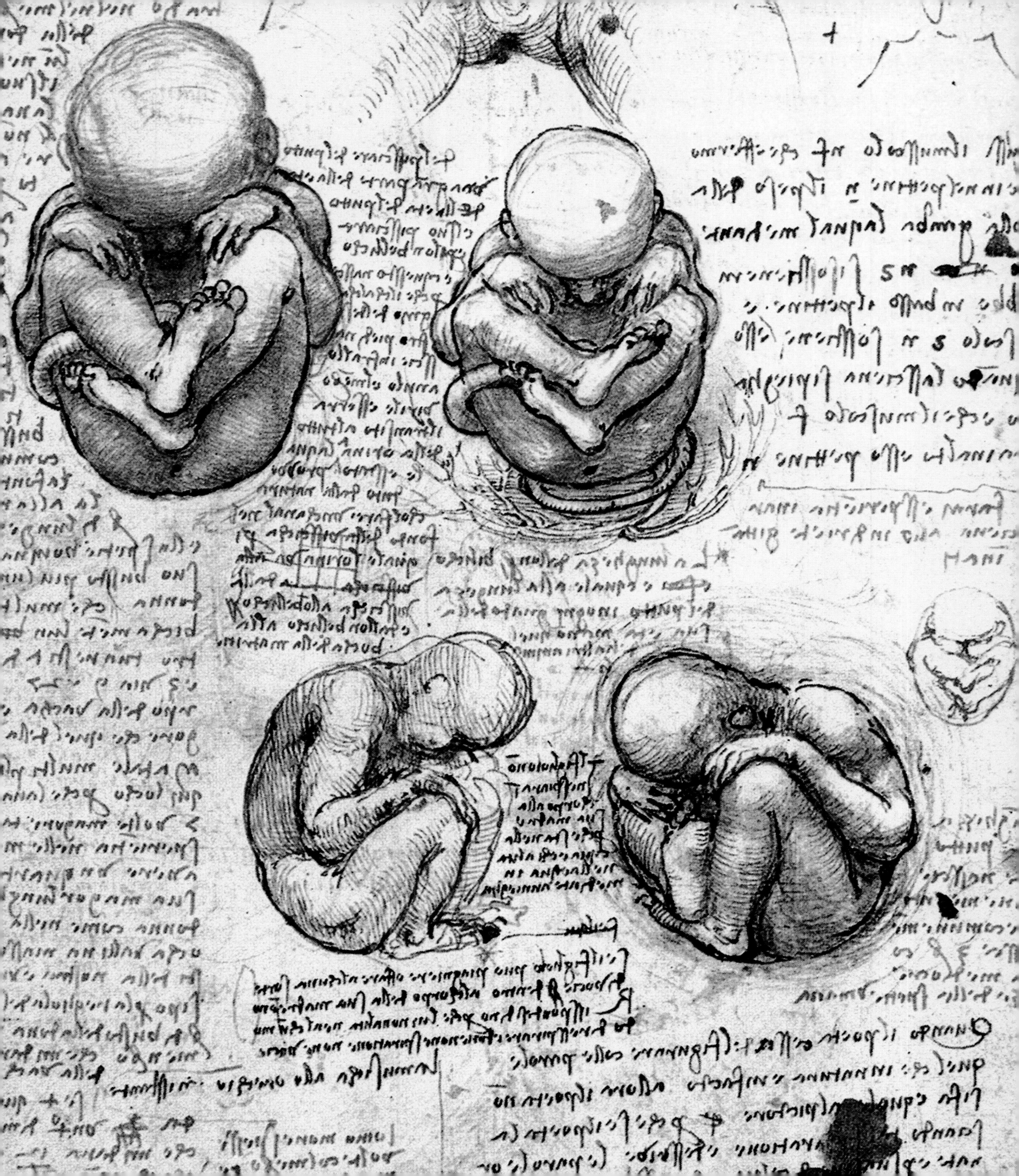

The telescope: overcoming optical distances

Hans Lipperhey (c. 1560-1619)

By the early 17th century, studying the heavens with the naked eye was no longer sufficient for astronomers and further discoveries depended on technical advances. The Dutch spectacle manufacturer Hans Lipperhey developed the "refracter telescope" for this purpose. But the credit for this invention was given to another scientist: Galileo Galilei.

In 1594 the Rhinelander Hans Lipperhey was working as a spectacle manufacturer in Middleburg in the Netherlands. Since the 13th century polished lenses mounted in a frame had existed to improve the vision of people suffering from long sight and short sight. But Lipperhey's interest in optical lenses went further.

In 1608 he invented the telescope, which made distant objects more visible by enlarging them. The original aim of his invention was to make objects look bigger by looking at them through a concave and a convex lens. To achieve this he built a tube with a lens at each end. The objective lens, that is the viewing lens that faced the object being examined, was a convex or converging lens. The eyepiece through which the observer looked was a concave or diverging lens.

The distance between the two lenses was determined by the difference in their focal lengths, which were unequal. The focal length is the distance from the center of the lens to the focal point, where the rays of the light converge again after being refracted through the lens. In the refracting telescope the magnification is determined by dividing the focal length of the objective by that of the eyepiece,

and the length of the telescope is relatively short. Lipperhey's telescopes could magnify an object from twice to ten times its size. The refracting telescope produces an upright virtual image, in contrast with the Kepler or astronomical telescope, which has two convex lenses and produces an inverted real image.

On October 2, 1608 Hans Lipperhey presented his invention to the States General in The Hague to be patented. But the patent office rejected the amateur's request. It recognized that the development of the telescope was worthy of a patent but it doubted that Lipperhey had discovered it himself. A year later Galileo Galilei built a telescope that was very similar to Lipperhey's version, even in its details. The Dutchman's telescope is often referred to as "Galileo's telescope" but it is not known whether Galileo was familiar with Lipperhey's invention. Galileo's telescope had a magnification from 20 to 30 times.

The telescope became the most important instrument in astronomy because it extended the range of observation of the universe and brought about the discovery of numerous planets and their moons. Using the Lipperhey telescope, Galileo himself for the first time observed the four large moons of Jupiter, known as "Galileo's moons."

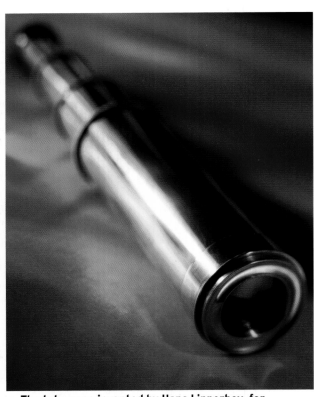

△ The telescope invented by Hans Lipperhey, for which he was refused a patent.

Galileo discovered the four moons of Jupiter using the telescope he had built, based on the principle of Lipperhey's telescope.

- > England settles 100,000 reformed Scottish Presbyterians in Northern Ireland, the "Ulster Plantation," to cement its claim to power.
- > The Catholic states of the German empire join the Catholic League against the Protestant Union.
- > Galileo Galilei formulates the principle of inertia. If no force is acting on a body, it will remain stationary or, if moving, continue with a uniform, linear movement.
- > The University of Marburg founds the first chair for chemistry in Europe.

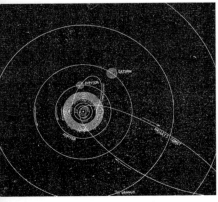

△ The closer a planet is to the sun, the more quickly it orbits around it.

The orbit of a planet? An ellipse!

Johannes Kepler (1571-1630)

Since ancient times, astronomers have observed the movement of the planets although they were not able to decipher the laws governing them. The more they looked, the more irregularities they found in the orbits of the planets. Using complicated models, astronomers tried in vain to explain these irregularities. It was not until Johannes Kepler appeared that the laws governing the solar system were really understood.

In 1543, Nicolaus Copernicus presented his revolutionary theory that the sun, and not the earth, is at the center of the planetary system. Copernicus also believed, as did Ptolemy, the creator of the old, geocentric world view, that the planets moved at a constant pace in a circular orbit around their center. The result was that the new models still could not explain the old contradictions in the movement of the planets. This was one reason why most leading astronomers of the time would not accept the theory of Copernicus.

The theology student Johannes Kepler became interested in this new view of the world. In 1596 he published a work with the title *Mysterium Cosmographicum* ("Mysteries of the Cosmos"). In this he formulated the theory that the sun exerts a pull on the planets that keeps them in their orbits. However, he still thought that the orbits of the planets were circular.

In 1600, Kepler moved to Prague and became a colleague of the imperial mathematician Tycho Brahe. This Danish scholar had collected an unmatched amount of data for determining the movements of the planets. In this period before the invention of the telescope, his astronomical calculations and measurements were more accurate than any other. After Brahe's death in 1601, Kepler took over his post as mathematician and astronomer at the imperial court of the emperor Rudolf II (1552–1612) of Bohemia-Hungary. He also inherited Brahe's collection of

data. With the help of this information he arrived at a remarkable conclusion: the planets did not travel in circular orbits but in elliptical ones. He also recognized that the planets move faster the closer they are to the sun. These two discoveries, known today as Kepler's first and second laws, were published by him in 1609 in his main work *Astronomia Nova* ("New Astronomy"). In 1619 Kepler formulated his third law. This stated that the square of period of each planet's revolution around the sun is proportional to the cube of its mean distance from the sun. It has been said that Isaac Newton evolved his theory of gravity from these laws and used them to calculate the mass of planets from the distances and orbital periods of their moons.

Kepler's laws gave people a realistic model of their solar system for the first time. For other astronomers the conclusiveness of the calculations was seen as decisive proof of the Copernican system. Kepler's theories finally made the orbit of the planets predictable and disturbances could be recognized. Kepler's last work, the *Tabulae Rudolfinae* ("Rudolfian Tables") formed the basis for astronomical calculations for the following 200 years. Kepler's laws are still of significance today. Using them, the orbit of the moon and of artificial satellites can be understood, since they behave in the same way as the orbits of the planets around the sun.

Johannes Kepler developed the first realistic model of the solar system.

The telescope: bringing the sky down to earth

Galileo Galilei (1564-1642)

By the late 16th century, astronomy had reached a dead end. Partly due to pressure from the censors of the Catholic Church, science still adhered to the Aristotelian idea that divided the natural world into two parts.

The earthly part could be researched by physics, but the heavenly part was not accessible to human logic. This was the basis for the geocentric world view of Ptolemy of Alexandria. He held that the moon, planets and stars all revolved in crystalline spheres around the earth, which itself was motionless. However, increasing numbers of scientists found irregularities in this system and supported the heliocentric system of Nicolaus Copernicus (1473–1543) that was published in 1543. But how could this theory be proved?

When Galileo Galilei, then a professor of mathematics in Padua, heard of the "Dutch telescope" for which Hans Lippershey had applied for a patent in 1608, he immediately set about making one for himself. Galileo mounted a concave (inwardly curving) and a convex (outwardly curving) lens in two pipes of different circumference. He slid the pipes into one another with the concave eyepiece through which the observer looked at one end and at the other the convex objective lens pointed towards the object to be observed.

Now Galileo could occupy himself with what really interested him. He pointed his telescope at the heavens and made some remarkable discoveries. The Milky Way was not a misty band but was composed of myriad points of light that could only be fixed stars. The moon had irregular, changeable light and dark areas. Galileo interpreted these as mountains and craters, valleys, and oceans, and he made some drawings of the rugged surface of the moon. The earth and the moon were therefore much more similar than had been thought previously, and the moon was not a perfectly smooth, unchanging globe. The astronomer could even see the planet Jupiter through his telescope, and he noticed that four moons revolved around it. Therefore it could not be surrounded by a Ptolemaic crystalline sphere, and significantly these heavenly bodies were not revolving round the earth.

In 1610 Galileo published his discoveries in his work *Siderus nuncius* ("Message from the Stars") and he published further observations in 1611 and 1613. He had noticed that Venus went through different phases like the earth. With this he proved that Venus revolved not round the earth but round the sun, whose light it reflected. He also observed sun spots, but these had already been seen by others before him. In 1611, Johannes Kepler (1571–1630) created a design for a superior astronomical telescope that was composed of two convex lenses that gave a clearer (albeit inverted) image and greater magnification.

In 1616 the Church censor banned the writings of Copernicus. But Galileo refused to comply. In *Dialogo*, his main work that appeared in 1632, he compared the geocentric to the heliocentric view of the world. This was the last straw for the Church authorities. Under threat of torture the refractory scientist was forced to repudiate the teachings of Copernicus before the Inquisition. Afterwards the Church court put him under house arrest.

Astronomical research was not to be halted on its new path, however, and with the aid of ever-improving telescopes it was proved that the theories of Copernicus and Galileo were correct.

With telescopes it became possible to prove that Galileo's view of the solar system was correct.

The submarine: down to the deep

Cornelius Jacobszoon Drebbel (1572-1633)

The dream of penetrating the depths of the sea in a boat capable of diving is as old as seafaring itself. The best-known designs are the drawings of an underwater boat by Leonardo da Vinci dating from about the year 1500. But it was not until the beginning of the 17th century that a Dutchman turned theory into practice. The first functioning submarine made by Cornelius Drebbel was launched in the River Thames in 1620.

At the request of King James I of England, the physicist and engineer Cornelius Drebbel came to London in 1606. The young Dutchman was to make a ground-breaking discovery under his patronage. Bur unfortunately when Drebbel presented the first functioning submarine in history the king did not realize its significance. In order to support the English fleet, the young researcher wanted to develop an armed vessel that could approach the enemy undetected below the surface of the water. The first submarine was conceived for military applications.

In constructing his submarine Drebell used the traditional ships of his time as his model. In principle, his ship was built like them. It differed only in that he moved everything that was normally on deck below it, and sheets of leather were stretched over the whole construction. By greasing the leather, Drebbel managed to make his diving boat almost completely airtight and waterproof. In the bows he fastened a long pole with explosive charges at its tip. Enemy ships were to be rammed under water and sunk by these spear-like torpedoes.

Inside the ship there was room for 12 rowers and a few passengers. They breathed through snorkels, which reached from the stern of the boat to the surface of the water where they were fastened to a raft in order to safeguard the supply of oxygen. It was hardly possible for those first submarine passengers to move in the cramped space. The members of the crew also had to remain at their stations and keep the boat moving by rowing steadily. Last but not least, the passengers and crew were bound to their places by their snorkels. The movement of the weight of a single body from the bow to the stern could easily have tipped the boat out of balance and made it sink. In spite of its successful maiden voyage on the river Thames, the inventor could not persuade King James of the usefulness of his diving boat.

More than 200 years were to pass before a submarine successfully engaged in a military encounter for the first time. The *Hunley* sank a blockade ship during the American Civil War in 1864, a feat assisted by the fact that the captain of the ship mistook the submarine for a porpoise or a piece of floating driftwood.

From the beginning of the 20th century, conventional submarines, and since 1954 nuclear-powered ones, have been built and operated throughout the world. In the meantime, their significance has far surpassed their use in military operations, since submarines and similar devices are also used as research vessels for underwater scientific work. In comparison with Drebbel's diving boat, modern submarines have a cigar-shaped hull with a central conning tower. The vessel is flanked by ballast tanks that enable the boat to rise and sink by being filled with air or water. The strongly reinforced inner chamber of the hull enables submarines to withstand the great pressure encountered underwater, and they can submerge to 500 ft, or in the case of nuclear-powered submarines, to 1,650 ft.

Although the invention of submarines dates from the 17th century, they have only been built and used on a large scale for under a hundred years.

The calculator: the automation of mathematics

Wilhelm Schickard (1592-1635)

1623

AROUND THE YEAR 1623

> 1623: A modern pharmacy in which medicines are produced is founded in London.

> 1623: Urban VIII is chosen as pope. During his pontificate, he is a patron of artists and scientists. In the Thirty Years War he supports France rather than the Catholic countries of Spain and Germany, since he wants to prevent the Habsburgs widening their sphere of influence.

> 1624: Cardinal Armand Jean du Plessis, later Cardinal Richelieu, becomes chief minister of the French king Louis XIII.

> 1626: The Dutch merchant Peter Minnewit acquires the island of Manhattan from the Native Americans for a price of 60 guilders. There he establishes the city New Amsterdam, which later becomes New York.

The people of the baroque era loved technical playthings. Automata including mechanically operated speaking dolls, flute players, and signing birds were constructed by ingenious mechanics to entertain the wealthy. But the theologian, orientalist and professor of mathematics and astronomy Wilhelm Schickard wanted to construct a genuinely useful device: he built a calculating machine from such mechanical components.

The sciences made crucial advances in the 17th century. With increasing interest in technical matters and improved instruments, the nature of the tasks performed and the calculations required became increasingly difficult. For example, with the telescope astronomers were venturing into new areas that they wanted to compute mathematically. Calculating machines were also to play an invaluable role in other areas: since the 16th century trade and the money economy were flourishing internationally, using abstract numbers. Measuring, counting, and arithmetic therefore became ever more important tasks, for which mechanical "helpers" were already being used: the abacus, the slide rule, and "Napier's bones" invented by John Napier (1550–1617).

However, Wilhelm Schickard's machine of 1623 was the first to mechanize the basic arithmetical processes of addition, subtraction, multiplication, and division. Schickard's calculator worked on the principle of clockwork. Addition and subtraction were carried out by ten-toothed wheels. Six ten-tooth wheels for six digits were connected and the user could read off the numbers 0 to 9 on each one through a little window. Each wheel rotated through 10 positions and 360 degrees. After a complete revolution, it returned once more to the starting position. At the transition from the digit nine to the digit zero, the counting wheel turned the next ten-tooth wheel one digit position further. Depending on whether the wheels were turned to the right or the left, they could add or subtract. The functions of multiplication and division were carried out in the upper part of the apparatus. Here the multiplication tables were read from revolving cylinders, one for each decimal place. The user selected the factor and could read off the product place by place.

Now a number of other mathematicians also tried their hand at constructing a calculator. In Paris, the philosopher and mathematician Blaise Pascal (1623–62) made a digital adding machine to help his father, a tax collector, with lengthy calculations. Also in 1673 the philosopher and polymath Gottfried Wilhelm Leibniz (1646–1716) presented a "living calculator" before the Royal Society. The construction of this machine was much more expensive, because the individual parts had to be made and assembled extremely accurately. According to own statements Leibniz spent some 24,000 thalers on the construction of his calculating machines.

With the opportunity presented by mass production, calculating machines came to be particularly widely used in the fields of commerce and insurance. Today, computers have largely taken over the task of automated calculation. At the time, however, Schickard's calculating machine marked an enormous step forward.

Calculators were able to carry out the operations of addition, subtraction, multiplication, and division as a completely automated procedure.

Circulation of the blood: systemic and pulmonary

William Harvey (1578-1657)

Until the 17th century the explanations of the function and operation of the heart and blood vessels still reflected the views held in antiquity. But increasingly these ancient theories failed to conform with the scientific discoveries of the time.

1628

AROUND THE YEAR 1628

> 1626: In Rome, St Peter's basilica is completed after 120 years of construction.

> 1628: The English Parliament presents the Petition of Rights to King Charles I. It includes demands for the right to approve taxes, the abolition of martial law, and the end of arbitrary arrests. Charles I accepts these concessions, but he did not summon Parliament again until 1640.

> 1628: Cardinal Richelieu captures the Huguenot city of La Rochelle.

> 1628: The Puritans in New England establish the Massachusetts Bay Company to accelerate the further colonization of the country.

The Greek physician Galen (131–201 BC), his theories on the circulation of the blood, and the role of the *spiritus* or *pneuma* continued to influence medicine for many centuries. According to him, nutrients were conveyed along the intestines to the liver, where the divine *spiritus naturalis* converted the nutrients into new blood as soon as the blood in the human body had seeped away. Galen was convinced that the blood flowed to and fro between two groups of blood vessels, moving through the heart from right to left. In order to explain the flow of blood through the heart, he claimed that there were tiny pores in the thick muscular partition, but it has to be said that these pores were never found. Nevertheless, physicians and anatomists firmly believed in their existence for 1,700 years after Galen's death.

The first observations of blood circulation were made by the Arab scholar Ibn an-Nafis (1210–80). In Europe it was the Spanish physician Miguel Serveto who first referred to the small blood circulation. The assumption that there were two blood circulations in the human body, one smaller and the other larger, was made by Andrea Cesalpino (1524–1603), physician to Pope Clement VIII.

But it was William Harvey, physician at the English court, who developed the first convincing theory on the circulation of the blood in the human body. This theory completely refuted existing beliefs and became the foundation of today's knowledge. In *De Motu Cordis* ("The Movement of the Heart"), published in 1628, Harvey described the two systems of circulation:

one from the heart through the body and back (systemic circulation), and the other from the heart to the lungs and back (pulmonary circulation). He proved his theory by many experiments and anatomical dissections. He studied the heart and dissected blood vessels, measured the amount of blood that passed through the heart at a particular moment, and identified the purpose of the valves in causing the blood to flow in only one direction. With his research Harvey was able to disprove Galen's theories completely. The blood does not seep out, but the blood pumped from the heart flows back to the heart. Because he was not familiar with the microscope, Harvey was unable to prove how the blood from the arteries ended up in the veins. It was the embryologist and zoologist Marcello Malpighi (1628–94) who first discovered the existence of capillaries.

Knowledge of the circulation of the blood opened up completely new insights into the workings of the human body. Where in the past treatment had been limited to simple bleeding, there were now new possibilities such as intravenous injection and blood transfusion. Because they often led to thrombosis and embolism, injections were not commonly given until well into the 19th century. In 1667 Jean-Baptiste Denis gave the blood of a sheep to a person as a transfusion, but fatal complications during this procedure led to the banning of further transfusions. These were only resumed in 1901 after the discovery of blood groups.

Today's knowledge of the two systems of blood circulation was developed in the 17th century.

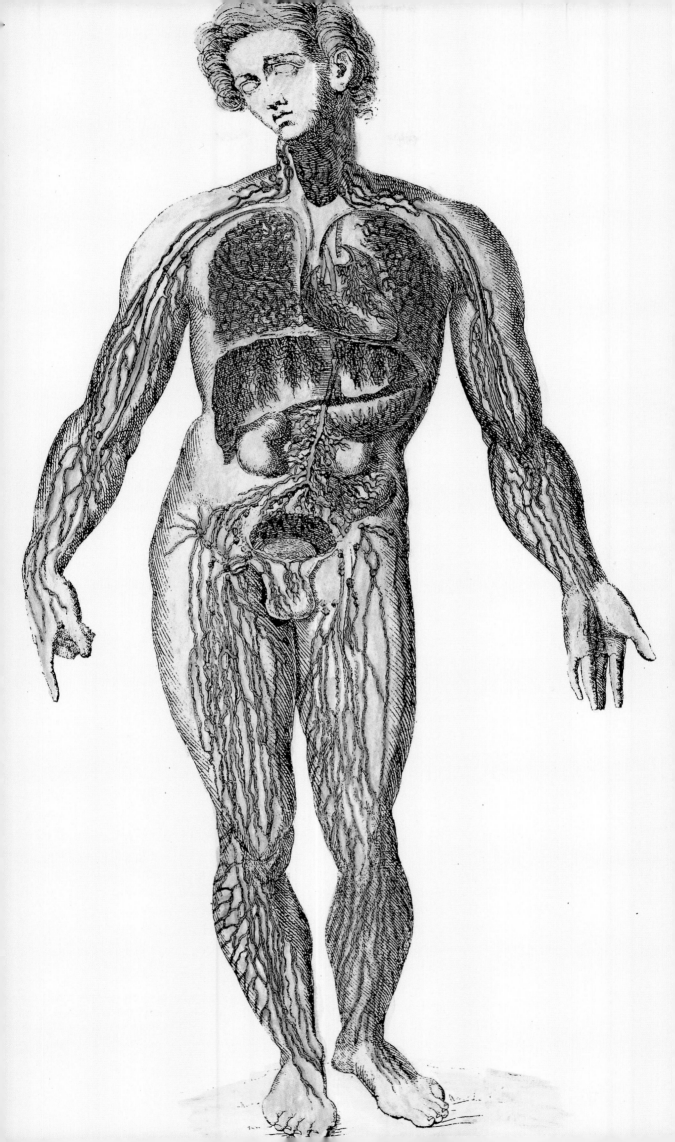

Analytical geometry: geometry assisted by algebra

René Descartes (1596-1650)

For a long time, two areas of mathematics appeared to be irreconcilable. There was geometry, concerned with the form of two-dimensional and three-dimensional objects, and there was algebra, for the solution of equations. René Descartes took up the topic and combined them.

1637

AROUND THE YEAR 1637

> **1633:** Under threat of torture by the court of the Inquisition, Galileo Galilei takes back his conviction that the earth rotates around the sun.

> **1636:** On October 28, the first university of the English colonies is founded in Cambridge, Massachusetts. It is named after the theologian John Harvard, who donated a large sum towards it.

> **1638:** Torture is abolished in England. In the same year, Christianity is prohibited in Japan.

> **1640:** King Charles I summons Parliament for the first time in 12 years. He wants to secure the financial resources to enable him to quell the rebellion in Scotland. Since Parliament will only approve the money if the king grants political concessions and religious rights, he immediately dissolves it again; hence it is known as the Short Parliament.

"*Cogito ergo sum,*" meaning "I think, therefore I am." Descartes' philosophy culminated in this famous quotation, which presupposes the superiority of reason and was the foundation of modern rationalism. The logical clarity of mathematics served Descartes as a methodological ideal in his reflections. Although his philosophical system did not deny the existence of God, he came into conflict with the Catholic Church. With the warning example of Galileo Galilei before him, Descartes published only three excerpts from his work *Le Monde* ("The World") under the title *Discours de la méthode* ("Discourse on Method"), and even then only anonymously.

His book was ground-breaking for modern mathematics. In it, Descartes established analytic (or coordinate) geometry, which fused algebraic and geometrical viewpoints. It enabled Euclidean space to be expressed algebraically and made it possible to solve geometrical construction problems by algebraic methods, and vice-versa.

The key to this achievement was the use of Cartesian coordinates, by which the position, construction, and projection of objects and points in three-dimensional space was expressed numerically. Two coordinates make it possible to locate any given point on a plane by giving the distance from the horizontal x-axis and from the vertical y-axis. For defining points in three-dimensional space an additional axis, the z-axis is used. Analytical geometry makes it possible to express the connection between points by means of an equation, as well as to position the positive and negative values of an algebraic solution geometrically. The three axes of the coordinate system can be added to as required, so that calculations in a theoretical space that has four or more dimensions can be made.

The possibility of representing space in ways other than by drawing later became a decisive factor in Einstein's theory of relativity. Over and above this, the geometrical representation of numbers and algebraic expressions created an important basis for the further development of the theory of functions and of differential and integral calculus.

Today the mathematical methods of Descartes have found their way into the work and leisure world of almost everybody by means of computer graphics and "virtual reality," whether these are used in creating the exciting worlds of computer games, or in the field of architecture for instance. Nowadays architects use special CAD (computer-aided design) programs to design buildings, however complicated, using a three-dimensional data model. Every single point of the building and its components is stored using Cartesian coordinates. The computer program manipulates these to create a three-dimensional view of the building from any angle, to move around within the space, and to show the perspective view of the interior from any chosen point.

The integration of geometry and algebra as analytic or coordinate geometry by René Descartes was a pioneering achievement in modern mathematics.

Vacuum: nothingness is no longer feared

Otto von Guericke (1602-86)

A vacuum is a space from which all air has been exhausted. Industry now uses vacuum technology for food packaging, such as coffee. Microelectronics would not be possible without this "pure space" technology. It was Otto von Guericke in the 17th century who was able to refute the obstinate belief that a vacuum could not exist in nature.

1654

AROUND THE YEAR 1654

> **1648:** The Peace of Westphalia between the German empire, Sweden, and France ends the Thirty Years War.

> **1652:** The Dutchman Jan van Riebeeck establishes Cape Town at the Cape of Good Hope.

> **1654:** The English physicist and anatomist Francis Glisson publishes his work on the anatomy of the liver.

> **1655:** The English Lord Protector Oliver Cromwell dissolves the first parliament.

△ **Otto von Guericke, a Magdeburg politician and engineer, proved the existence of the vacuum.**

The Latin word *vacuum* means "empty," or "empty space." A perfect vacuum is a space completely empty of matter. As this is impossible in practice, science uses the word "vacuum" to describe the conditions inside a container that has had all the air pumped out of it. Investigations of vacuum have led to many interesting discoveries about air pressure, but in order to achieve these successes, the resistance of scientists who insisted that there was no such thing as a vacuum had to be overcome.

The idea of "nothingness" was for a long time accompanied by the fear of emptiness, known as *horror vacui.* Aristotle (384–322 BC) denied the existence of a vacuum for this very reason, the fear of losing one's bearings. The Church too was of the opinion that nature abhors a vacuum, so a contradictory opinion was equivalent to heresy. The first theories on the existence of vacuums arose at the time of the Reformation.

An experiment by the physicist Evangelista Torricelli (1608–47) in the year 1644 brought the first proof. He inverted a glass tube sealed at one end and filled with mercury in a bowl that was also filled with mercury. The level of the mercury sank in the tube, leaving an "empty" space above the top of the mercury in the tube, a vacuum. Torricelli's experiment was the cause of heated argument, most scientists believing that the empty space was "ether." Blaise Pascal (1623–62) commented on the experiment with the words "Nature would rather face her own demise than the smallest empty space."

Otto Guericke, a politician and engineer from Magdeburg, Germany, also carried out experiments dealing with air pressure and vacuum. In 1650, he invented a pump with which he clearly demonstrated the existence of vacuum. Guericke took two metal hemispheres and placed them together to make a globe. He pumped the air out of the globe, so the internal pressure fell below that of the atmosphere. He then harnessed eight horses to each half of the globe, which then tried unsuccessfully to pull the two halves apart. The external air pressure pressed the "Magdeburg hemispheres" together with great force, since there was no internal pressure to oppose it.

It was held that the hemispheres could not be completely empty; how otherwise could light waves be carried in a vacuum? This misconception was based on the persistent theory that the "ether" acted as a "carrying medium" for light. In the 20th century physics began to change traditional ideas of space. Since the special theory of relativity of Albert Einstein (1879–1955), scientists have regarded "relative" space as dependent upon the movement of the observer. The emptiest space that current science can imagine is indeed filled not by matter but by a "field." The "Higgs field," a crystalline structure, is supposed to have similar characteristics to water. But to prove this disputed theory another scientist like Otto von Guericke will be needed.

In 1654 horses were harnessed in a vain attempt to separate the Magdeburg hemispheres in Regensburg, Germany.

Fig I.

A

B

Fig IV.

Fig V.

N N N N

Fig II.

D

Fig III.

Probability theory: unraveling the mystery of coincidence

**Pierre de Fermat (1601-65),
Blaise Pascal (1623-62)**

Science often progresses along unusual paths in acquiring new knowledge. For instance, the discovery of probability theory was due to a game of chance. Can a player calculate a win in advance? Or is it all a matter of chance?

In about 1650 the passionate gambler and writer Antoine Gombaud Chevalier de Méré (1607–84) questioned the French mathematician Blaise Pascal (1623–62) about the outcome of a bet. How often was it possible to throw a double six with two dice, throwing the dice several times? Pascal answered that in the case of six times six, that is 36 possible throws, it would on average happen once. The chances of throwing a double six were therefore 1 to 36. It was now up to the Chevalier de Méré to decide whether to bet on this double six over 36 attempts or not to run the risk.

But Méré had yet another question that was much more difficult to answer. How should the players in a game divide the pool when they break up the game prematurely? It was necessary to divide the money according to each player's chances of winning at the moment that play was ended.

In 1654 de Méré discussed this problem with his colleague Pierre de Fermat (1601–65) in an extensive correspondence. This correspondence marks the beginning of methodical probability theory, which was followed by the birth of the science of the uncertain.

Towards the end of the 17th century the Swiss mathematician Jakob Bernoulli (1654–1705) published *Ars conjectandi sive stochastice* ("The Art of Conjecturing or Speculating"), providing a systematic foundation to the study of chance. He also recognized other practical applications for the new science of probability. Important questions about human life, such as diseases, life expectancy, and death rates, as well as decisions made by the legal system, could be better understood through a fundamentally new classification and meaning.

Bernoulli tried to assess the cogency of an argument based on the "degree of certainty." For him, to "presume" something meant to "measure" the probability. According to the law of large numbers, the number determined by mathematical probability and the actual frequency observed will tend to converge as the number of examples increases. For instance, the more often two dice are thrown, the closer the actual total of double sixes will approach the mathematically calculated total (one thirty-sixth of the total number of throws). Today this law is the foundation of probability theory.

In the 19th century the insurance business developed as an economic sector in its own right as a result of the laws of probability, which enabled it calculate the risks against which people insure. Without probability theory modern physics (quantum physics) would be unimaginable, while decisions in business and politics are also frequently based on the degree of probability of certain events. However it should always be remembered that individuals will often act irrationally.

The theory of probability was discovered accidentally through of a game of chance.

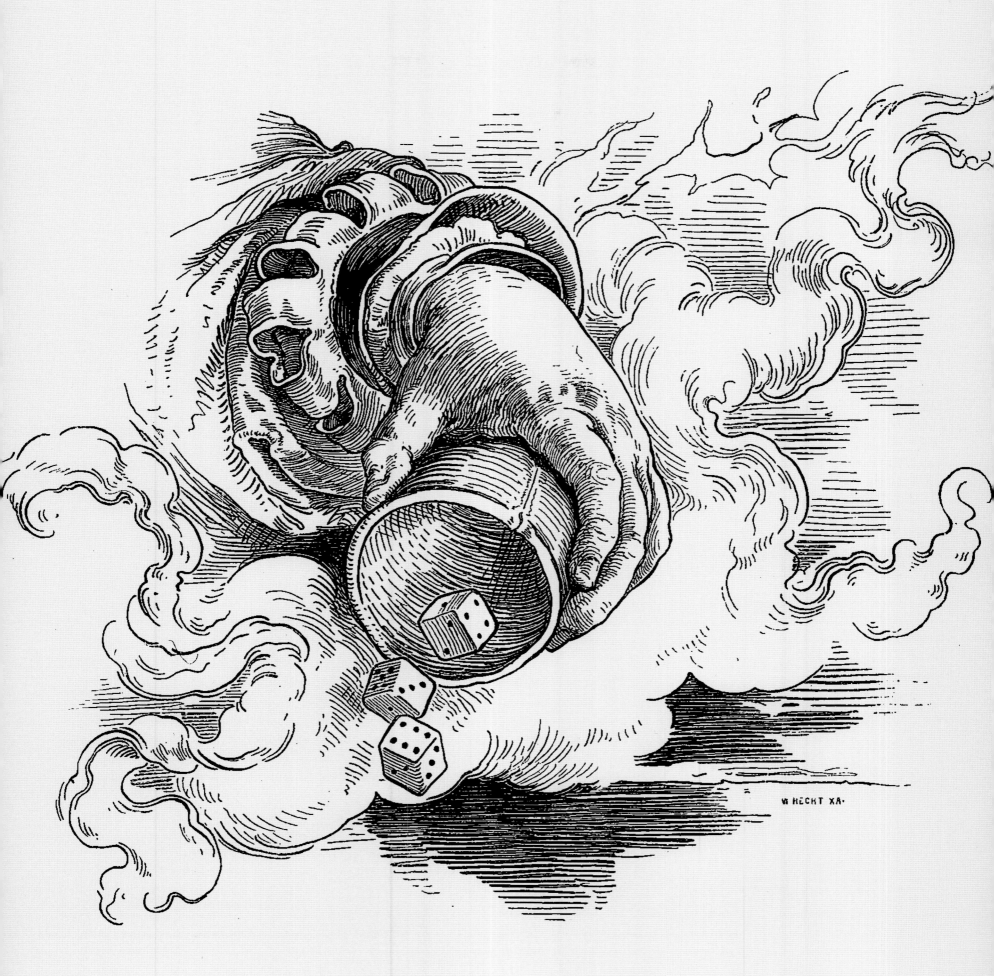

Blood corpuscles: what is blood made of?

Antonie van Leeuwenhoek (1632-1723)

Antonie van Leeuwenhoek was a Delft city official who devised and built microscopes, and also made practical use of them. He made numerous observations of such quality that they were published by the Royal Society. In 1673 he became the first scientist to identify the composition of blood and to see red blood corpuscles.

1673

AROUND THE YEAR 1673

> 1669: The last day of the Hanseatic League of Bremen, Lübeck and Hamburg marks the end of the formerly influential association that once included 200 cities.

> 1670: The fur trading Hudson's Bay Company is established in North America.

> 1672: The mathematician Wilhelm von Leibniz discovers the electric spark while carrying out experiments with friction.

> 1673: With the Test Act, the English Parliament decrees that only people who dissociate themselves from the Catholic faith can occupy public offices.

> 1674: The Reichstag in Regensburg declares war against France.

Antonie van Leeuwenhoek is one of the fathers of modern medicine and the founder of modern hematology, the science of blood. He worked with microscopes that magnified objects about 270 times. With these he ventured into previously unknown worlds, and his findings unsettled not only the doctrine of the Church but also several current scientific theories. For example, the discovery that weevils, fleas or mussels did not grow from grains of wheat or sand but from tiny eggs, weakened the view of the theory of spontaneous generation. By microscopic examinations of plants and muscle tissues Leeuwenhoek was one of the first to discover the three forms of bacterium, bacilli, cocci, and spirilli. With unconscious foresight he bluntly named these microorganisms "disgusting beasts." Science only found out the diseases they could cause much later.

However, the brilliant amateur scientist was concerned not only with plants and animals, but also with the human organism, particularly blood. The English doctor and anatomist William Harvey (1578–1657) had already discovered the circulation of the blood in 1628 and suspected that arteries and veins were connected together by very fine vessels that could not to be perceived with the naked eye. The opinion expressed by the anatomist and physiologist Marcello Malpighi (1628–94) in 1661 was that particles of the blood circulated through a so-called capillary system, a large widely branching network of blood vessels. However, Antonie van Leeuwenhoek in 1668 was the first to see red blood corpuscles thus confirming the earlier theories. With his microscope, van Leeuwenhoek observed red blood corpuscles flowing through the capillaries of a rabbit's ear and a frog's leg. But their function – the transportation of oxygen – was not yet known to van Leeuwenhoek.

From 1673 onwards, the scientist, who had never enjoyed an academic education, relayed his findings to the Royal Society in London in a total of 190 letters. This renowned institution tested his statements and confirmed them in every detail. As acknowledgment, it elected van Leeuwenhoek a member of the society in 1680 and promoted his works. Important scientists and even royalty visited this self-taught man, who was also in correspondence with several foreign scholars. Van Leeuwenhoek wrote his reports only in Dutch, and they were translated into English and published in the *Philosophical Transactions the Royal Society* up to 1724. In1696, van Leeuwenhoek published many of his observations in the book *Arcana naturae detecta*. His insights into the structure of blood are still part of the basic knowledge of medicine.

Leeuwenhoek kept the secret of his outstanding lenses resolutely, even taking his knowledge to the grave. Only in the 19th century were microscopes with better lenses produced.

Antonie van Leeuwenhoek discovered the existence of red blood corpuscles while working with his microscope.

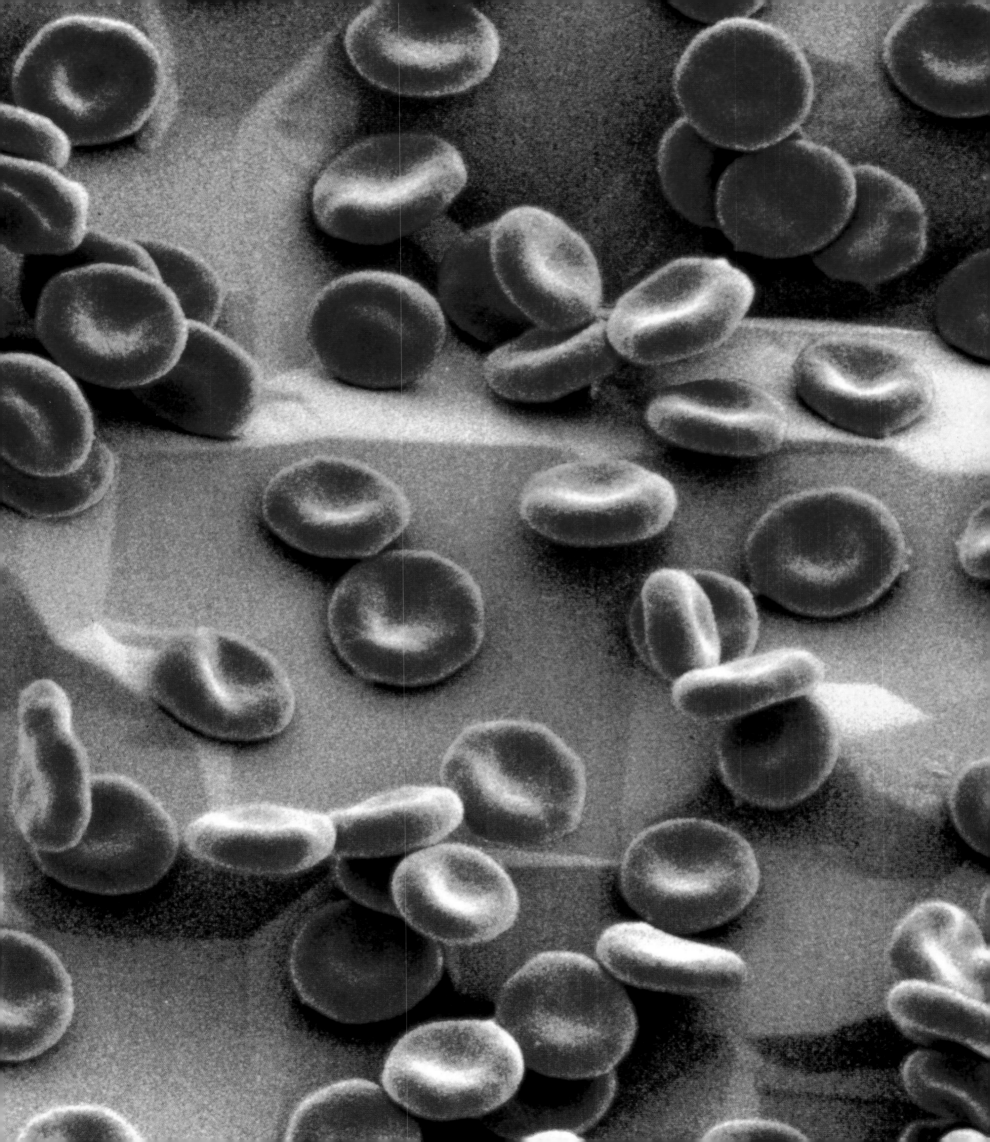

Communication: From jungle drums to space satellite

Civilization without communication?

Human beings can hardly survive on their own and they depend on social contact with their surroundings. In order for this communal living to succeed they must make themselves understood to others. Prompted by the development of personal conversation in which two people alternately play the part of the sender and receiver, people soon felt the need to communicate between each other over longer distances. But that required an additional aid: the communication channel.

Indian smoke signals, African drums, and Roman torches that transmitted information visually or acoustically might be described as the text message services of early civilization. In about 1500 BC the Persians, Greeks, and Romans used messengers who delivered oral information, messages on clay tables or scrolls that were originally made from parchment and later from paper. In 27 BC the emperor Augustus set up a network of mail coaches, but a real postal service in the present sense of the word was only introduced at the end of the 15th century. The growing importance of written speech and increasing literacy of the population gradually led to a culture of letterwriting, no longer the preserve of the Church and state authorities.

It is true that books, although handwritten, played an important part in carrying and distributing information, but it was only when Gutenberg invented printing in the mid-15th century that books became a mass-produced source and distributor of information. The next 400 years were marked by the spread of books throughout the world and the development of related print media such as newspapers, magazines, comics, and written material of every kind.

New possibilities

In the 19th century electricity made a triumphant entry into people's life and opened up new dimensions of communication. After various experiments Samuel Morse developed the electric telegraph in the 1830s. The code he developed and

Letterwriting shaped the cultural and social exchange of information for many centuries.

which was named after him formed the basis on which the apparatus converted the information into electrical impulses and conveyed it to the receiving station across a connecting link. Because telegraphs only recognized two signals, current and no current, they were based on a binary code, the same principle used by computers today. In the 19th and 20th centuries the telegraph contributed to the acceleration of the speed of information distribution; instead of days it only took hours to convey information.

But new technology changed the form of communication as well as its speed. Alexander Graham Bell's invention of the telephone (1876), which is based on the electromagnetic transmission of speech, discovered by Johann Reis in 1860, demonstrates this very clearly. People who were spatially separate from each other could speak together without any time delay for the first time (leaving aside the ancient, equally synchronous, forms of communication of smoke signals and fire signals; but these only provided a very limited exchange of information). People suddenly felt closer than had ever been possible with written communications. It is true that it was still not possible for the people talking to see each other, but the speech was audible and could therefore contain much information; a voice can reveal whether a person is laughing or crying, while the modulation and expression, the speed of speech, and the volume of the sound build a more complete image of the speaker and thus facilitate interaction. Because of this more personal form of communication, which almost resembled a face-to-face conversation, it became apparent at the same time that the "absence" of the other person led on the one hand to more objectivity and shorter telephone calls, and on the other to a kind of loss of inhibition; people tend to be more relaxed and words come more easily if they cannot see each other when speaking. The influence of technical communication media on content has been recognized since the introduction of the telephone.

Mass media

The 20th century was entirely under the influence of the emerging mass media of film, radio and television, which broadcast their message to large numbers of individuals at the same time without these individuals being able to interact directly with each other. This new, one-sided communication soon became generally accepted. When the first radio broadcasting station was set up, there were very few receivers but by 1924 there were 1,500 and by the end of 1925 there were over one million. When television was introduced it too quickly became an indispensable part of most homes, first in black and white, then in color, and finally on broadband cable networks and satellites.

The invention of the telephone and radio telephone made it possible for people in different places to speak to each other without any time delay.

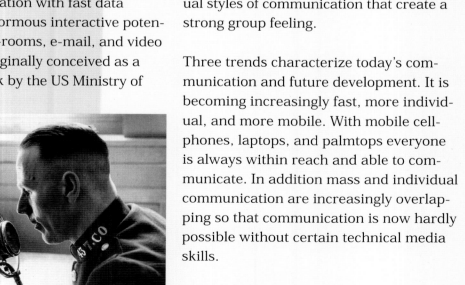

The incredibly fast development of computer technology soon had a revolutionary influence on all areas of communication. After the first computers using relays and vacuum tubes, scientists turned to semiconductor technology. By the end of the 1960s micro-processors were launched onto the market. They were the heart of the first "personal computers" that appeared in the late 1970s. Since then computers have been constantly improved as far as efficiency and storage capacity are concerned.

The digital age is converting all means of communication and information-handling processes into digital signals in order to integrate "older" media such the telephone and radio into a comprehensive multimedia system. It is the high level of interlinking between computers through the Internet that makes possible effective global communication with fast data exchange and enormous interactive potential, such as chat-rooms, e-mail, and video conferencing. Originally conceived as a safe data network by the US Ministry of

The global interlinking of computers makes possible worldwide communication and fast exchange of data.

Defense, the whole world can now communicate through the virtual channels of the Internet. Communication is primarily text-based so that the individual almost disappears behind the characters on the screen of the monitor. The risk of this type of communication is that it may become depersonalized, but the potential disadvantages of virtual communication compared to face-to-face exchanges are compensated for in other ways: in e-mails, chat rooms, and video conferencing, the written message often takes the form of spoken language. The mood of the discussion may be enhanced and conveyed by the use of emoticons such as smileys. These create their own atmosphere, giving clues as to how a written statement should be interpreted, thus replacing the clues that are usually missing in non-verbal communications. Meanwhile members of mailing lists have developed clear, individual styles of communication that create a strong group feeling.

Three trends characterize today's communication and future development. It is becoming increasingly fast, more individual, and more mobile. With mobile cellphones, laptops, and palmtops everyone is always within reach and able to communicate. In addition mass and individual communication are increasingly overlapping so that communication is now hardly possible without certain technical media skills.

The binary system: zero and one, the basis of the universe

Gottfried Wilhelm Freiherr von Leibniz (1646-1716)

1679

AROUND THE YEAR 1679

> 1675: King Charles II sets up an observatory at Greenwich in England. The location of the building is fixed as the zero meridian.

> 1679: To protect itself from France, the main cities of Franconia and the upper Rhineland form the Frankfurt alliance.

> 1679: Charles II passes the Habeas Corpus Act whereby arrests are only possible with a judicial warrant and people may only be imprisoned on decision of the court.

> 1680: Louis XIV declares Alsace French territory, apart from the cities of Strasbourg and Mulhouse.

In 1679, the mathematician and philosopher Gottfried Wilhelm Freiherr von Leibniz invented a mathematical notation in which only the numbers "zero" and "one" existed. While Leibniz described one number as the "Godly" one and the other as the "devilish" one, in modern data processing the binary number system stands for other conditions, such as "go" and "not go," "true" and "false," or "yes" and "no."

△ The scholar Gottfried Wilhelm Freiherr of Leibniz developed the mathematical techniques of differential and integral calculus as well as the binary system.

The polymath Gottfried Wilhelm Freiherr of Leibniz came to scientific honors as an engineer, a natural scientist, a mathematician, and a philosopher. Important mathematical concepts such as "function," "constant," "variable," "coordinate," "parameter," "algebraic," and "transcendental function" go back to him. One of his many ideas in the mathematical field found its widest use in modern data processing – the binary system of numbers.

In 1679 Leibniz published this new binary number system that used not ten but only two digits. With this notation, each number can be expressed by a series of just two symbols. In the opinion of Leibniz, this number system was symbolic of creation "because empty depth and darkness belong to zero and nothingness, but God's spirit with his light belongs to the omnipotent one." Therefore, he expressed the binary numbers as 0 and 1. In the binary system, 2 is represented as 10, 4 as 100, 8 as 1,000, and so forth. As Leibniz proudly stated, the addition of numbers is so easy with this method that they can be added more quickly than it takes to dictate them. Addition using the decimal system requires considerable thought, but the ones and zeroes of the binary system practically sort themselves out on their own. Leibniz applied his binary system to more than mathematical equations. He represented God's creation of the world in seven days as 111 – three "godly" ones without a "devilish" zero – and proposed to use the binary system for the conversion of heathens. Admittedly this plan did not work, but in other areas his system became irreplaceable, since it prepared the way for modern electronic data processing.

Leibniz also designed a binary mechanical calculator, a predecessor of today's computers. In the 20th century, with the aid of electricity, the binary system developed its full capabilities. Digital data processing systems are based on binary numbers, because electric appliances can be controlled with the symbols one and zero indicating the switch conditions "go" and "no go," or "on" and "off." The binary mathematics of Leibniz has attained incalculable significance as the basis of computer and telecommunications technology.

All the processes of modern computer and information technology are based on zero and one.

0	0	25	11001
1	1	26	11010
2	10	27	11011
3	11	28	11100
4	100	29	11101
5	101	30	11110
6	110	31	11111
7	111	32	100000
8	1000	33	100001
9	1001	34	100010
10	1010	35	100011
11	1011	36	100100
12	1100	37	100101
13	1101	38	100110
14	1110	39	100111
15	1111	40	101000
16	10000	41	101001
17	10001	42	101010
18	10010	43	101011
19	10011	44	101100
20	10100	45	101101
21	10101	46	101110
22	10110	47	101111
23	10111	48	110000
24	11000	49	110001

The laws of motion and gravity: the earth's force of attraction

Isaac Newton (1643-1727)

> 1685: Louis XIV revokes the Edict of Nantes, which had guaranteed religious freedom to the Huguenots.

> 1687: For the first time a lecture at a German university is delivered in the German language.

> 1688: Elector Frederick William the Great dies in Potsdam. Under his rule, Prussia had become greatest power in Europe.

> 1689: King William III of England enacts the Bill of Rights, making England a constitutional monarchy and establishing important human and civil rights.

An apple that drops from the tree falls straight down to the earth below it. A stone that is thrown describes an arc before falling on the ground. The laws governing these everyday experiences were defined by the English mathematician and physicist Sir Isaac Newton.

In August 1684 Sir Isaac Newton, professor of mathematics at Cambridge, met Edmond Halley, professor of geometry at Oxford. They discussed the subject of planetary motion. At the beginning of the 17th century Johannes Kepler had discovered the paths of the planets as they orbited the sun, but the explanation of planetary motion was still a mystery to scholars. Newton was prompted by his conversation with Halley to take up once more his research into universal gravity that had already fascinated him when he was a student.

Starting from the premise that there must be a fundamental force of attraction between the sun and the planets in order to maintain the balance of the system, Newton reflected on the interactions between bodies and thus also on the principles of motion. Kepler's laws on the path of planetary orbits could only be explained by accepting that there was a force of attraction between the planets themselves as well as the force of attraction of the sun. Eventually, Newton formulated three laws of motion that made him the founder of a completely new science, dynamics.

Newton's axioms or laws of motion are:
1. Every object in a state of uniform motion tends to remain in that state of motion unless an external force is applied to it.
2. The acceleration of an object is directly proportional to the force applied to it and inversely proportional to its mass.
3. For every action there is an equal and opposite reaction.

On the basis of these considerations Newton decided that there was one force of attraction that affected all bodies in space. The law of universal gravitation formulated by Newton states that the mutual force of attraction depends on the mass of the bodies and their distance apart. In other words this means that the attraction between two bodies due to gravity is directly proportional to the product of their masses and indirectly proportional to the square of the distance between their centers. These forces are so small that a sizable object, such as the planet earth, is required to have a significant effect on other bodies in motion.

Newton published his theory in 1687 in his most important work *Philosophiae naturalis principia mathematica* ("The Mathematical Principles of Natural Philosophy"), supported and funded by his old friend and admirer Halley. The idea that every single body in the universe is subject to gravity marked a turning point in the history of science and remained the foundation of the scientific conception of the world for the following 200 years and more. As well as defining the force of gravity, Newton discovered one of the fundamental forces that determines the interactions of matter. It was many years before any other similar forces – such as those between fundamental nuclear particles and electromagnetic interactions – were discovered.

In 1687 Isaac Newton published his major work *Philosophiae Naturalis Principia Mathematica* in which he explained the Law of gravity.

Halley's Comet: the return of the comet

Edmond Halley (1656-1742)

1705

AROUND THE YEAR 1705

> 1700: Antonio Stradivari makes his first violins.

> 1703: The War of Spanish Succession breaks out over the throne of Spain. With the death of King Carlos II in 1700, Habsburg rule ended in the country. With support of England, Archduke Charles of Austria fights against the Bourbon Philip V. Only in 1713 with the Peace of Utrecht is Philip V's claim to the throne secured.

> 1703: After his victory over Sweden Tsar Peter I founds St Petersburg on the site of the Swedish fortress Nyenschanz. Nine years later it becomes the capital of Russia.

△ The astronomer Edmond Halley discovered that comets moved on an elliptical orbit.

At the same time as the Norman Conquest of England was taking place in 1066, there was a spectacular comet in the skies that was later depicted in the Bayeux tapestry recording the Conquest. 650 years later the English astronomer Edmond Halley discovered the reason for this phenomenon.

Until 1577 comets were believed to be atmospheric phenomena, comparable to lightning and the northern lights. It was the Danish astronomer Tycho Brahe who proved in 1577 that they were in fact celestial. Over 100 years later Edmond Halley put forward the theory that comets, like planets, move around the sun in an elliptical orbit. From this it followed that comets reappeared on a regular basis.

Halley applied Kepler's discoveries concerning the orbital course of the planets and Newton's laws of gravity to a particular phenomenon: a comet that could observed in 1682. He calculated that it had a period of revolution of 76.2 years and maintained that the comets seen in 1607, 1531, and 1456 were the same comet. He calculated the appearances of the comet back to 240 BC and identified it with the comet depicted in the Bayeux tapestry. He also predicted the comet's return in 1758. In 1705 Halley published his discoveries in the treatise *Astronomiae Cometicae Synopsis* ("Synopsis of the Astronomy of Comets"). In 1718 he also established that the "fixed" stars that were thought to be anchored in space actually moved, albeit extremely slowly.

With the comet named after him, Halley had discovered a celestial body that was to be the darling of future astronomers and space research. When Halley's comet returned again in 1986, several countries sent space probes to observe the phenomenon. The European Space Agency Giotto probe came within 370 miles of Halley's comet and was therefore able to take pictures of the nucleus of the comet, a sight never seen before. Scientists believe that the nuclei of many comets are as old as the solar system and have barely changed since then, so they hope that research on the clumps of dust and ice that are comets will provide clues about the origin and development of the solar system. Up to now scientists have concentrated mostly on the matter that burns out in the tail of a comet. But the European Space Agency (ESA) is planning a landing on comet 46P/Wirtanen with the Rosetta comet probe in 2011.

Scientists also hope that comets will provide new information about cosmic catastrophes. Unlike planets, comets are very unstable celestial bodies. They burn out slowly and can be pushed out of their own orbit into the gravitation field of planets, or they may be shattered by the driving force of its own gases. This means that parts of comets may fall onto planets. In 1992 the comet Shoemaker-Levy 9 broke up. Two years later debris of the comet fell onto Jupiter for weeks on end, causing visible disturbances, including fireballs larger than the earth. This led to a number of catastrophe scenarios speculating that earth could suffer a similar fate.

Halley's comet is due to pass the earth again in 2061 – if nothing unforeseen happens in the meantime.

Halley's comet returns every 76 years when it provides a fascinating spectacle in the night sky.

The blood pressure test reveals how hard the heart works

Stephen Hales (1677-1761)

1726

AROUND THE YEAR 1726

> 1725: Catherine I, the wife of Peter I, becomes tsarina of Russia.

> 1726: Jonathan Swift's novel *Gulliver's Travels* is published anonymously.

> 1726: The construction of the Frauenkirche in Dresden begins. It will take 12 years to be completed.

> 1727: The English mathematician, physicist, and astronomer Sir Isaac Newton dies in London.

> 1727: Russia and China agree that the Amur river should be the border between their empires.

Since ancient times, it was believed that the liver was the center of the circulation of the blood . But in 1628 William Harvey disproved this view and stated that the blood circulated round the body from the heart. A century later, experiments carried out by Stephen Hales, an English clergyman, resulted in important findings concerning blood pressure.

As so often in the history of medicine, it was research on animals that formed the starting point for scientific investigation of the human body. In 1726 Stephen Hales performed an animal experiment that finally clarified the concept of blood pressure. He introduced a thin brass tube into the carotid artery of a mare. This tube was connected to a vertical glass tube about 10 ft long. The pressure of the circulation pushed the blood in the tube up to a height of well over six ft. The blood in the glass tube moved in time with the heart beat. Hales recognized that the highest pressure corresponded to the pressure created by the heart when contracting. The lowest pressure represented the level of resistance presented by the blood vessels in the body. Obviously this invasive method of testing blood pressure was not suitable to be applied to humans and it therefore played no part in medicine.

In 1881 the Viennese university lecturer Ritter von Basch (1837–1905) invented an instrument that measured blood pressure without needing to tap into an artery. Called a sphygmomanometer, this had an inflatable bag that constricted the arm and measured systolic pressure when the pulse disappeared. The instrument enabled scientists to check blood pressure, discovering more about it and its changes. But the meaning of different values of blood pressure remained a controversial topic among doctors. Even at the turn of the century many still believed that blood reflected the strength of the heart, rather than the pressure produced by it, so high blood pressure was mistakenly considered to be a sign of good health.

The prototype of von Basch's instrument to measure blood pressure was the forerunner of the improved model made by the Italian pediatrician Scipione Riva-Rocci (1863–1937) in 1896. His instrument had an inflatable rubber arm cuff and a mercury manometer for carrying out external blood pressure measurement on the patient's upper arm. In 1905 the Russian surgeon Nicolai Sergejewitsch noticed that by decreasing the pressure of the cuff while listening through a stethoscope, he could hear a murmur in the artery of the upper arm as the heart relaxed between beats. Using this method it was now possible to measure diastolic pressure for the first time.

The pumping action of the heart takes place in two phases, systole and diastole. They correspond to the two parts of blood pressure measurement: systolic pressure, when the heart contracts and the blood flows out, and diastolic pressure, when the heart relaxes. As Stephen Hales had already noted, the pressure in blood vessels is at its highest when the heart contracts.

The experiment by Stephen Hales on a live horse contributed significantly to the progress of medicine. Today, measuring blood pressure is one of the most important standard tools of medical diagnosis.

Measuring blood pressure is still one of the most helpful ways to provide a clinical picture of a patient.

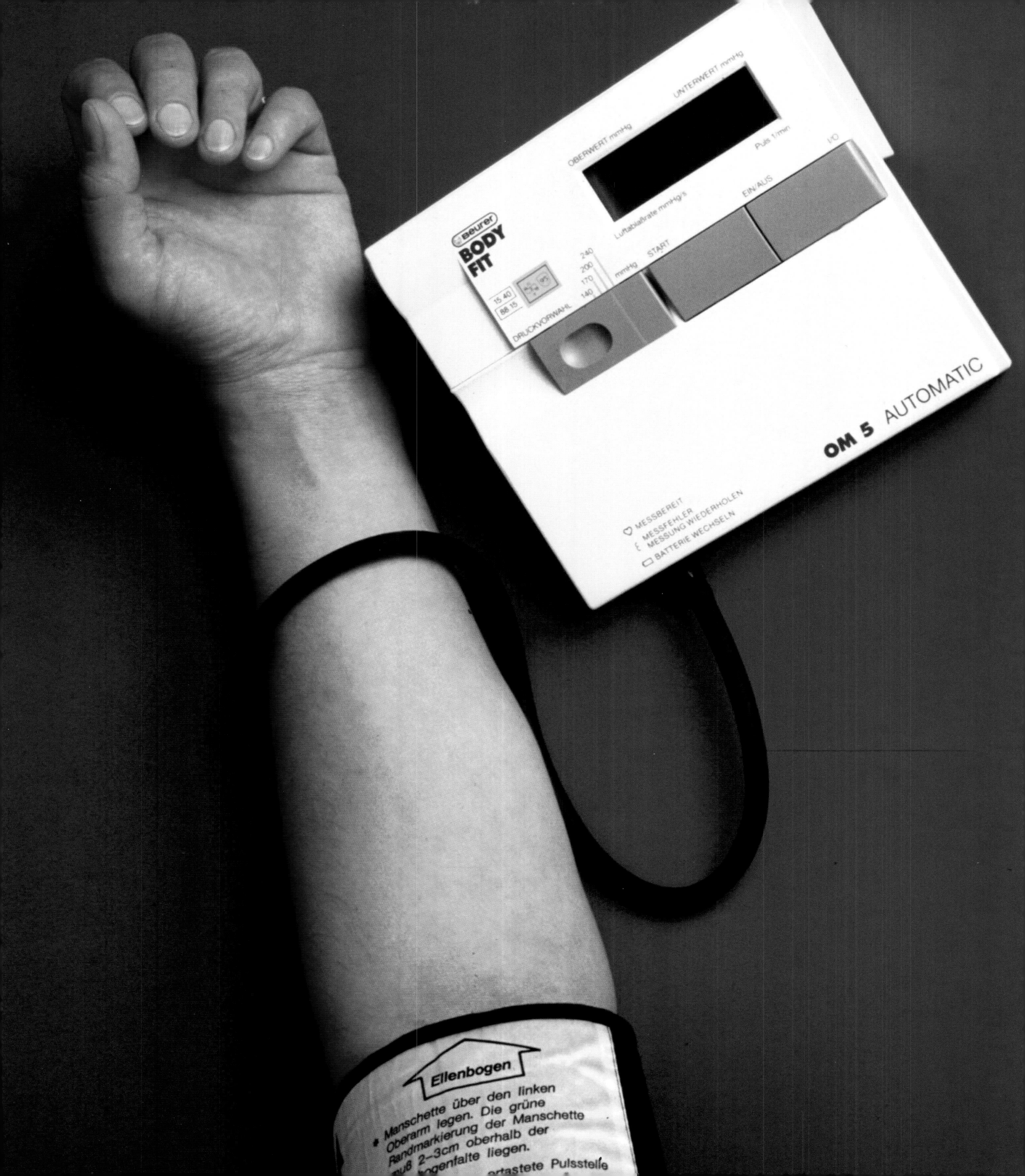
Beurer
BODY FIT
OBERWERT mmHg
UNTERWERT mmHg
Puls 1/min
I/O
Luftablaßrate mmHg/s
EIN/AUS
START
mmHg
240
200
170
140
DRUCKVORWAHL
OM 5 AUTOMATIC
MESSBEREIT
MESSFEHLER
MESSUNG WIEDERHOLEN
BATTERIE WECHSELN
Ellenbogen
Manschette über den linken
Oberarm legen. Die grüne
Randmarkierung der Manschette
muß 2–3cm oberhalb der
liegen.

The classification of flora: families of flowers

Carl von Linné (1707-78)

The Swedish doctor and biologist Carl von Linné, known as Linnaeus, revolutionized botany. The scientist developed a method for naming plants known as the "binomial system of nomenclature." This system still forms the basis of botanical classification today.

1735

AROUND THE YEAR 1735

> **1733:** With the Molasses Act, Great Britain imposes heavy duties on sugar, molasses, and rum that do not come from its colonies.

> **1736:** Two French expeditions explore Peru and Lapland to establish whether the earth's polar circumference and the equator are round, or flattened at the poles.

> **1736:** The German Reichstag declares the renunciation of Lorraine.

> **1737:** The first Masonic lodge in the German empire is established in Hamburg. In the following year Pope Clement XII prohibits Catholics from adopting Freemasonry, declaring that anyone opposing this would be excommunicated.

The 18th century was the century of natural science. Zoological and botanical gardens sprang up everywhere where people could see and be amazed by the unique creatures and strange plants brought from exotic lands. The great voyages of discovery made in the 16th and 17th centuries had made all this possible.

The circumnavigators of the globe had worked so hard that the sheer mass of previously unknown plants and animals soon exceeded the boundaries of the traditional classification systems of zoologists and botanists. The question arose as to how to deal with this problem. In 1735, Carl von Linné, also called Carolus Linnaeus, came up with a new systematic foundation for the two branches of science. He suggested naming all plants and animals consistently with a genus and a species name. In 1730 he had already published a first treatise on the sexual system of plants in which he had ordered them according to the characteristics of their reproductive organs. Two years later, sponsored by the Swedish Royal Society of Science, he undertook a six-month research journey through Lapland. Illustrations of the time show him in the traditional dress of the Lapps with a drum for collecting botanical specimens hung over his shoulder.

After his return, Linnaeus sat for his medical exams in 1735. In the same year he published the first version of his famous work *Systema Naturae*, in which he classified plants according to the existence, number, and growth of their stamens and pistils. He grouped similar species under the same "genus," related genera under "orders," and orders into "classes." He also used this system to classify animals. Linnaeus gave each species a double Latin name; the first was used to define the genus and the second the particular species. This form of binomial nomenclature has been used in biology ever since, and it gave scientists an international technical terminology that diverted the terminological chaos that had seemed imminent. The scientist gave humans an official name too: *Homo sapiens.*

Linnaeus' system rapidly became widespread. In 1741, he was appointed Professor of Botany at the University of Uppsala in Sweden. He built up a museum of natural history and classified the botanical garden according to his system. Consequently Uppsala developed into a center of scientific botany, and few natural scientists had as many students as Linnaeus. He sent his pupils out to all parts of the globe to collect new material. His original *Systema Naturae,* which had originally been only a few pages in length, grew to a work of several volumes by 1768.

The classification system was successful because it was easy to learn and simple to apply. But since it mainly used the reproductive organs for its structural divisions, some of the groupings seemed arbitrary. The German philosopher Immanuel Kant (1724–1804) criticized it as an "artificial system" and called for a "natural classification" of plants and animals. This demand was met in the mid-19th century when the biologist Charles Darwin (1809–82) appeared on the scene with his theory of evolution.

The classification of plants according to Linnaeus.

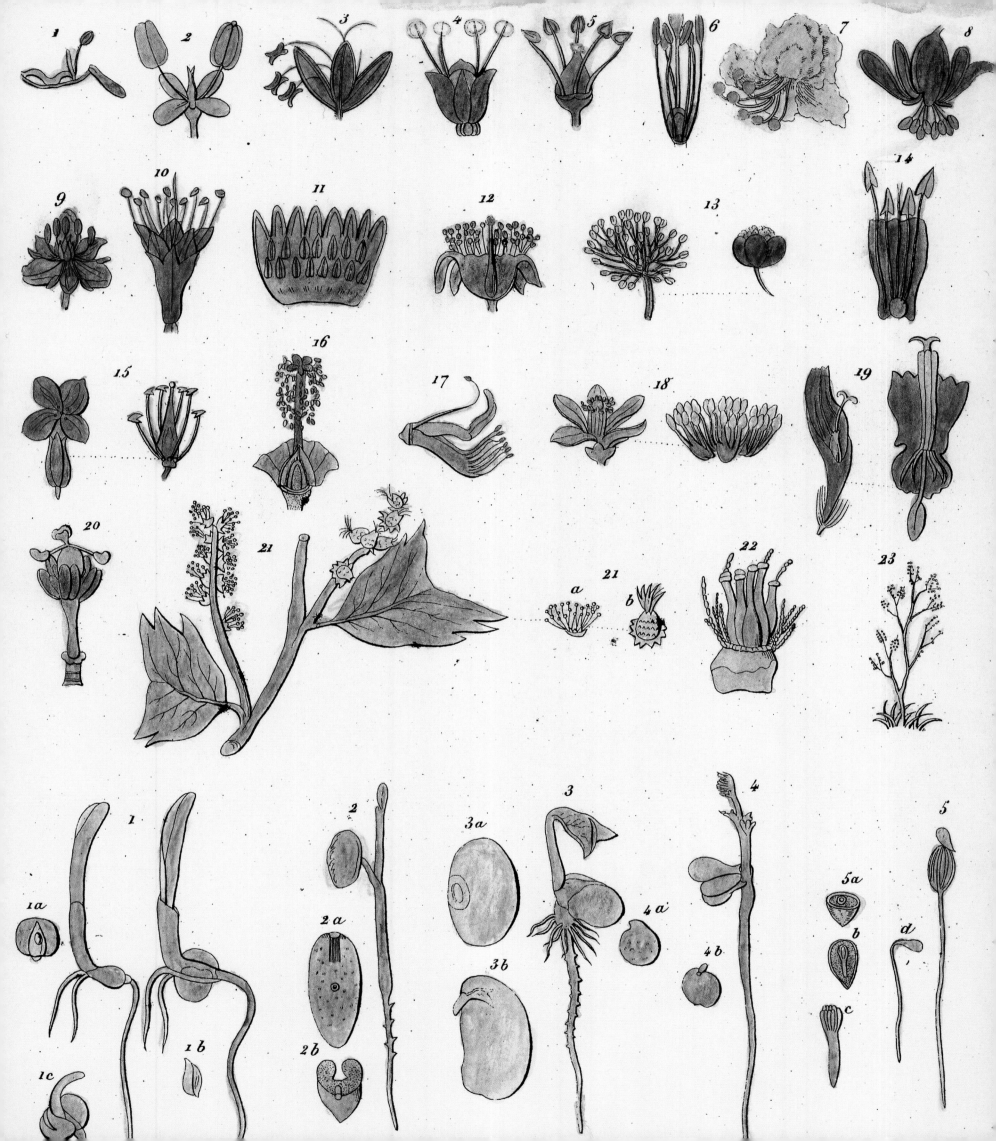

The Milky Way: the heavens become clearer

Thomas Wright (1711-86), Immanuel Kant (1724-1804)

The Milky Way is a mysterious, diffuse band of light across the sky that has fascinated people for thousands of years. In about 1750 the English scientist Thomas Wright came to the conclusion that the Milky Way was a disc. Based on this theory, the philosopher Immanuel Kant made some bold speculations about the structure of the universe.

According to Greek mythology, the Milky Way was created while Zeus's son Hercules was suckling at the goddess Hera's breast as she slept. Zeus had placed him there to ensure that Hercules sucked in immortality together with the goddess's milk. But some of the milk was spilt and became a luminous band of light in the sky.

Democritus suggested that the white nebula was made up of a mass of separate stars. This was eventually proved centuries later by Galileo Galilei, who studied it through his telescope. It was the Englishman Thomas Wright who first brought some order to the Milky Way and its fixed stars. He held that the Milky Way was not a "way" but a disc-shaped grouping of several planetary systems. Seen from the earth, the curve of this disc encompasses the sky in a circular manner and only part of its radius can be seen; therefore the earth and its solar system must lie on its surface. In 1750 Wright published his work *An Original Theory and New Hypothesis of the Universe*. This prompted the young Immanuel Kant to develop his own ideas on the structure and origin of the universe. In 1755 he published *Allgemeine Naturgeschichte und Theorie des Himmels*, whose full English title is the "Universal Natural History and Theories of the Heavens, or: an Attempt to Treat the Condition and Mechanical Origin of the Whole Universe According to the Laws of Newton."

Kant took an important step beyond Wright in his theory. Like Wright, he believed that the Milky Way or the Galaxy (from the Greek *gála* = milk) was one of many stellar systems, or "world islands," that made up the universe. He also believed that he would discover similar galaxies in the neighboring nebulous stars that today are known as the Orion and Andromeda nebula. Kant concluded from the proximity of the nebulas to the Milky Way that their systems shared a similar organization, with a common structure and similar properties. For instance, he assumed that every galaxy had a similar disc shape with a concentrated grouping of stars in the center, and the same rotation on its own axis. In order to support the theory of a common origin that was implied by this assumption, Kant referred to Newton's laws of motion. The force of gravity – the mutual attractive force of masses – and a force of repulsion had an interactive effect on prime matter and determined the shape of the galaxies. This process, an alternation of order and chaos, continued endlessly.

Instead of seeing the whole universe as the result of a divine act of creation, Kant explained the origin of the universe through the laws of natural science. Many of Kant's contemporaries dismissed his theory as mere speculation. Although Kant's work is mainly admired for its visionary power, many of Wright's and Kant's ideas were later confirmed by astronomers using improved technical instruments.

According to Greek mythology the Milky Way was created from milk spent while Hercules was being suckled by Hera.

1750

AROUND THE YEAR 1750

> Doctor John Hunter succeeds for the first time in the artificial fertilization of a human being.

> Spain and Portugal contractually agree on the borders of their South American colonies.

> Frederick II drastically cuts the rights of the Jewish citizens of Prussia.

> The composer Johann Sebastian Bach dies in Leipzig.

△ **Immanuel Kant was encouraged by Thomas Wright's discoveries about the Milky Way to reflect on the creation of the universe.**

The lightning conductor: nature is outwitted

Benjamin Franklin (1706-1790)

It was once believed that lightning was an expression of God's anger, because a direct lightning strike often caused disastrous damage. How could anyone protect themselves against it? In 1752 the American natural scientist and politician Benjamin Franklin invented a device that intercepted lightning and conducted it to the earth without danger. As so often in research, it was coincidence that helped him to the breakthrough.

1752

AROUND THE YEAR 1752

> 1752: The French Estates General confiscates the private property of the archbishop of Paris. Louis XIV dissolves parliament, but recalls it in 1754 because of the renewed danger of civil war.

> 1752: Great Britain introduces the Gregorian calendar.

> 1753: The British Museum opens in London.

> 1754: In Prussia, the use of torture in criminal proceedings is abolished.

△ Benjamin Franklin discovered the principle of the lightning conductor by chance.

A summer thunderstorm gave Benjamin Franklin the idea for the lightning conductor. He was flying a kite during a storm when a flash of lightning struck it and was conducted to earth by the string. The scientist felt a slight electric shock through it. At that time it was already scientific knowledge that electrically charged bodies could discharge themselves through a pointed conductor. Franklin now perceived from the experience of his own body that lightning was an electrical phenomenon, and from this deduction he developed the principle of the lightning conductor. On September 1, 1752, he installed on his house in Philadelphia an iron rod fitted with a steel tip, projecting over 6 ft above the roof. The rod was grounded by being buried 5 ft deep in the ground.

Within 20 years this system was widely accepted. It was simple to install and gave effective protection against damage by lightning. Even the Church, which had once opposed this outrage against the wonders of God, soon recognized the advantage for its tall steeples. It is said that the British King George III deplored Franklin so much as a fighter for American independence that he was determined that his invention should not be "uncritically" adopted. So he ordered that the lightning conductors at his palaces should have rounded ends rather than Franklin's pointed ones. Ironically, it was found that the rounded-end construction was more effective, but this was only discovered by comprehensive experiments carried out in the late 20th century.

So how does Franklin's invention work? The "trick" of the lightning conductor is to attract the lightning and then conduct it safely to the ground. Lightning always seeks the easiest, most direct route to the ground. Usually it strikes tall buildings, or the pointed lightning rod on the roof itself. The current is then conducted through a cable or thick copper strip to copper netting or a copper plate that is buried in contact with ground water. The three components forming the lightning conductor must survive a lightning current of up to 200,000 amperes.

Nevertheless it is dangerous to stay close to a lightning conductor. The lightning may leap across and flow to earth partly through the human body. For this reason, all gas and water pipes, telephone and electricity cables, aerials, heaters, electrical appliances, and metal rain gutters must also be connected to the ground. In spite of these precautions an apartment may not be completely secure, so during a thunderstorm metal objects such as faucets, plumbing fittings, television aerials, and telephones should not be touched, nor is it advisable to take a bath. Lightning may also hit power lines causing excessive voltage surges that can destroy electronic components. To prevent this the sockets supplying sensitive equipment should have surge protection. The best protection against lightning is to stay within a "Faraday cage," a grounded metallic enclosure, such as an automobile.

Benjamin Franklin's brilliant idea was to attract the lightning and conduct it safely to the ground.

Pathological anatomy: learning about life by studying the dead

Giovanni Battista Morgagni (1682-1771)

IN THE YEAR 1760

> With the conquest of Montreal, New France becomes a British colony.

> Russian landowners can banish impertinent serfs to Siberia.

> The Scottish chemist Joseph Black propounds the theory distinguishing heat and temperature from each other.

> The potato is brought to Prussia and establishes itself as a basic food.

The doctors of the Middle Ages were still very skeptical about autopsies, the dissection of corpses. However, in the 17th century scientists recognized the significance that the study of the dead could have for the living. It allowed deductions to be made that were of benefit to the living body and its illnesses.

The word "pathology" is first found in the work of the Greek doctor Galen of Pergamon (131–201 AD). It comes from *pathos* (suffering) and *logos* (teaching), and therefore means "teaching of suffering." Galen, the private doctor of Marcus Aurelius, founded humoral pathology, which states that the reason for all disease is the imbalance of the different bodily humors, or fluids. In some later autopsies there were obvious discrepancies between the visible cause of death and the ancient theories of Galen, but the people who noticed these preferred to believe that the human body had changed in certain ways over the years rather than admit that the great master of antiquity had made a mistake.

In its present form as the study of disease, pathology goes back to the teachings of the Italian doctor Giovanni Battista Morgagni from Padua. His five-volume work, *De sedibus et causis morborum* ("On the Seats and Causes of Sickness"), published in 1760, was the result of almost 700 autopsies. It is regarded as the basis of all pathological research that succeeded it. His book impressively illustrates the connection between clinical symptoms and the results of the autopsies. It was Morgagni's objective to demonstrate the relationship between symptoms of disease, the causes of disease, and the findings of the postmortem. It was no longer the "dissection" of the human body itself that was at the forefront of the operation, but the possible correlation between illness and changes found in the organs.

However, the doctors soon ran into a number of difficulties. Not only did they have to put up with the stigma of being reproached as graverobbers, but the unpleasant aftermath of dissection was that the doctors themselves were responsible for removing the corpses when they had finished with them. This is why most professors preferred to teach from books rather than from the object itself.

It was not until the end of the 18th century that hospitals and universities hired prosectors especially for the job of dissecting (Latin *prosecare* = cut). While the professor was giving his anatomy lecture, these specialists, who were usually surgeons, pointed out the organic and anatomical changes in the dead body.

Pathological anatomy is one of the fundamental medical sciences, since it conveys an unparalleled insight into the complex structures of the human body and therefore helps towards a better understanding of its functions.

△ **Galen and Hippocrates, the most famous physicians of antiquity influenced medicine until the modern age.**

In the 17th century scientists realized that the study of dead bodies provided important information about the living and the diseases that affected them.

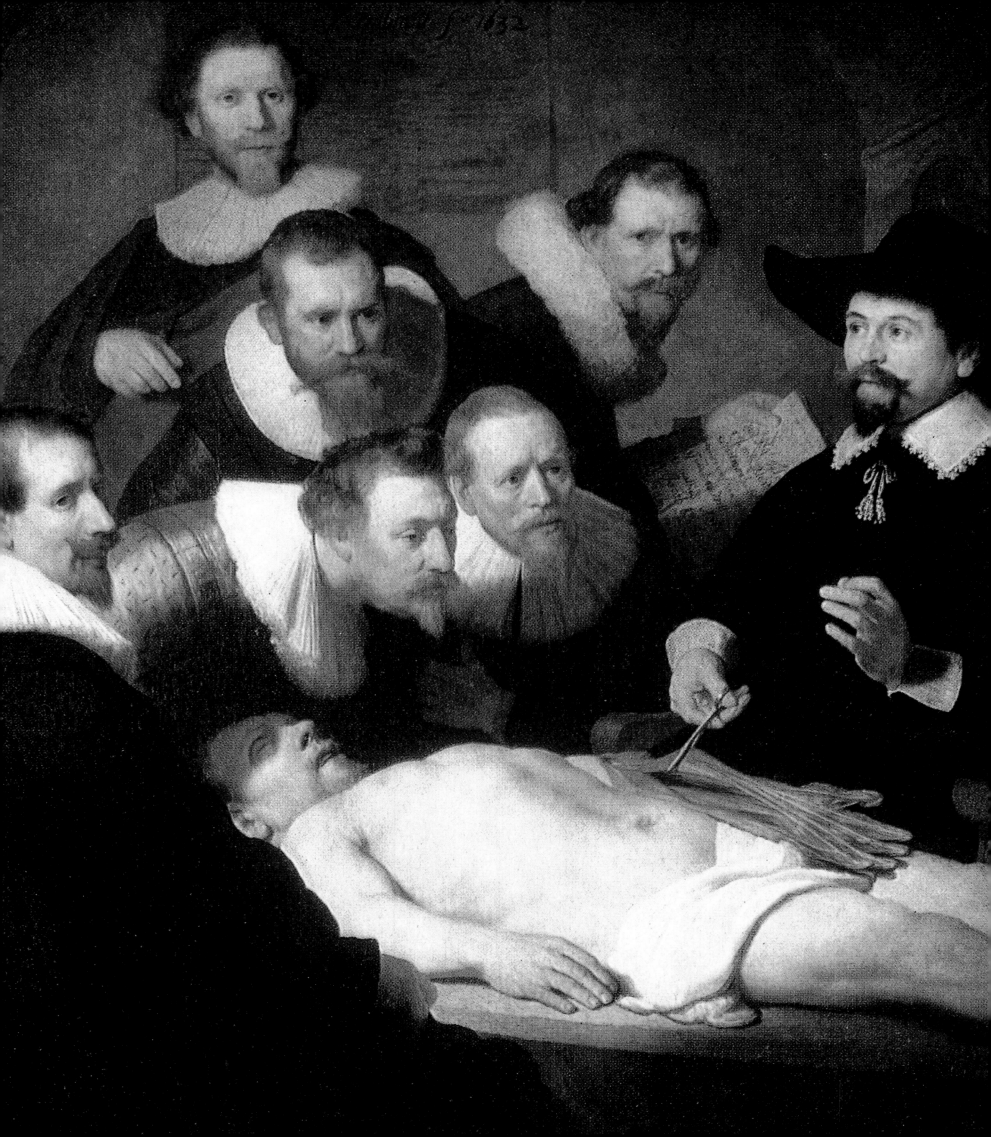

The low pressure steam engine: low pressure, high performance

James Watt (1736-1819)

Everybody who has heard the whistle of a steam kettle as the steam escapes knows something of the power that there is in boiling water. As far back as antiquity, scientists endeavored to find a way of harnessing the power of steam. The first practical applications of the principle did not become possible until the 18th century, but thereafter the discovery of the steam engine changed people's lives and working conditions fundamentally and permanently.

1765

AROUND THE YEAR 1765

> 1763: Wolfgang Amadeus Mozart appears before Empress Maria Theresa at the age of only six.

> 1764: Russia expels a settlement of German farmers from the Volga.

> 1765: Great Britain imposes the Stamp Act, a tax on printing and documents, on the North American colonies. The colonies declare the tax unlawful since it was introduced without the consent of any North American representatives in the British Parliament. They demand the right to return delegates chosen by the people to Parliament: "No taxation without representation."

In 1712, the English blacksmith Thomas Newcomen (1663–1729) built the first efficient steam engine to power water pumps in coal mines. This engine operated on the principle of atmospherics, that is, the actual work was performed by air pressure. The pump linkage was connected to a piston inside the cylinder in such a way that the weight of the linkage forced the piston upwards. At the same time, steam was admitted to the cylinder from a separate boiler. With the piston in the upper position, the steam was cut off and condensed by cold water. This caused a vacuum within the cylinder, so that atmospheric pressure pushed the piston down again, which in its turn caused the pump linkage to rise.

Newcomen's machine proved to be a true friend of the miners by removing water from mine workings. After an improvement by John Smeaton (1724–92), which reduced the amount of coal needed to run it by 50 percent, it rapidly became established in coal mines throughout Britain.

It was coincidence that led to the further development of this machine. While repairing a Newcomen engine in 1765, the mechanic James Watt observed the great wastage of energy caused by the process of alternately cooling and heating the cylinder. Watt believed that the problem could be avoided by using a separate condenser, so that the power cylinder was always hot and the condenser always at the same cool temperature. On January 5, 1769 Watt applied for a patent for his invention of an efficient low-pressure steam engine, so named because of the low pressure of the exhaust steam. The patent was for "A New Invented Method of Lessening the Consumption of Steam and Fuel in Fire Engines."

The Watt steam engine with its separate condenser used only one-quarter of the coal needed to run a Newcomen engine. James Watt rented out his machine for one-third of the cost of the coal saved. His business partner, Matthew Boulton (1728–1809), put their business policy in a nutshell when he said: "I sell what the whole world wants to have: power!"

The textile industry was the first to use the Watt steam engine in production. In 1785 the first steam-driven spinning machines were introduced, and in 1806 the steam-driven mechanical loom followed them. As a source of energy available anywhere and at any time, it enabled the production industry to move to the cities, where the rapidly growing population could provide the numbers of workers needed. But there was a negative aspect to this development. It resulted in the creation of grim factory towns in which child labor, low wages, and long working hours were the predominant characteristics.

James Watt applied for a patent for his direct working low-pressure steam engine.

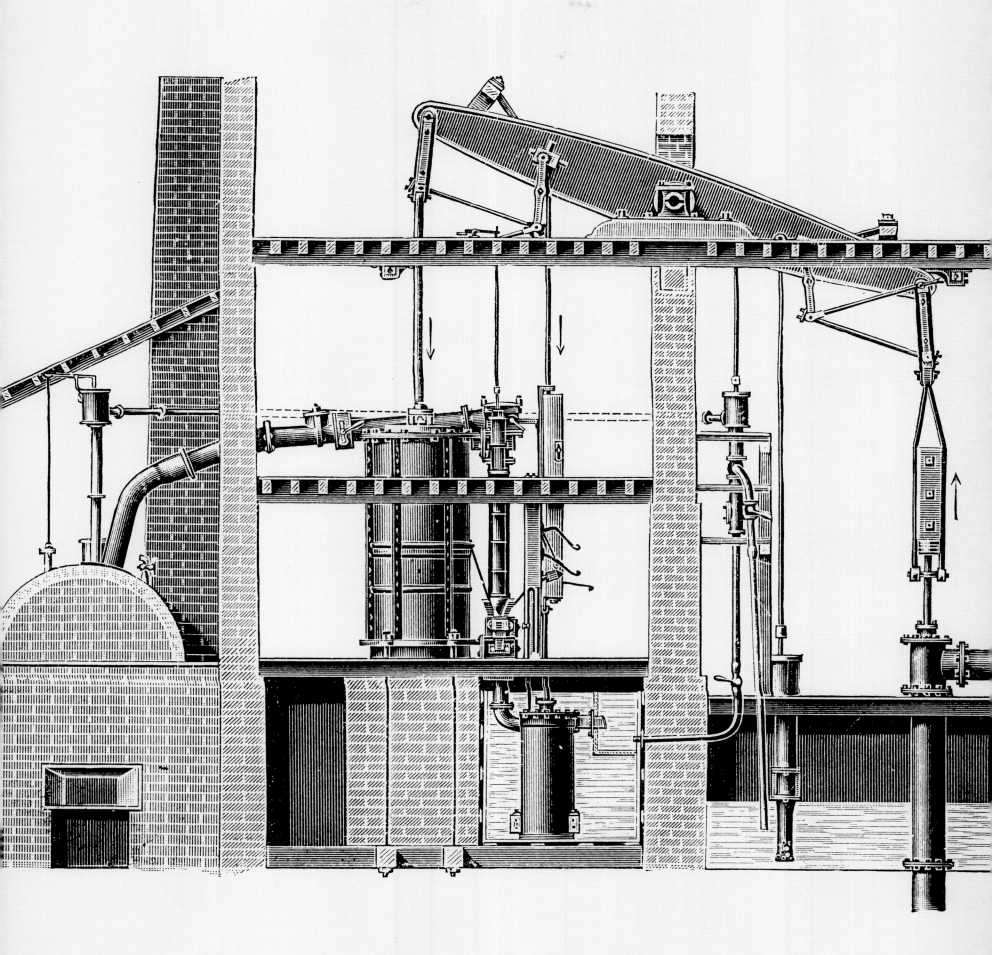

The parachute: only flying is better

Louis-Sebastien Lenormand (1757-1839)

"If a man equipped himself with a dome of cloth stretched on a frame, (...) he could jump from any height without danger," wrote the artist-scientist Leonardo da Vinci in 1495. However, he did not try out this hazardous venture himself.

1783

AROUND THE YEAR 1783

> **1783:** Great Britain and its former colonies end the American War of Independence with the Peace of Paris. The mother country acknowledges the United States of America as a sovereign state.

> **1783:** Margrave Karl Friedrich of Baden is the first German elector to abolish serfdom.

> **1783:** The Russian Tsarina Catherine II annexes the Crimea.

> **1784:** The British factory owner Henry Cort invents the technique of "puddling" pig iron. It is melted and stirred while oxygen is added to it. Accordingly the carbon is oxidized and the molten metal becomes steel.

△ The folding automatic parachute was first developed in the early 20th century.

The mathematician Fausto Veranzio, a fellow-countryman of Leonardo, was the next to leave information about parachutes. It is possible that he might even have tried it out experimentally, since at least his instructions sound very practical. It takes quite a while, he warned, until enough air collects under the canopy of the parachute so that a human can float to the ground without danger. He also pointed out that the area of material must be increased in proportion to the increase in weight of the body to be carried.

Reliable information about parachutes was not available until after the experiments of two Frenchmen, Joseph Montgolfier and Louis-Sebastien Lenormand. Montgolfier threw himself off the roof of his house with a home-made parachute, and the physicist Lenormand jumped from a tree using two small parachutes. His horrified family forbade Montgolfier to participate as the subject of any further experiments. So it was that in 1779 he floated a ram in a wicker basket gently down to earth from the top of the Papal Palace in Avignon, a height of 115 ft. Lenormand, however, dared to make the first proven jump from the tower of the observatory in Montpellier.

Lenormand believed that a parachute would be a useful piece of rescue equipment in the event of fire in a building. The contemporary discovery of the hot-air balloon, however, resulted in further possible uses. The French balloonist Jean-Pierre Blanchard was the first to take a parachute on board as an item of safety equipment. Its use became an urgent necessity in 1785 when Blanchard's balloon threatened to burst due to too much pressure and the parachute saved him from a fatal fall. Further development was rapid. In 1797 Jean Garnerin constructed the first parachute without the rigid wooden frame that had been customary until then. His brother, André Jaques, the first man to jump out of a balloon at a height of about 3,000 ft (1,000 m), added a hole at the top of the canopy to release air, which prevented it oscillating dangerously as it fell. In the 19th century, parachuting developed into an adventure sport and public entertainment in which women also took part.

The decisive impulse to make parachutes into effective rescue equipment came from two Germans in the early 20th century. The parachute jumper Käthe Paulus invented the folded parachute, and Otto Heinicke the first automatic one that was attached to the body of the parachutist, opening once the wearer was free of the aircraft. This prevented the danger of a parachute becoming entangled with a falling plane.

The life of the aviator Charles Lindbergh was saved four times by parachute. However the military did not permit their pilots to carry parachutes during World War I. They thought that parachutes would encourage the pilots to abandon their aircraft too quickly. It was not until the end of the war that the parachute became standard issue for a fighter or bomber pilot.

One of the first applications of the parachute was as life-saving equipment on early hot-air balloons.

> 1783: Charles Alexandre de Calonne, the new controller of France's public finances, cannot rescue the situation. The financial crisis will lead to the French Revolution.

> 1783: The French author Nicolas Chamfort utters the famous cry, "War to the châteaux! Peace to the cottages!"

> 1783: The French marquis Claude-Francois Dorothee Jouffroy d'Abbans builds the first seaworthy steamship.

△ Today, hot-air ballooning is a popular pastime and a sport with international championships.

The hot-air balloon: traveling above the clouds

Joseph Michel (1740-1810) and Étienne Jacques (1745-99) de Montgolfier, Joseph Gay-Lussac (1778-1850), Jean-Baptiste Biot (1774-1862)

Hot air rises. This principle was celebrated by the Chinese as long ago as the Middle Ages with a special ritual. They lit candles beneath paper balloons, the air in the balloons became hot, and they rose up into the sky. How could this simple principle be transferred to a balloon that could carry people into the air?

Two men who wanted to attempt this in the 18th century were the Montgolfier brothers from near Lyon in France, the heirs to a paper mill 400 years old. The French king nominated them paper suppliers to the royal court. As well as the honor, this title more importantly brought them a large fortune that enabled them to finance their attempts at flight. They did this not to gratify scientific or economic interests but because they were patriots. With the aid of their balloons they wanted to smuggle soldiers into Gibraltar and recapture it from the English.

In 1782 they experimented with a model balloon, a fabric bag filled with hot-air, that flew for 1,650 yards, climbing to a height of 330 ft. It is said that a wet shirt billowing in front of an open fire gave them this idea. In June 1783 the first public demonstration took place at Annonay near Lyon. The balloon was made of paper and canvas, and reached an altitude of 6,000 ft. When Louis XVI heard of this, he ordered a special presentation in Paris. This took place at the beginning of September 1783 with an even larger balloon. On this occasion no people were carried in the attached basket, but just a rooster, a duck, and a sheep. This demonstration fascinated the French physicist Jean-François Pilâtre de Rozier to such a degree that he wanted to try flying himself. Just one month later, he rose 85 ft (26 m) into the air in a tethered balloon. A month later, the Montgolfier brothers also made a manned flight attempt, with the "air traveler" Rozier as their passenger. This trip lasted 25 minutes and carried Rozier over the center of Paris into the suburb of Gentilly. Two years later, in 1785, Rozier lost his life in a balloon crash.

The physics professor Jacques Alexandre César Charles (1746–1823) designed a balloon that used hydrogen gas instead of hot air as a lifting medium. Following the example of the "Montgolfière," the name of the famous brothers' balloon, he named his own balloon "Charlière."

In the year 1804, Jean-Baptiste Biot and the physicist Joseph Gay-Lussac made the first balloon ascent with a purely scientific objective. Measurements of the temperature, atmospheric pressure, air composition, and magnetic field at a height of 13,100 feet revealed no significant differences from the respective values at the ground. Gay-Lussac reached a height of 23,280 feet in a second attempt on his own, thus showing that such a height was not harmful to a human being.

In 1785 Jean-Pierre Blanchard (1750–1809) crossed the English Channel in a balloon for the first time, while the first solo flight circumnavigating the globe was made by the adventurer Steve Fossett in June, 2002.

The Montgolfier brothers presented their hot-air balloon in 1783 in a public display after the French king Louis XVI expressed his interest in their flying experiments.

The mechanical loom: the beginning of industrialization

Edmund Cartwright (1743-1823)

The mechanical loom, an invention of the country parson Edmund Cartwright, woke the textile industry from its torpor. It gave industrialization in Europe a decisive boost, and radically changed the lives of craftsmen and laborers and their families.

The manufacture of textiles has always been a driving force in economic development. With the invention of the foot loom and the hand-held spinning wheel in the Middle Ages, mechanical methods took over from purely manual processes in European textile manufacturing. The decisive push for the development of mechanical spinning machines was given in 1733 by the Englishman John Kay (1704–64) with his "flying shuttle," an invention that enabled the shuttle to move much faster through the gap between the warp threads, thus accelerating the process of weaving. This meant that more fabric could be produced, and this in turn caused the demand for yarn to increase dramatically.

In order to satisfy demand, the spinning mills looked for ways to speed up their production process and make it more efficient. In 1767, the English weaver James Hargreaves (*c.* 1745–78) invented the "spinning jenny," which he named after his daughter. This mechanical hand spinning wheel could spin eight threads at the same time. Two years later another Englishman, the manufacturer Richard Arkwright (1732–92), constructed a spinning wheel with an automatic feed for the thread. In 1775 he modified it to be driven by water power and then again in 1785 to be run by a steam engine. His invention took the textile industry a significant step further and made him the greatest textile manufacturer of his time.

All that was missing now in order to perfect the manufacture of cloth was a functional powered loom. The English country parson, Edmund Cartwright, applied for a patent for such a machine in 1785. The first piece of cloth to be woven mechanically earned him the derision of manual weavers since the quality was so poor. The technology still needed perfecting. Eventually, in 1803, after years of work, Cartwright introduced an efficient mechanical loom that, by 1806, could be driven by steam. This new invention enabled the manufacturers to produce cloth in hitherto unbelievable quantities, and this was not only true of the cotton trade. With slight adjustments, the looms could spin other materials too, such as wool, flax, and silk. By 1830 there were 55,000 power looms in England and Scotland.

This of course was the death knell for the traditional cottage industry of weaving. Production moved from its place in the home and small workshops into factories and factory cities, and the working conditions of the weavers changed dramatically for the worse. The revolt of the weavers of Silesia in 1844 is probably the best-known example of the struggle for better working conditions. This rebellion was dramatized in the politically provocative drama *Die Weber* ("The Weavers") written by the German poet Gerhard Hauptmann (1862–1946).

As a result of technical innovations after World War II, such as the introduction of artificial fibers and sophisticated production techniques, the textile industry has now become a capital-intensive industry with enormous increases in production.

The invention of the mechanical loom was a prerequisite for the industrialization of textile production.

Galvanic current: dead frogs brought back to life

Luigi Galvani (1737-98)

It had been possible to produce electric charges since the early 17th century. However, there was no means of creating a continuous flow of electricity. It was the jerking of a frog's legs that gave Galvani the idea that led to the production of an artificial source of electric current.

1791

AROUND THE YEAR 1791

> **1789:** The French Revolution breaks out with the storming of the Bastille.

> **1789:** George Washington is sworn in as first president of the United States of America.

> **1791:** France becomes a constitutional monarchy by virtue of its new constitution.

> **1791:** The Bill of Rights, ten amendments to the American constitution, comes into force. It protects important rights of freedom.

> **1791:** Wolfgang Amadeus Mozart dies in Vienna.

The Italian doctor Luigi Galvani had long been interested in the phenomenon of electricity. He was fascinated with it in relation to animals, particularly the frog. So, he prepared some frogs' legs for his experiments. He cut off the legs with part of the back, removed the skin, and exposed the nerves of the spinal cord. When an assistant happened to touch a prepared frog's leg with the blade of a scalpel while an electrostatic machine nearby was creating large sparks, the frog's leg began to twitch severely. Galvani himself was extremely surprised, since the frog could certainly no longer be alive.

So what had happened? Without suspecting it, Galvani had produced a current that released itself in the muscles of the frog. Galvani was quite right in recognizing that the phenomenon had to do with electricity; when he touched the frog's nerves with a scalpel while the electrostatic machine was switched off, nothing at all happened. However they also twitched when he touched the nerves with two different metals, again with the machine switched off.

Galvani then transferred his experiments outside. He stretched an iron wire from the roof of his house and insulated it. On the wire, he hung up a number of frogs' legs that he fixed with brass hooks at the nerve endings. From the frogs' legs he led wires down to the ground, finishing in the water of a well. Galvani then waited for a thunderstorm. When one took place, he observed that each bolt of lightning caused the frogs' legs to twitch. However they also twitched if they touched the iron railing of Galvani's balcony in the wind, and when there was no thunderstorm and no electrostatic machine as a source of electricity.

The scientist had therefore demonstrated a circuit. The electricity flowed from the brass hooks through the frogs' legs to the iron balcony. The legs, as Galvani correctly recognized, had to be touching two different metals for the twitches to appear. In 1791 Galvani published his essay *Commentary on the Effect of Electricity on Muscular Motion* in which he argued that animals contained an "animal electric fluid" that was conducted to the nerves and muscles.

The first person to recognize the true reason for the twitching of the frog's legs was the physicist Alessandro Volta (1745–1827). He maintained that the legs were simply acting as an indicator of the passage of electric current, like a measuring instrument. He debated the causes of the twitches vehemently with Galvani until the latter's death. Volta carried out further experiments with two metals and an electrolyte, which showed that the frogs' legs were not necessary. In 1799 he build the first Voltaic cell or battery.

It was the twitching of frogs' legs that led to the development of the first artificially produced source of electro-chemical current.

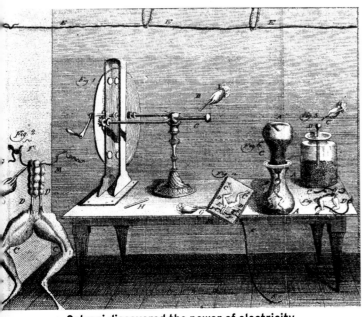

△ Galvani discovered the power of electricity accidentally while experimenting on animals.

Medicine: The art of healing

The scourge of humanity

Sickness and injury have troubled mankind since the beginning of time. In early cultures wounds were cauterized, bandaged and sewn up, dislocations put back in place, and bone fractures set and splinted. People knew about emetics and laxatives, diuretic draughts, and enemas as well as many kinds of tranquillizers and stimulants. If the medicine had no effect, then it was the fault of evil spirits. Medicine men usually tried to drive out the symptoms with spells but in the hope of a cure they also sometimes beat or starved the patient, or drilled holes in the skull. This procedure, known as trepanning, was carried out in the early Neolithic period and is the oldest known surgical operation.

First signs of science

In the advanced ancient cultures, apart from magic rituals there was also a rational and pragmatic approach to medicine, especially with regard to easily diagnosable suffering such as eye or skin problems or external injuries. The profession of physician, distinguished from the medicine man by using a scientific approach, arose in Egypt in the 3rd millennium BC. In temple schools, the aspirants learned to examine patients and to ask them questions. However, apart from trepanning, the Egyptians only carried out simple surgical operations.

In ancient India on the other hand it is probable that the healers knew about skin transplants and operations on the nose. The writings of the doctors Charaka (2nd century AD) and Susruta (4th century AD) show that anesthesia was known at that time. Cannabis was used as an anesthetic. However, with the rise of Buddhism all surgical operations were forbidden. In ancient China dissection was also forbidden on religious grounds, but traditional Chinese medicine was familiar with acupuncture, massage, and cupping over 4,000 years ago. Doctors also had a large selection of healing remedies at their disposal, including opium, sulfur, and arsenic. In Jewish culture, the Bible offered detailed strictures on hygiene, for instance that the sick should be placed in quarantine and the objects that they had been in contact with disinfected.

The first breakthrough

The real changeover in medicine from a religious to a scientific-secular study took place in ancient Greece. Philosophers no longer regarded the sick as being punished by the Gods, but saw sickness as an imbalance in the mixture of the elements. There were two famous schools of medicine, in Knidos and Kos. The latter was also the birthplace of Hippocrates (460–370 BC), who is regarded as the first modern doctor. Not only did he develop a standard of ethics for the medical profession with his

Natural medicine, the oldest and most traditional method of healing, continued long after the Middle Ages.

Hippocratic oath, but he handed down writings and case studies that were used by doctors well into the 18th century. The next most eminent physician of ancient times was Galen of Pergamon (AD 129–199). He made significant discoveries in the areas of inflammation, infections and medication, as well as in the function of the muscles and the spinal marrow.

A step back

These high medical standards fell severely during the Middle Ages. In Europe only fragments of the classical teachings were still extant. However, in the 7th century the Greek writings were brought to the Arab world by a Christian sect. Here, they were translated and distributed. There were also many distinguished Arab and Jewish doctors who had handed down important knowledge on infectious diseases, eye disease, nutrition, and new medicines. The most famous was Ibn Sina (c. AD 980–1037), also known as Avicenna. In the areas under Arab domination qualifications were requred to become a member of the medical profession, acquired through study and examinations. In Europe however it was not until the care of the sick was undertaken in monasteries that a certain professionalism arose

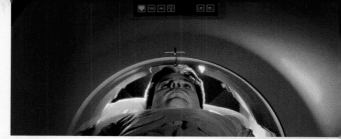

The English hospital reformer and philanthropist Florence Nightingale (1820–1910) encouraged nursing and the training of nurses.

The technology developed in the 20th century has created new possibilities of treatment.

in medical care. It was the Benedictines in particular who studied the Arabic translations of the ancient Greek texts and, in order to make them available to everyone, began to translate them into Latin. Then with the founding of schools of medicine in the 12th century, the art of healing again became a more secular profession. From the 13th century onwards there was also an obligatory examination to be taken by doctors. Hygiene was improved and in spite of all the prejudice against dissection, surgery began to make progress

The fascination of the body

During the Renaissance, scholars and artists discovered the human body for themselves, as the anatomical drawings of Leonardo da Vinci show. Therefore, it was surgery that made the greatest progress at this period. At this time too, diseases such as typhus and syphilis were discovered, and it was learned that bleeding could be stopped by clipping or sewing the edges of the wound together instead of cauterizing it. Slowly people began to realize that disease could be transmitted by organisms that could multiply. A milestone in the history of medicine was the discovery of the circulation of the blood by the English doctor William Harvey in 1628. Following on from this, research was done into blood vessels and the lymphatic system. Slowly, the functions of the body were becoming

less like a puzzle composed of many individual pieces, and more comprehensible as a system. As Descartes put it, the body functioned like a machine.

Now chemistry began to play an important part. Scientists investigated the metabolic and digestive systems. The significance of treatment with medication gained rapidly. New knowledge led to a number of eccentric teachings such as mesmerism, which propagated the effect of magnetism on the human organism, or phrenology, the research into the form and size of the human skull. The only one of these that is still of interest today is homeopathy, developed by Samuel Hahnemann.

Medicine becomes specialized

Slowly but surely, the different schools of medicine fanned out into individual branches. Neurology and pathology were established as independent subjects. So far, the medical profession had been more concerned with curing sickness, but now prevention was gaining in importance. Edward Jenner discovered the principle of inoculation and introduced the smallpox vaccination in 1796.

In the 19th century it was mainly in the field of diagnosis that the greatest progress was made. Sicknesses such as Parkinson's disease, Hodgkin's disease, and Grave's disease were discovered. The cell theory of the German botanist Matthias Jakob Schleiden explained the development of a living organism and led to the microscopic examination of diseased tissue. Using this as a starting point, the pathologist Rudolf Virchov came to the important realization that the seat of sick-

ness is found in the human cell. Another milestone in the history of medicine was the pioneering work of Louis Pasteur, Ignaz Philipp Semmelweiss, and Robert Koch. These men showed how sickness is transmitted by bacteria, and, therefore, how it could be prevented by hygienic measures and vaccination. Within a few decades, Koch and his colleagues had isolated the bacteria causing anthrax, diphtheria, tuberculosis, leprosy, and the plague, and had developed protective vaccines. The British surgeon Joseph Lister introduced phenol as an antiseptic. This was the beginning of the age of sterile surgery. Many new medical innovations came from the field of chemistry, biology and physics, for instance X-rays, or the proof that malaria and yellow fever are transmitted by mosquitoes.

Technical methods of the 20th century enabled investigation of previously unexplored areas such as the function of the brain, the nerves and the hormone system. The defense mechanisms of the immune system were discovered in the 1930s. This knowledge is the necessary basis for successful organ transplants, but it is also of significance for the whole field of allergy sicknesses.

Alternative medicine is still used in the treatment of diseases.

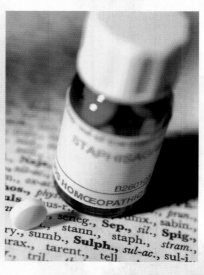

Vaccination: preventing epidemics

Edward Jenner (1749-1823)

△ Vaccination reduced the threat of a number of dangerous epidemic diseases, including smallpox.

Until the early years of the 19th century, plague was one of the greatest scourges of humanity, spreading like wild fire and killing thousands of people, especially children. Doctors were almost powerless in the face of these recurrent mass epidemics, since there were no effective measures against the spreading of pathogens. Eventually Edward Jenner's discovery of vaccination provided immunity.

The principle on which the concept of vaccination is based is that the body needs antibodies to fight off illness. Either the body builds the antibodies itself or it receives them from another source. The first method is known as active vaccination, whereby the patient is given weakened or dead pathogens. With the second method, passive vaccination, the person who is vaccinated is given "ready-made" antibodies that have an immediate effect. In both cases the person will at first suffer from a mild form of the illness but the body will then be immune from possible infection in the future.

Even before the discovery of these methods of vaccination, healers in the East and in China were already practicing a kind of inoculation against smallpox known as "variolation" (from the Latin *variola* = smallpox). Using a needle, the physician transferred pus from the pustules of a person suffering from smallpox into the body of one who was not yet affected. The method of inoculation became known in Europe through the writings of the physician Emanuel Timoni (1713) and Lady Mary Wortley Montagu (1718), the wife of the British envoy to China. Unfortunately the technique was not without danger, since this deliberate infection often resulted in a full-blown case of the disease and sometimes even in the death of the patient.

In 1796 the English physician Edward Jenner decided to carry out a similar experiment. He had observed that milkmaids infected with the harmless cowpox hardly suffered when they became sick with actual smallpox. Having noticed this, Jenner took a few drops of fluid from the cowpox pustules on the hands of a milkmaid, Sarah Nelmes. He then made a small cut in the skin of eight-year old James Phipps and injected the fluid into it. The young boy reacted by developing the typical cowpox pustules, and the smallpox virus that he subsequently introduced into the boy's body had no effect. Jenner published his results in 1798 and was recognized as the inventor of vaccination. Smallpox vaccination (from the Latin *vaccinia* = cowpox) soon became widespread in Europe, thus reducing the threat of the disease throughout the continent.

But doctors still knew nothing about the origin of infectious diseases, and for this reason it was impossible to produce vaccines in advance. This only became possible when the botanist Ferdinand Julius Cohn (1828–98) of Breslau discovered bacteria in 1872. In 1885 the physician and chemist Louis Pasteur (1822–95) produced vaccinations against anthrax and chicken cholera, and most importantly rabies. In honor of Jenner, he called all these types of inoculation "vaccinations."

Today serious diseases such as poliomyelitis and tuberculosis can also be prevented by vaccination. But the threat of biological weapons in the hands of terrorists has made further research imperative. The isolated spread of the anthrax virus has reawakened the nightmare of a possible epidemic that it was believed had been eradicated completely.

Before the discovery of vaccination, measures against the transmission of pathogens were ineffective because of poverty, misery and lack of hygiene.

Black holes: everything or nothing in the universe?

Pierre Simon Marquis de Laplace (1749-1827)

In 1798 the astronomer Marquis de Laplace put forward a theory that he himself considered unbelievable. He postulated the existence of a planet with a force of gravity so strong that even light was unable to resist its force, as a result of which the planet was completely darkened and invisible.

△ When Laplace put forward his theory of the "black holes" he himself could hardly believe in their existence.

The physicist, mathematician and astronomer Pierre Simon Marquis de Laplace made detailed studies of the universe and the planets. His work on astronomy was based on the theory of gravity developed by Isaac Newton in 1666. He investigated such phenomena as the effect of the elliptical shape of the earth on the course of the moon and on the dynamic theory of tides. Laplace applied Newton's law of gravity to the whole solar system, using complex mathematical calculations to explain why Jupiter's orbit appeared to be shrinking while Saturn's seemed to be expanding. He proved the stability of the planetary system and calculated the escape velocities, the lowest speed needed to leave the gravitational field of a celestial body.

In 1798 when Laplace put forward the theory of the "black stars," he could hardly believe it himself. He found it hard to comprehend that a star could exist of such a mass and density that light was unable to resist its gravitational attraction.

In order to escape the gravitational field of these small stars, a speed greater than the speed of light would be needed, and that is of course impossible. So not even light can escape from black holes, and they are therefore the blackest of all known bodies.

Because black stars cannot be seen, Laplace's theory soon fell into oblivion. It was only when Albert Einstein published his general theory on relativity in 1915 that new research into the phenomenon of black holes became possible. Black holes, defined as mass-rich objects in space, were believed to have strong forces of gravity.

Today black holes are thought to be the final stage of very mass-rich blue stars. In principle any celestial body can become a black star – which the physicist John Archibald Wheeler named a "black hole" in 1969 – although only after enormous compression. There are probably many black holes in the Milky Way although they are only as heavy as a few sun masses. Proof of the existence of black holes can be found in the movement of stars in their close vicinity; because of a black hole's great force of attraction the stars move faster the closer they are to it, revolving around an apparently empty space. The usual concepts of time and space are completely irrelevant inside a black hole, where time changes into space and space into time.

Laplace's theory was that when a planet was completely blacked out, its force of gravity was so strong that not even light could escape from it.

The battery: the discovery of how to store electricity

Alessandro Volta (1745-1827)

At the end of the 18th century electricity was merely a subject of conversation in learned circles. Physicists created sizeable sparks with "electricity machines" and set light to inflammable liquids with wires. This only sparked and blazed away for a brief moment, then it was all over. How electricity could be produced continuously was still a mystery to scientists.

The physicist Alessandro Volta (1745-1827) was interested in the experiments that the physician Luigi Galvani (1737–89) had carried out with frogs' legs; Galvani had accidentally touched a frog with the blade of a knife and an electricity machine nearby suddenly produced a large spark. The frog's leg jerked violently. Galvani concluded that the animal had a kind of "animal electricity," but Volta disagreed with this theory. While recognizing that electricity played a part in the jerking of the frog's leg, he believed that it was the contact between two different metals that had released the current. The frog was merely a "conductor," and as it were the display unit. In order to prove this by producing electricity, Volta carried out an experiment on himself. He placed a sheet of tin foil on the tip of his tongue and under it a silver coin. As soon as these two objects made of different metals touched each other, Volta was aware of an acid taste on his tongue. He noticed a similar taste but of different strengths when using other metals.

As a result Volta categorized metals in an "order of tension." If two metals touch each other in an electrolyte (a liquid that can conduct an electric current), the "non-precious" metal, for instance zinc, transmits electrons to the "precious" metal, for instance copper (oxidation). The zinc element produces kations (positively charged zinc ions) and the metal begins to dissolve slowly. At the same time the metal ions can now absorb electrons. If the two metals are separated from each other spatially but connected to each other, a current develops that goes from the precious to the non-precious metal. The "order of tension" categorizes metals according to their ability to release or absorb electrons.

Dating from 1799, Volta's first "battery," the Voltaic pile, was based on his earlier experiments. Volta arranged copper and zinc discs in alternate layers on top of each other and placed a piece of cardboard soaked in a saline solution between each layer. These voltaic piles produced current as soon as the discs were connected together by wires. A circuit of several voltaic piles connected in series produced a higher tension, whose strength was expressed in "volts" after the inventor. However, the electric voltage soon faded away as soon as the electrolyte solution had been used up or the non-precious metal had corroded. It was Johan Wilhelm Ritter (1776–1810) who discovered the rechargeable battery or "accumulator" by conducting current through it.

In the late 19th century, new inventions such as the dynamo and the light bulb created a growing need for storing electricity. The first lead-acid batteries were produced industrially in 1880, and by the turn of the century the first nickel-cadmium rechargeable cells were developed. Life today would be extremely difficult without the electro-chemical energy storage provided by the battery. Automobiles would still be started with a crank handle, telephones would still need cables, and kerosene or gas lanterns would be used instead of flash lights.

Illustration of a Voltaic pile, an early form of battery producing electric current.

1799

IN THE YEAR 1799

> Napoleon Bonaparte overthrows the ruling Directory and nominates himself First Consul – in fact the autocratic ruler – of France.

> French archaeologists find a stone carved in three languages in the Egyptian city of Rosetta on the Mediterranean. The Rosetta Stone carries the same text in demotic script and Greek, which can be understood, as well as in hieroglyphics, which cannot. With its help, Jean-François Champollion decodes the hieroglyphics in 1822.

> George Washington dies in the United States.

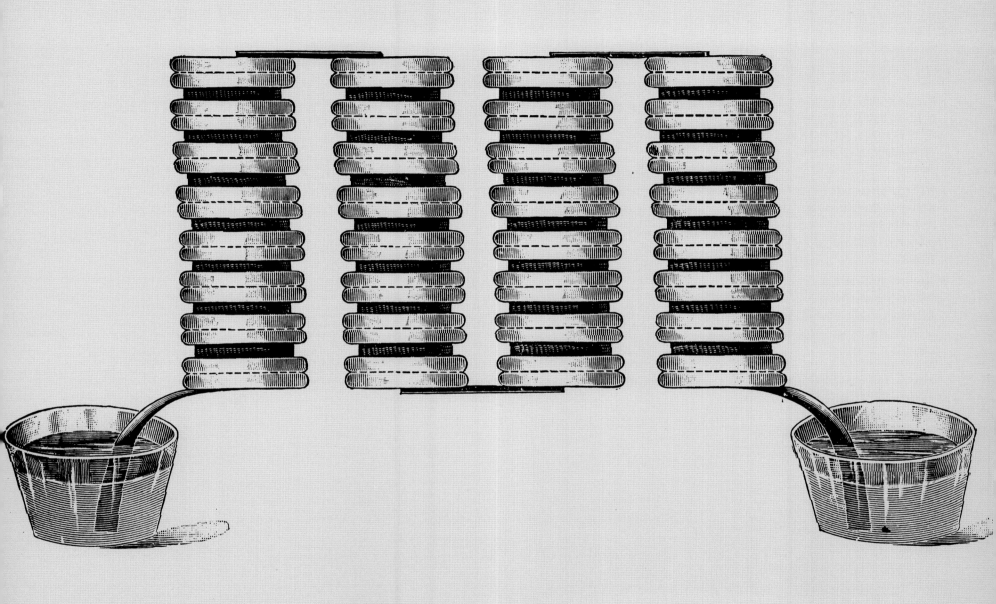

High-pressure steam engines: full steam to industrialization

Richard Trevithick (1771-1833)

At the beginning of the Industrial Revolution, one of the main priorities in economics was the fast and smooth transport of people and freight. What would such a machine look like? The English engineer Richard Trevithick (1771–1833) found the solution to this problem; he combined his two inventions, a high-pressure steam engine and a vehicle that ran on tracks, to make the first steam locomotive. The vehicle went on its maiden run in South Wales in 1804.

Between 1765 and 1784, the Glaswegian mechanic James Watt (1736–1819) perfected the low-pressure steam engine for use in industrial production. Nevertheless, it was not suitable for powering vehicles, since in order to build such a powerful low-pressure engine, the engine parts would have to be huge. The development of the steam locomotive, therefore, had to come from another quarter. The high-pressure steam engine was smaller, weighed less, and the steam pressure that it could produce was significantly above one atmosphere.

Shortly before 1800, Richard Trevithick had built his first workable model in Cornwall. Almost simultaneously, the American inventor Oliver Evans (1735–1819) also built a stationary high-pressure engine. However, Trevithick recognized the value of his invention immediately. It only took him until 1801 to design a steam-powered vehicle for the road, and soon afterwards it was able to run on tracks.

The birth of the steam locomotive was of great significance for the English coal mines. By 1800 coal mines already had nearly 300 miles of tracks, along which carts full of coal were pulled by horses. In 1803 Trevithick received a commission from an iron foundry in South Wales to construct a steam-powered locomotive. On a track 12 miles long made of cast-iron rails, the world's first steam locomotive drove along at roughly 5.5 mph.

Against popular opinion, Trevithick had proved that enough friction could develop between the iron wheel and the rail to provide traction. However the cast-iron rails were not strong enough to carry the weight of the locomotives indefinitely. Broken rails (such as the one that featured in the play *Catch me who can* shown in London in 1808) cast a shadow over Trevithick's delight in his invention.

From 1814 onwards, it was chiefly the mining engineer George Stephenson (1781–1848) who worked at solving this problem. In October 1829 he presented a more modern type of the steam locomotive. The *Rocket* was fitted with a new water-tube boiler with firebox that achieved greater and more constant power from the steam cylinder. At the same time as these innovations, stronger rails were developed. On May 3, 1830, the regular passenger service along the six miles between Canterbury and Whitstable was inaugurated. Much earlier than this, in 1812, the first steamship, the *Aetna*, had been launched, powered by a high-pressure steam engine made by Oliver Evans. However, after ten successful years, the ship suddenly exploded, a risk that was only eliminated later with the development of better boiler-making techniques and the invention of the safety valve.

A high-pressure steam engine and a vehicle running on a track led to the development of the steam locomotive: the start of the age of mass transportation.

1800

IN THE YEAR 1800

> Napoleon delivers Austria a crushing defeat at the battle of Marengo. The victory consolidates his power in Europe.

> With the agreement of San Ildefonso, Spain transfers its North American property, Louisiana, to France.

> The British physicists William Nicholson and Anthony Carlisle prove in an experiment that water consists of one part hydrogen and two parts oxygen. This marks the first application of the process of electrolysis.

△ The high pressure steam engine: smaller, lighter and more effective than its predecessor.

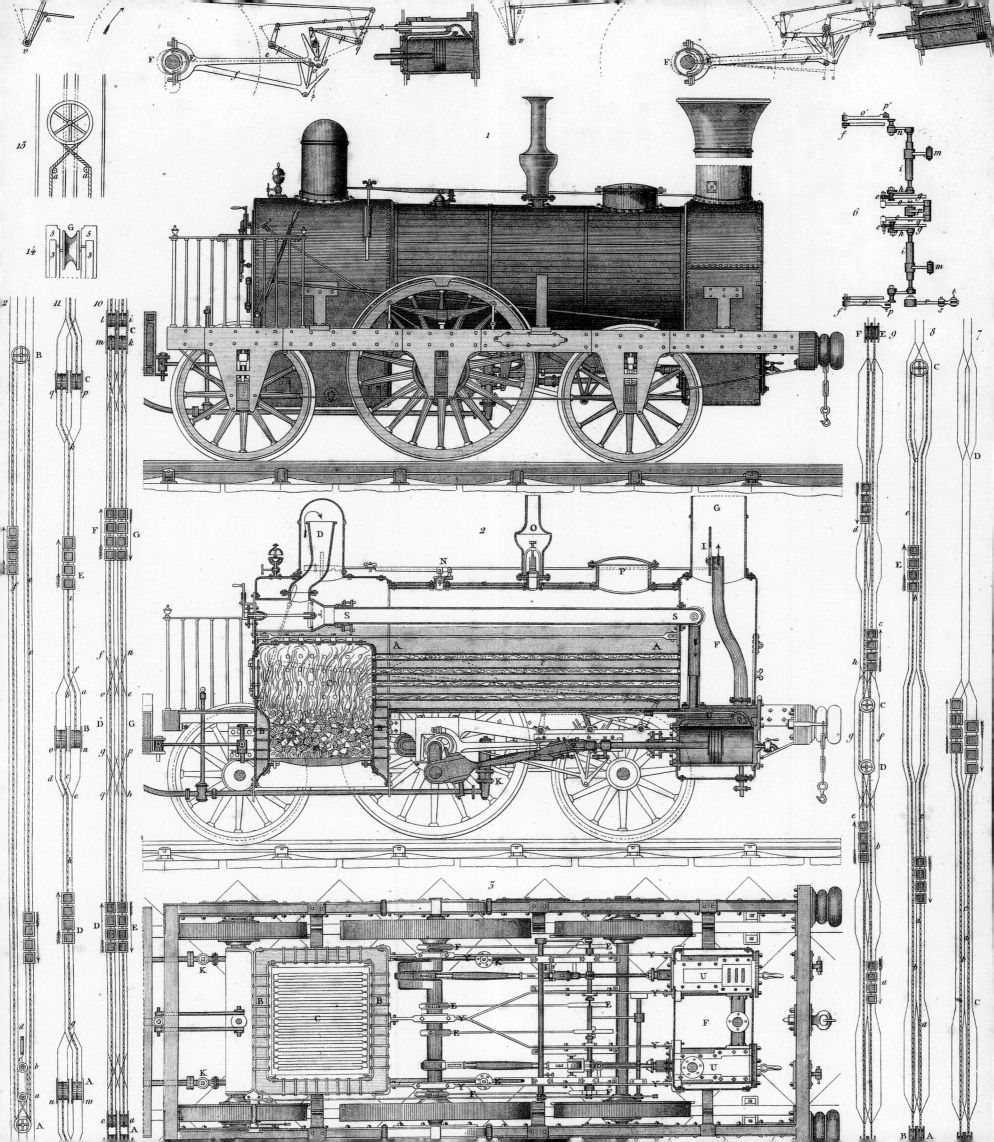

Ultra-violet light: at the end of the rainbow

Johann Wilhelm Ritter (1776-1810)

With the discovery that sunlight can be split up into colors, a completely new chapter in the history of optics was opened. But this was only the beginning. In 1800–01, scientists succeeded for the first time in detecting the invisible components at each end of the visible rainbow, ultra-violet and infra-red light.

In 1666 Isaac Newton (1643–1727) split white sunlight into its component colors by refraction through a glass prism. The visible spectrum was broken up into its separate components as occurs in a rainbow; starting with violet, it goes to indigo, blue, green, yellow, orange, and finally red. But in fact, beyond the spectrum that was now visible, the actual wavelengths of light extended further in both directions. The pioneering discovery of the spectral color sequence covered only a part of the overall spectrum of the beams of light emitted by the sun. The decisive turning-point came in 1800–01 when scientists succeeded in detecting the electromagnetic rays of other wavebands.

Friedrich Wilhelm Herschel (1738–1822) in 1800 proved for the first time that the sun emits invisible infra-red rays (thermal radiation) at the long-wave end of the visible spectrum, in other words beyond the color red. He ran a blackened thermometer over an artificially reproduced solar spectrum and noted that the temperature rose as it approached the color red. When he held the thermometer beyond the color red, the column of mercury rose even further, although no rays could be seen there. These findings indicated that the spectrum of light was much wider than could be perceived with the naked eye.

In 1801 Johann Wilhelm Ritter (1776–1810) discovered that invisible radiation also reached the earth at the short-wave end of the light spectrum, that is, beyond the color violet. Herschel's earlier work played an instrumental part in Ritter's discovery. Indeed, Ritter repeated Herschel's experiments but under different conditions. He already knew what he was looking for, an invisible radiation similar to thermal radiation but one that was at the opposite end of the spectrum from the color red. All he needed was proof, and this he found remarkably quickly.

In his experiments on the thermal radiation produced by the various wavebands, Ritter took into account a discovery made by the chemist Carl Wilhelm Scheele. He had shown that the colorless salt silver chloride (AgCl), was turned black by light rays at the violet end of the spectrum but not by those from the red end. Being aware of this distinctive feature, Ritter now introduced silver chloride specimens into the spectrum, slightly beyond the visible violet light, and discovered that this too caused intense blackening. This demonstrated that there was light invisible to the human eye at this end of the spectrum too, ultra-violet.

This discovery caused a great stir among scientists. As well as ultra-violet light itself, Ritter also discovered the most chemically active rays present in this waveband. This discovery was of fundamental importance for physics, and it marked the starting point of the science of photochemistry.

Light can be split into the colors of the spectrum by being shone through a prism. In 1800 scientists proved that there was also invisible radiation beyond the spectrum.

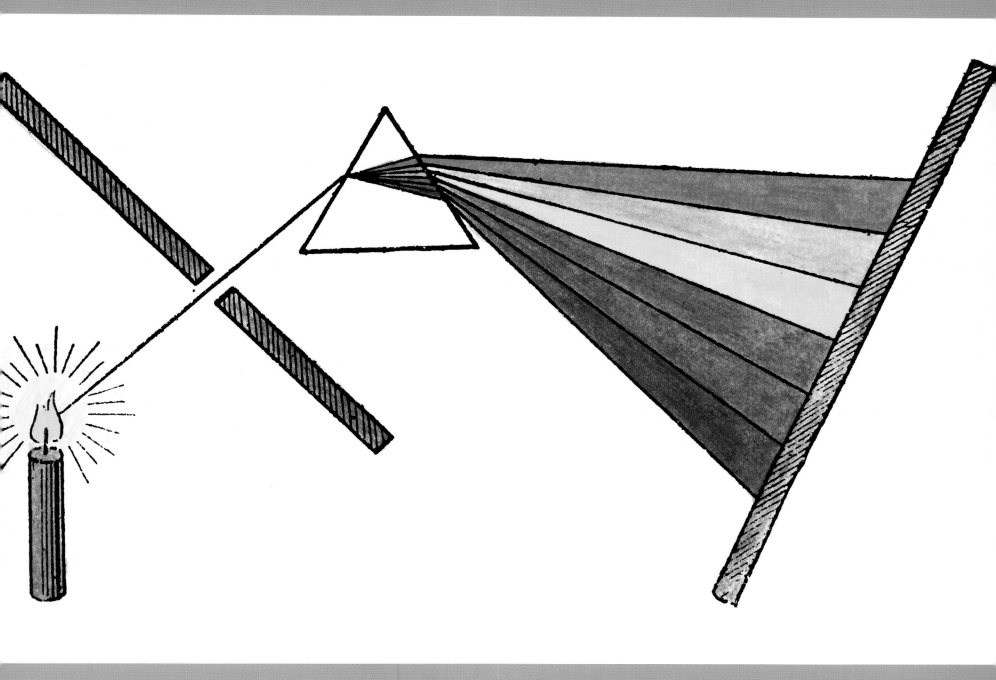

Fossils: the classification of geological eras

William Smith (1769-1839)

In January 1796 the English surveyor William Smith discovered that certain types of fossils such as ammonites only occurred in particular layers of rock. He wondered if it might be possible that each stratum represented a geological era.

1801

AROUND THE YEAR 1801

> 1801: The British prime minister William Pitt announces his resignation.

> 1801: Ireland is united with Great Britain by the Act of Union.

> 1801: The first German factory for refining sugar from sugar beets is established in Silesia.

> 1803: France sells Louisiana to the United States for 60 million francs.

In the mid-18th century naturalists came to recognize that the rock strata of the earth's crust could not all have been created at the same time as the result of a single act of creation, and that they were much more likely to be the result of a long process of development.

At the same time the remains of prehistoric fossils, the petrified remains of animals and plants, became sought-after collector's pieces that filled the curio cabinets of royal palaces and monasteries. But no one had ever thought of studying and systematically categorizing these "curiosities."

In 1794 the English surveyor William Smith was charged with the task of building a canal in the county of Somerset to transport the coal that was mined there. In his surveys for this purpose, Smith traveled all over England to view other canal projects, and in the process he also studied the soil from which each canal had been dug. He made a discovery that puzzled him enormously: the fossils buried in the rock strata were clearly distributed evenly, and each stratum contained "fossils peculiar to itself." He identified an order that in every case ran from bottom to top, and, most significantly, the same order was found in places far distant from each other.

Smith suspected that rock strata found in different places containing identical fossils dated from the same period. He recognized that fossils provided an unmistakable source of information on the basis of which rock strata could be systematically categorized. But his theory also had an invaluable practical application, because it enabled scientists to determine where to look for mineral resources. For instance, there were now criteria indicating where to look for coal.

As the discoverer of the index fossil principle, according to which the fossils present in a geological layer indicate its chronological order, Smith is recognized as the founder of stratigraphy, the science of the composition and chronological order of rock strata.

In 1799 he proposed the drawing up of a geological map of England and Wales on the basis of his guiding principle. In 1802 he submitted his project to Joseph Banks (1743–1820), the president of the Royal Society in London, who gave him his lasting support.

Nevertheless Smith had to struggle for financial resources for his travels and research, so that it was only in 1812 that he began to produce his geological map. His work was eventually published on August 1, 1815, under the title *A Delineation of the Strata of England and Wales*. It became the model for all subsequent geological maps, and Smith's index fossil principle is still valid today. His fossil collection was sold to the British Museum when he needed to raise money for his map.

The systematic classification of geological deposits started by William Smith has proved invaluable in the search for mineral resources.

Electric light: a brilliant idea

Humphry Davy (1778-1829)

At the beginning of the 19th century scientists had already been experimenting with electrical energy for some 200 years but it had yet to find any practical use. Then the British chemist Humphry Davy had a flash of inspiration.

> 1806: Great Britain annexes the Cape region in southern Africa.

> 1807: The kingdom of Bavaria leads the way in compulsory vaccination as the first country in which everyone must be immunized against smallpox.

> 1808: Napoleon nominates his brother Joseph as the king of Spain.

> 1808: The German New Yorker Johann Jacob Astor founds his American Fur Company, which will make him one of the richest men in the USA.

Davy was interested in electricity from a chemical point of view. His observation of the action of electrolytic cells gave him the idea of using electrolysis to break down substances into their component elements. He conducted strong electric currents through various fluids on the assumption that they contained hidden, undiscovered chemical compounds. As well as discovering elements such as potassium, sodium, calcium, and later boron, Davy also established that sparks develop between two carbon electrodes when a strong current flows through them. In subsequent experiments he eventually succeeded in producing a stable electric arc.

To achieve this, two pencil-shaped electrodes, usually carbon, were brought into contact with each other. A very strong current of about ten amps was then conducted through them. Heat developed at the point of contact. When the two electrodes were slowly separated, a very intense, flame-like luminous electric arc was created. Depending on the type of carbon used, the light was distributed along the entire arc or concentrated at the tip of the positive electrode. The high temperature produced ions between the two electrodes. If the current was sufficiently strong the ionized light track remained stable.

This is what enabled Davy to develop continuous electric lighting in 1808, rather than intermittent sparks. To present his discovery to the public, in 1813 he built the largest battery that had ever been made up to that time.

But it was some time before the principle of the arc lamp was sufficiently perfected to be used on a large scale. In 1853 the French physicist Jean Bernard Léon Foucault developed the first serviceable arc lamp. The first durable application of Humphry Davy's original invention was made in 1862 for the lighthouse at Dungeness in England. An economically viable model was eventually built by the American Charles Francis Brush in 1878.

Because arc lamps can reach an extremely high temperature of up to 6,330° F they are not suitable for use in the home. They are exceptionally bright and, using the appropriate technique with reflectors, they provide a very concentrated light that makes them ideal for certain specialized applications. Originally used for street lighting and in lighthouses, they are also used for lighting movie sets and in movie projectors, for instance.

Sodium and mercury vapor lamps are electric discharge lamps similar to enclosed arc lamps. Because of the heat it produces, the electric arc also has applications other than lighting, for instance in industrial furnaces for melting metals. Similarly, the process of electric arc welding is based on the same principle as Humphry Davy's invention. In the 19th century Davy's inventions stimulated many other scientists to produce light using electric current.

△ Davy discovered that a strong current between two electrodes produced a stable arc emitting light.

Originally arc lights were mainly used in lighthouses because of the brilliant illumination they provided.

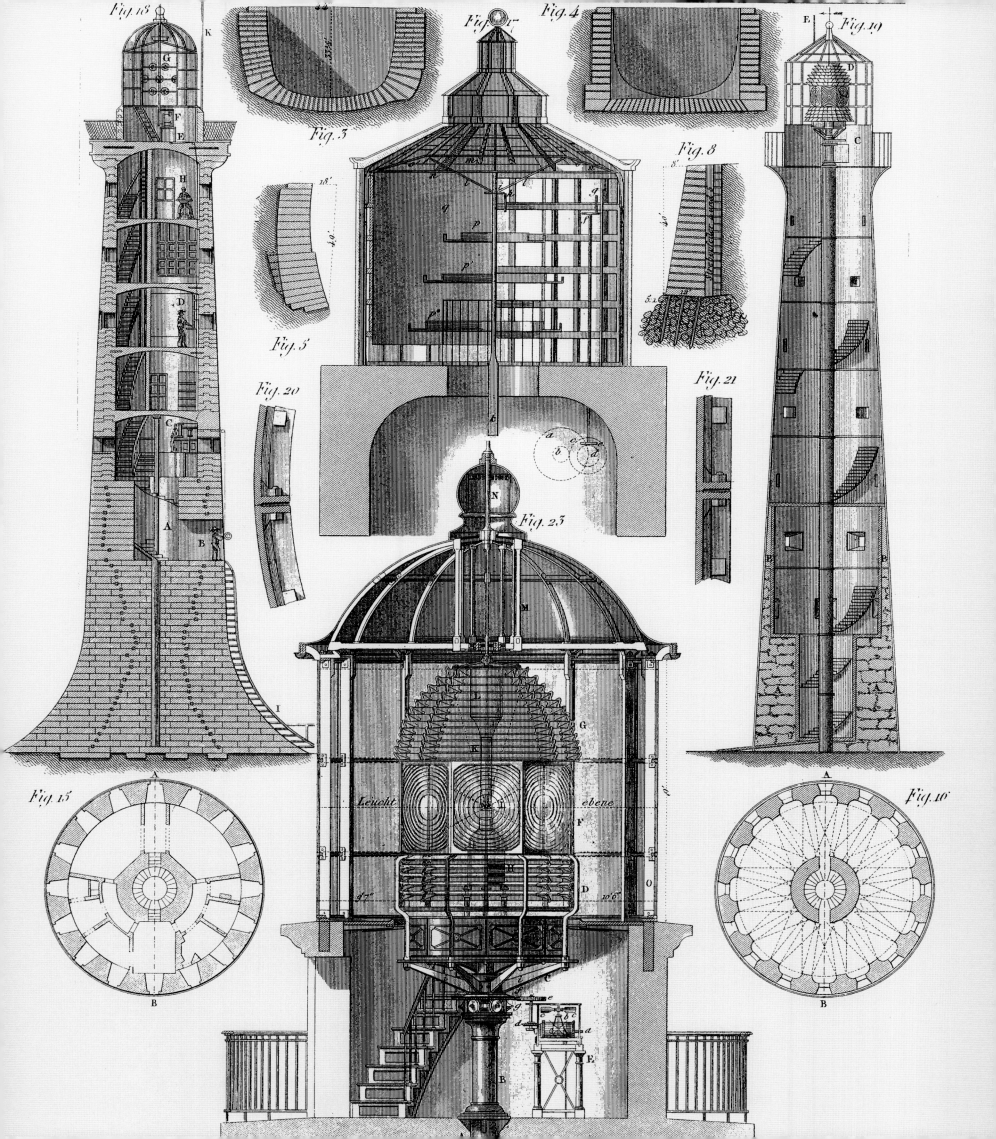

Fig. 18   Fig. 3   Fig. 17   Fig. 4   Fig. 19

Fig. 8

Fig. 5

Fig. 20   Fig. 21

Fig. 23

Leucht   ebene

Fig. 15   Fig. 16

Aerodynamics: a lift for fliers

Sir George Cayley (1773-1857)

There is an age-old dream that has long fired the imagination of mankind and in particular of scientists: to fly like a bird. Leonardo da Vinci had made a study of air currents and the flight of birds, but every attempt to keep a body in the air for any length of time remained unsuccessful. So scientists who were fascinated by flying used balloons, which were lighter than air. Nevertheless the desire to conquer gravity remained.

Birds too are heavier than air, so scientists wondered how they could soar up high into the sky without apparent effort and even glide without beating their wings.

The British scientist Sir George Cayley had been interested in this problem since he was a child. In his efforts to solve this mystery he became the founder of the science of aerodynamics, the study of the laws of motion of gaseous substances. He divided the complex phenomenon of a bird's flight into three parts: lift, thrust, and flying. This expressed the fundamental problems of aviation in general terms.

In his experiments with kites Cayley observed that with particular shapes of wing section, the air flowed faster over the top of a wing than underneath it. As a result the air pressure decreased above the wing while it increased below it. The suction on the top surface of a wing combined with the pressure on its underside creates a lift that enables even heavy bodies to float in the air.

The starting point of George Cayley's research was Bernoulli's principle. This was named after the mathematician and physicist Daniel Bernoulli, who in 1738 had discovered that the pressure in a flowing gas or liquid decreases as its velocity increases. Cayley was now able to prove that the lift of a bird in flight also depended on this principle, the lift being generated by the slightly cambered shape of the wings. Cayley built a kite-like flying machine with large, cambered wings, based on his findings of the effect of the dynamic lift, thrust, and air resistance on a wing. He used a tail fin as a stabilizer and steering device, a similar configuration to that of aircraft today. In 1809 one of Cayley's model gliders succeeded in lifting a small boy up into the air. He continued his researches and experiments, and in 1853 he built a glider that carried his coachman on the first manned glider flight.

Cayley's theories on the flying machine of the future inspired subsequent aviation scientists, including Otto Lilienthal. Like Cayley, Lilienthal started from the assumption that the prerequisite for flying was the development of a perfect gliding machine. Using willow canes and cotton fabric, he built an airplane with slightly rounded wings. Lilienthal's glider also had a tail fin and it was controlled by the pilot shifting his weight. Leaping from a hill in Berlin, Lilienthal successfully flew into the air for the first time. With the help of constantly improved gliders and biplanes he undertook over 2,000 flights until his fatal accident in 1896.

There is no doubt that Cayley's fundamental discoveries in the field of aeronautics made a vital contribution to the development of aviation in the 19th and 20th century by providing it with a scientific basis.

Flying like a bird became a reality when Otto Lilienthal first succeeded in flying with his aerodynamically shaped gliders.

The bicycle heralds the era of mobility

Baron Karl Drais von Sauerbronn (1785-1851)

A rider on an early bicycle presented an amusing sight, sitting on a saddle fitted to a framework mounted on wheels and pushing the bicycle along with his feet in a walking motion on the ground. In this way the bicycle began its triumphal progression into the age of mobility.

Following the wishes of his father, the young Baron Karl Drais von Sauerbronn graduated in forestry before devoting himself to his real interests, which were physics and mechanics. From 1813 onwards, the forestry commissioner tinkered with the construction of vehicles that could be driven by muscle power alone. In 1814 he presented his first model to the public, a four-wheeled trolley that ran on rails and was powered by the driver pumping a lever up and down. These rail trolleys were in use on railroads for a long time as repair vehicles. For this invention Drais was appointed to Professor of Mechanics by the Grand Duke of Baden and given a ten-year patent on his machine.

As the roads of his time were not suitable for four-wheeled vehicles, Drais turned his attention to the development of a more flexible two-wheeled model, that would be able to avoid potholes more easily. In 1817, he introduced his "draisienne," a wooden rider-propelled bicycle that could be steered. On the face of it, the machine was uncomfortable and likely to attract ridicule from passers by. Nevertheless, the rider, or rather the "walker," on this machine was able to reach maximum speeds of nearly 10 mph.

In fact these early push bikes became remarkably popular among the well-to-do and free-thinkers who wanted to provoke bourgeois society with their style. Sport clubs bought push bikes to be used for exercise, and in England push bike races and competitions between horse riders and bicycle riders became all the rage. The metal variation of Drais' wooden bicycle that was popular in England was called a "dandy horse" or "hobby horse." The proliferation of bicycles was so great that from 1818 onwards they were only permitted on the roads. There were push bicycle schools, where drivers could learn how to use the machine, and the invention attracted the attention of caricaturists and satirists.

Drais continued to improve his invention, adding, for instance, a luggage carrier and a brake. A special accessory was a sail for using wind power to propel the bike. However the bicycle did not bring its inventor much financial gain. The Englishman James Starley and the Frenchman Pierre Michaux developed similar push bicycles at the same time. The result was a series of lawsuits as to whose bicycle was the original one.

The fashion for push bicycles did not last long. The machine could not be improved any further and was hard to produce commercially. While trying to open a push bicycle factory, Drais eventually overstepped himself financially and died in 1851 as a penniless showman. The real breakthrough for bicycles came when models equipped with pedals appeared on the market. It was particularly the development of the English "hobby horse," such as that of the Scotsman Kirkpatrick Macmillan (1813–78), that finally established the bicycle worldwide in the second half of the 19th century.

The boneshaker or velocipede was uncomfortable and people thought of ways to improve its comfort, such as by the addition of arm supports and pedal cranks.

Dinosaurs: the fearful saurians with big teeth

Gideon Algernon Mantell (1790-1852)

Dinosaurs were the largest land animals that ever lived and 170 million years ago they were masters of the earth. It was in 1822 that an English country doctor found the first signs of the "terrible lizards." Their sudden disappearance at the end of the Cretaceous period is still unexplained.

The discovery of dinosaurs came about because of the English country doctor Gideon Algernon Mantell's passion for collecting. Since his schooldays Mantell had always been enthusiastic about minerals and fossils. His home in the county of Sussex, with its extensive deposits of the Cretaceous period, was in this sense a true gold mine.

In 1822 Mantell (or according to some reports, his wife), made a finding that would revolutionize research into primeval life on earth: he came upon a strikingly large tooth with a smooth, worn surface. The appearance of the tooth indicated a herbivorous animal and Mantell at first thought of an elephant. But the knowledgeable fossil collector knew that no remains of mammals had ever been found near where he lived. Perhaps the tooth came from one of the widely dispersed reptiles? But these did not crush their food in the manner for which the tooth was obviously positioned.

The puzzle was finally solved by coincidence. In 1825, Mantell found a considerably smaller but otherwise identically molded tooth in the museum of the Royal College of Surgeons in London. This came from the mouth of a South American iguana. The fossil collector therefore concluded that the tooth must be that of a gigantic lizard. He named it "iguanodon" after the iguana; today it is called *Ornithopoda*. Mantell was therefore the first person to track down a land dinosaur. Two years later, the clergyman and naturalist William Buckland (1784-1856) reconstructed a carnivorous land dinosaur "megalosaurus," today called *Theropoda*. In 1832, ten years after his first great discovery, Mantell described *Hylaeosaurus*, thus identifying the first group of strongly armored dinosaurs, today called the ankylosaurs.

These findings attracted the attention of the anatomist Richard Owen (1804–92). In 1842 he gave the odd giant creatures the name "dinosaurs," meaning "terrible lizards." Two years later, on the basis of further bone finds Owen succeeded in making a complete reconstruction of Mantell's *Iguanodon*. In 1861, he identified *Archaeopteryx*, which had been discovered in shale by Solnhofen a year earlier, as a connecting link between the classes of reptiles and birds.

But not until the second half of the 19th century were finds made (first in America and then particularly in the Belgian coal fields) that provided a more precise picture of these primeval giants. Dinosaurs belong to the order *Ornithischia* or *Saurischia*, the thecodonts, that is, animals with teeth set in sockets. Crocodiles also developed from this type. The evolutionary success of the dinosaurs can be attributed to their physique. In contrast with other reptiles, their legs were not at the side of the body but underneath it. The legs could therefore carry greater weight, and the animals could move quickly and agilely instead of being able only to crawl. Dinosaurs lived exclusively on land and were probably warm-blooded creatures. Technically, flying saurians and those that live in the water are not actually dinosaurs.

It was in 1822 that remains of dinosaurs were first discovered. Here is a reconstruction.

The electro-magnet: great power from electricity

William Sturgeon (1783-1850)

1825

IN THE YEAR 1825

> After the death of Alexander I, Nicholas I succeeds him as tsar. A few days later, a group of liberal officers tries to overthrow him. This conspiracy of the Decembrists is however immediately suppressed.

> The Erie Canal connecting New York with the Great Lakes is opened. As a result, canal navigation develops into an important engine of economic development.

> Louis Braille, a blind French teacher, develops braille, the writing system of raised dots that is still in use today.

> The first public steam railroad in Great Britain connects Stockton and Darlington.

His interest in the phenomenon of electricity caused the English physicist William Sturgeon to carry out a great number of experiments. When he wound wire around an iron core and conducted electric current through it, he produced a power that was able to move a heavy object. It was now possible to use electrical energy directly.

In the 18th century, electricity was regarded as a fascinating phenomenon, which was used mainly for entertainment value, but during the 19th century many practical applications were found for it. The English physicist William Sturgeon contributed to this development with his experiments with electrical charges. The son of a shoemaker from Whittington, England, he enlisted in the army at an early age. There he taught himself mathematics, physics and Greek. From 1824, Sturgeon taught natural science and philosophy at the East India Company's Royal Military College in Addiscombe. He built scientific apparatus and taught his students natural laws and technical matters in innovative ways.

The chance observation of a Danish physicist interested him greatly. In 1819, while preparing a lecture, the professor Hans Christian Oersted (1777–1851) inadvertently dropped a wire connected to a voltaic battery onto a compass. To his surprise he saw that the compass needle rotated and did not return to its original position until he removed the wire. He surmised that there must, therefore, be some connection between electricity and magnetism.

Sturgeon was of the same mind. He sought to reproduce Oersted's experiment by simple means. In 1825, with the help of his assistant Francis Watkins, he developed an experimental construction. He wound 16 pieces of copper wire that did not touch each other round a horseshoe-shaped piece of iron about 12 in (30 cm) long. He attached the wires to individual batteries. When he passed current through the wires, the piece of iron became magnetized and exhibited the same properties as a rod-shaped permanent magnet. When he switched off the current, the iron became demagnetized.

With this experiment Sturgeon demonstrated that electricity was able to magnetize iron, which in itself was not magnetic. The electricity built up a magnetic field which was concentrated in the iron core. The coils of wire amplified each other in their effect, since the electricity flowed in the same direction in all of them. Sturgeon observed a further phenomenon in his device. If he suspended the wire-wrapped iron core, which weighed about 7 oz (200 g), and magnetized it, it could lift 9 lb (4 kg) of metal pieces. This was 20 times its own weight! When the electricity was turned off, the pieces fell off. Sturgeon had taken the decisive step towards the practical use of electromagnetism. He had demonstrated that electricity could produce a magnetic effect that multiplied the power of the source of energy – in this case a single cell – many times.

Sturgeon's model was exhibited in London and the inventor was honored with the silver medal of the Royal Society of Arts. Sturgeon's electromagnet became the vital component of many electrical devices, without which modern life cannot be imagined. Notably, the electric telegraph and the electric motor were applications of his discovery.

The principle of the electromagnet: an iron core round which wire is wound, through which a current passes.

Fig. 1.

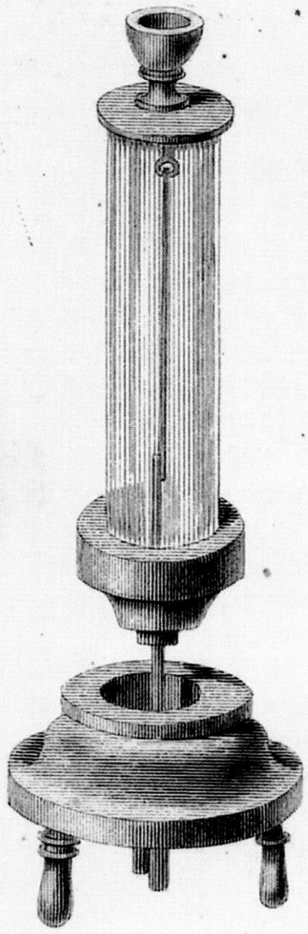

Fig. 2.

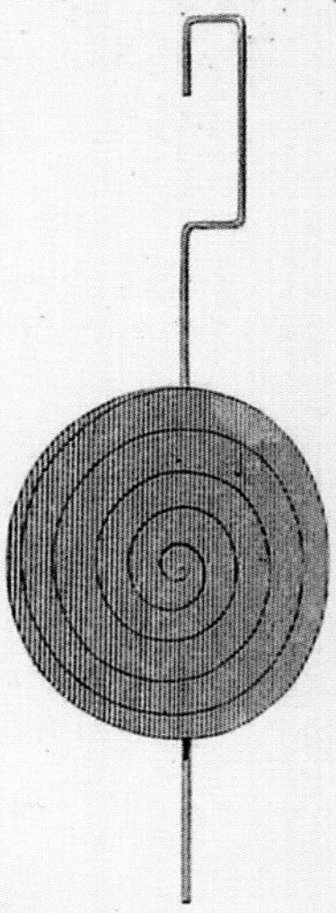

Fig. 3.

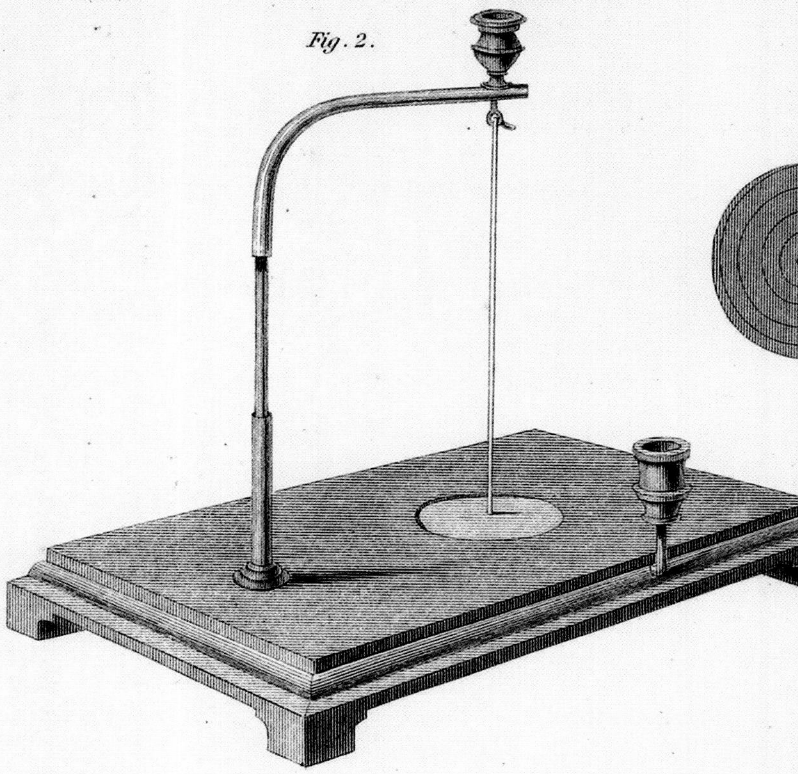

Fig. 4.

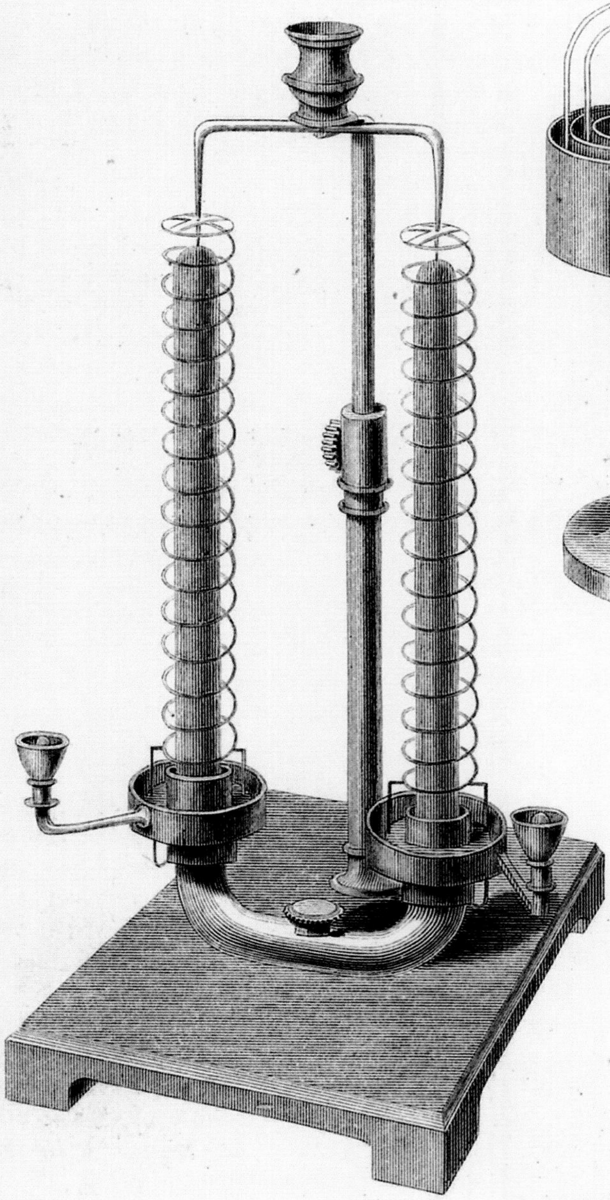

Fig. 5.

Fig. 6.

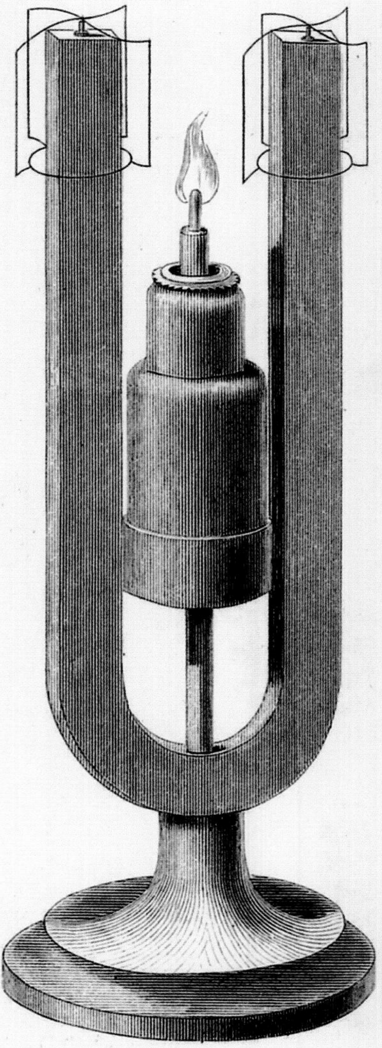

The propeller: new life for old ships

Josef Ressel (1793-1857)

While working on a new mechanism for powering ships in 1826, the Austrian inventor Josef Ressel built an underwater propeller. Until his death, Ressel fought unsuccessfully for recognition as the inventor of the ship's propeller. Meanwhile, the British Admiralty took over his idea and awarded other claimants a bonus for this ground-breaking development.

1826

AROUND THE YEAR 1826

> 1825: the Scottish researcher Gordon Laing succeeds in crossing the Sahara from north to south. He is the first European to reach Timbuktu.

> 1826: Tsar Nicholas I creates a secret police force to suppress liberal movements.

> 1826: Karl Liebknecht, who will become the founding father of German social democracy, is born in Giessen.

> 1826: The Austrian actor and lawyer Alois Senefelder develops the technology of color lithography.

For thousands of years mankind has sailed the seas in order to trade, to conquer strange lands or merely to travel from place to place. The development of ships went hand in hand with technical improvements. The first ships were moved by oars using muscle power, by sails that caught the wind, and later by steam engines. At the time of Josef Ressel, ships were still using paddle wheels to move through the water. In Austria, Ressel was working as a naval forester in a region where the navy obtained its wood. He was therefore also a naval officer, and his interest in shipping encouraged him to construct a better method of driving them.

His first drawings were for a drive using an Archimedean screw. The Greek mathematician and physicist Archimedes (c. 285–212 BC) had designed this for pumping water from a lower level to a higher one. The device consisted of a spiral screw revolving in a cylinder. Up to the 18th century, designers had already made several attempts to power ships with this kind of propeller but the experiments all failed, with the result that shipbuilders still used paddle wheels to convey the motive power to the water.

Josef Ressel set about constructing a propeller that would be attached to the bow of the ship. On November 26, 1826, he applied for a patent for his ship's screw. The Austrian navy agreed to build a steamship using Ressel's propeller, on condition that the ship would be built in Austria. However there were difficulties with the delivery of the steam boiler equipment, and Ressel therefore traveled to Paris where a French company had shown interest in his patent. The test was successful but it did not completely convince the firm of the utility of this invention.

Ressel did not have enough money to carry on in Paris, so he returned to Austria. On August 4, 1829, back in Trieste, then still Austria, he started on a new test with a ship driven by his propeller. The screw worked perfectly, but a fault in the steam boiler called a halt to the voyage. The ship had to be towed back to port and the authorities forbade any more test runs, citing "security measures."

In the meantime, Ressel's documents about the construction of his propeller had appeared in England, then the largest seafaring nation in the world. In 1850 the British Admiralty offered a prize of £2,000 for the inventor who could conclusively prove that he had developed the propeller. Josef Ressel wrote to the authorities but never received an answer. Even an intervention on his behalf by the Archduke Ferdinand Max was unsuccessful. Instead, the Admiralty divided the prize amongst various British applicants. Ressel fought for the recognition of his rights for the rest of his life, but it was not until after his death that he was recognized as the inventor of the ship's propeller.

The propeller was invented by Josef Ressel, who tested his invention in 1829 on a ship fitted with this new device.

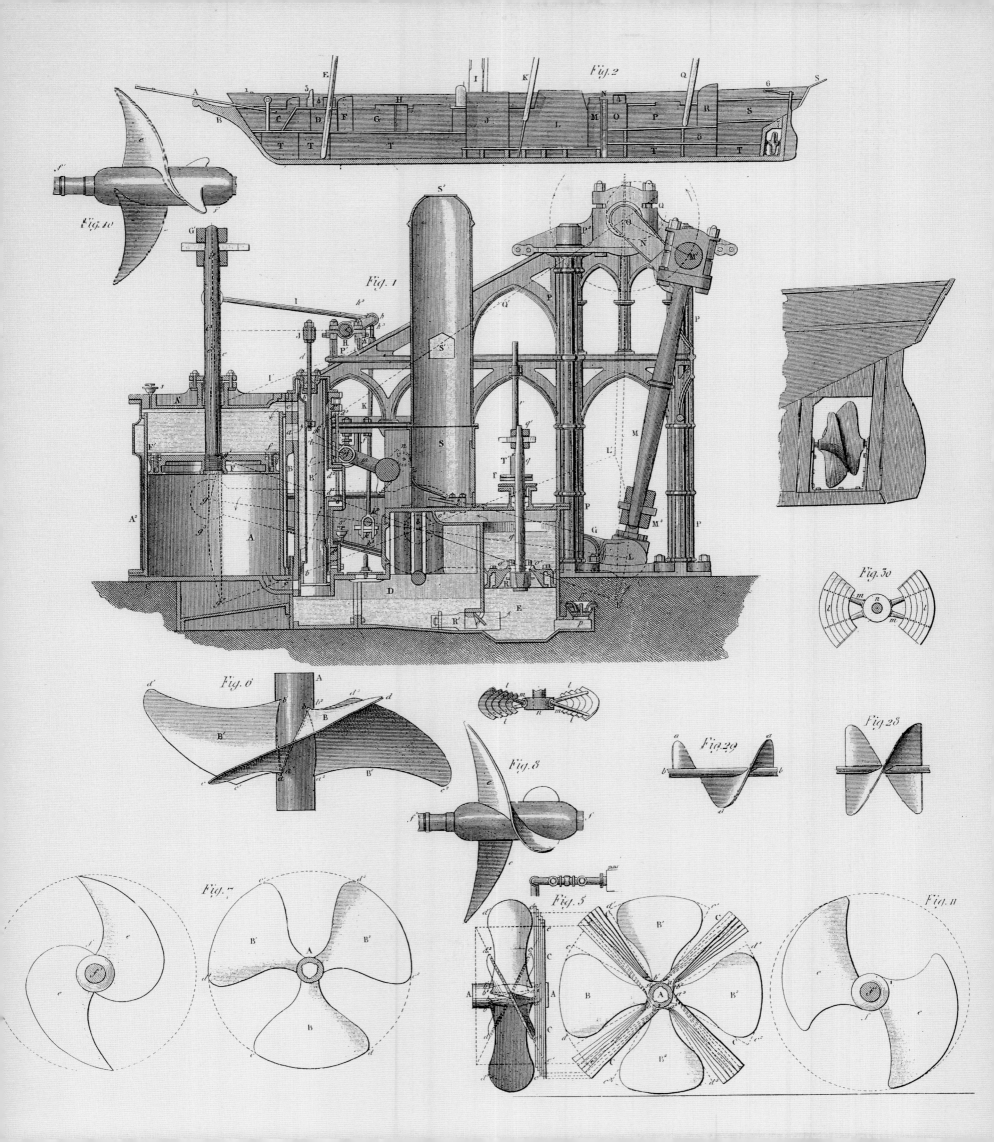

Fig. 2

Fig. 1

Fig. 10

Fig. 30

Fig. 6

Fig. 8

Fig. 29

Fig. 28

Fig. 7

Fig. 5

Fig. 11

Geography:
Mankind explores the world

The voyages of discovery had dramatic consequences for mankind at the start of the modern age.

The development of economics and trade has always gone hand in hand with exploration. Where people are exclusively occupied with the struggle for daily existence, there is neither the need nor the urge to explore strange lands. Only when forced by external circumstances such as drought or over-grazing did people dare to move outside their traditional territories. However, in advanced cultures, a mixture of curiosity and the prospect of wealth has always inspired travel to other regions. From about 2000 BC, the Minoans of Crete began to explore the Mediterranean and by 1400 BC they had more or less mapped the

coastal areas. Egyptian hieroglyphs tell of lucrative expeditions to the Land of Punt, which must have lain in the region of what is today Somalia or Eritrea. In 600 BC the Phoenicians sailed around Africa and the Iberian peninsula to reach the south coast of England.

What does the earth look like?

Exploration inevitably led to a general question about the shape and composition of the earth. The philosopher Aristotle recognized in the 4th century BC that the earth was round, since it threw a round shadow onto the moon. The geographer Eratosthenes calculated the circumference of the earth very accurately in the 2nd century BC. He was also the author of a famous map that shows the then known world, from Great Britain in the northwest to the mouth of the Ganges in the east and Libya in the south. In the 2nd century AD, the astronomer Claudius Ptolemy collected the geographic knowledge from ancient times and suggested new methods for making maps and charts. In his famous *Geography* he divided the circle of the equator into 360° and established a grid of lines running sideways and lengthways for locating countries and sea routes.

The inheritance of the ancient geographers was taken up not by the Europeans, but by Arab scholars. They translated the works of the Greeks and also explored Africa and

Asia on their own behalf. One of the most eminent Arab geographers was Al Idrisi, who drew remarkably detailed maps. The only significant European explorer in the Middle Ages was the Italian Marco Polo. Using Arab and Chinese trade routes, he traveled to the Far East in the 13th century. While on his second journey to China, Marco Polo entered the service of the Mongolian ruler Kublai Khan, whom he accompanied on many of his travels. For a long time the reports he wrote were the only source of information about Asia.

Europe goes forth

The age of discovery in Europe started with the Renaissance. Again, economic interests were the motivating force. One of the greatest patrons was the Portuguese prince Henry the Navigator (1394–1460). He founded the first school for geographers and navigators in Europe and instigated countless improvements in shipbuilding. As a patron he also supported important voyages of exploration, particularly along the west coast of Africa. It was his goal to find a sea route to India, since the land route was controlled by Arab merchants. However, the circumnavigation of Africa was only achieved in 1494 by Vasco da Gama. Two years earlier, Christopher Columbus had tried on behalf of the Spanish crown to find a route to India by sailing from Europe to the west. He based his decision on the theory that the world was round, which had still

Vasco da Gama (1469–1524)

Christoph Columbus (1491–1506)

not been conclusively proved, but he depended on the calculations of an Italian astronomer that proved to be erroneous. This man believed that the world was much smaller than previously supposed and that it was composed mainly of land. As is well known, Columbus actually discovered America, and this "new world" then became the main goal of European explorers and adventurers who hoped to find valuable resources and costly goods. In the early 16th century Hernando Cortez conquered the empire of the Aztecs, and Francisco Pizarro that of the Incas. Ferdinand Magellan sailed round South America while looking for a new route to the Orient, and later he was the first man to circumnavigate the globe.

Traveling for science

From the 18th century, knowledge for its own sake became a more important factor in expeditions. Alexander von Humboldt was largely responsible for exploring Latin America. He not only traveled down the Orinoco river for its whole length and a large section of the Amazon but he also studied the ocean currents, temperatures, flora and fauna, minerals, and much more. The expedition of James Cook to the Pacific was initiated by the Royal Society, the British scientific institution founded in 1666. Cook mapped New Zealand as well as the east coast of Australia and brought many unknown plants and animals back with him to Europe. The exploration of Africa was promoted largely by the African Association, the predecessor of the Royal Geographical Society in London. The most famous explorer of Africa was the Scottish missionary David Livingstone, who crossed the Kalahari desert and mapped a large part of Angola up to the mouth of the Zambezi river.

In contrast with Africa, America and Oceania, in Asia Europeans came up

Adventurous men such as Roald Amundsen could not resist the attraction of the last few blank spaces on the map of the world.

against solidly established empires that were not so easy to enter. The first information came from missionaries in the 16th century. Two Jesuits, Franz Xavier in Japan and Matteo Ricci in China, were among the first to make reports. Later, it was courageous adventurers, often without companions and disguised for instance as Muslim merchants, who traveled in Asia.

The last blanks on the map

Eventually, only the polar regions of the earth were left as the last great goals for the explorers. Who reached the North Pole first is still unclear. Several travelers have claimed their right to this title, including Robert E. Peary in 1909. The journey to the South Pole became a race between the Norwegian Roald Amundsen and the Englishman Robert Scott, which Amundsen won. Scott and his team lost their lives on their way back from the Pole.

The journalist Henry Morton Stanley set off on a search expedition to find the missing explorer David Livingstone.

Ohm's law: a new impulse for electrical engineering

Georg Simon Ohm (1789-1854)

IN THE YEAR 1827

> Simón Bolivár is appointed lifetime president of Peru.

> The American treasure-seeker Joseph Smith declares that the angel Moroni had appeared and given him gold plates engraved with the Book of Mormon. In 1830, Smith would establish the church of the Mormons, the first Christian religion founded on American soil.

> Germany's first life-insurance society is established in Gotha.

The German mathematician and physicist Georg Simon Ohm discovered the interrelationship of voltage, resistance, and current in 1827 and expressed these in his celebrated "Ohm's law." His formula is still the basis of all electric circuits today.

The experiments of the doctor Luigi Galvani (1737–98) and the physicist Alessandro Volta (1745–1827) brought electro-technology at the end of the 18th century decisively to the forefront, with Volta constructing the first battery. This "Voltaic pile" delivered electric current as a result of chemical reactions. But the researches of Galvani, Volta, and scientists of the early 19th century were usually carried out on the principle of trial and error. No scientist had yet discovered the laws governing the behavior of electricity.

Another scientist provided the mathematician and physicist Georg Simon Ohm (1789–1854) with a starting point in his search for these laws. In 1820 the scientist Hans Christian Oersted (1777–1851) of the university of Copenhagen had discovered that direct current would deflect a magnetic needle.

Ohm's experiments were founded on this discovery. He constructed a measuring instrument in which a needle was suspended by a gold thread between the poles of a magnet. When the device was connected to a circuit, the needle moved. Called the galvanometer, this instrument enabled Ohm to measure the strength of a current accurately for the first time.

In numerous related experiments with the galvanometer, Ohm made a fundamental discovery about the flow of current. He passed current through wires of different length and diameter and observed the deflection of the meter connected to them in each case. He discovered that with constant voltage and temperature the current depended on the length and diameter of the wires used. Ohm drew the conclusion that this phenomenon was attributable to the resistance with which the wire opposed the current.

From his experiments, the physicist eventually derived the following law. The electric current I flowing through a wire is directly proportional to the difference in the voltage V at each end of the wire, and inversely proportional to the resistance. The quotient of I divided by V is the electrical resistance R. With direct current, the formula of Ohm's law is: V equals I over R, or amps equals volts over ohms.

In 1827 Ohm published his results in the book *Die galvanische Kette, mathematisch bearbeitet* ("The Galvanic Circuit, Calculated Mathematically"). At first the work found little approval, because many of his colleagues refused to accept his findings. Only in countries outside Germany did scientists recognize the practical benefit of Ohm's law, which soon opened up new possibilities in telegraphy and measuring techniques.

With time, German engineers also recognized that the development of electrical engineering and electronics was impossible without the knowledge of the correlation of voltage, current, and resistance. Ohm's law is still today the basis of the circuit diagram of every electrical device.

Georg Simon Ohm made discoveries about electric current that led to significant developments in the field of electrical engineering and electronics.

The typewriter: revolutionizing the world of work

William Austin Burt (1792-1858)

In the woods of Michigan, far from the economic centers of the United States of America, the land surveyor, civil servant and brilliant inventor William Austin Burt invented the prototype of a typewriter in 1829. His invention revolutionized the working world and speeded up clerical work.

△ The development of the typewriter accelerated office productivity. This tendency has been further speeded up by the development of modern computer technology.

Inventors in many countries had experimented with automating the writing process. In 1714 the British inventor Henry Mill patented such a machine, but not much notice was taken of it since he was unable to convince people of the necessity of his invention. A whole century passed before the idea was taken up again. In Germany, Karl Friedrich Drais (1785–1851) worked on a similar machine and in 1820 he built an apparatus with 16 types (cast printed letters) that was to facilitate speedwriting.

Meanwhile, in the state of Michigan, USA, William Austin Burt was tinkering with his invention. Burt started work on his "Typographer," as he called it, in 1829, with no idea of how radically his invention would influence the working world. He built his first machine of wood and it was impressively large. Burt fixed the types to a metal wheel supported by a semi-circular frame. Using a crank, the writer moved the wheel until the desired letter was in the correct position, then pressed a lever that pushed the type against the paper where it left an ink imprint.

Burt worked on improving his model. He constructed a new device that was the size of a modern pinball machine. With practice he was able to type with it as fast as he could write by hand. His friend, the founder and editor of the *Michigan Gazette*, John P. Sheldon, recognized the possibilities inherent in the invention and applied for a patent for Burt. This gave Burt sole rights to construct and sell other Typographers. However, he could not find any buyers, probably because he was an inventor at heart and was not a marketing strategist.

However, Burt had prepared the ground for further developments. The American inventor Christopher Latham Sholes (1819–90) took up the challenge in 1867. Together with his friends Carlos Glidden, James Densmore, and Samuel Soule, he designed a machine that boasted such modern characteristics as a rubber roller, line spacing and carriage return, and the QWERTY type sequence that is still used today. In 1873, Sholes sold the rights to his typewriter to the gunmaker Philo Remington and his firm E. Remington & Sons. Remington mass-produced the typewriters and sold them to writing offices, lawyers, industrial companies, and even to authors. With his book *The Adventures of Tom Sawyer*, Mark Twain was the very first author to hand his editor a typewritten manuscript.

Since that time the typewriter has climbed a steep career curve. It has speeded up the writing process and increased productivity enormously, a development that is still continuing, with the invention of electric typewriters followed by the computers, electronic notebooks, and personal digital assistants of today. Social structures were also changed forever by this machine. For the first time women entered the work force in large numbers, which in turn caused fundamental changes in the industrial countries.

The invention of the typewriter revolutionized the working life of women in particular.

The telegraph and morse code

**Wilhelm Eduard Weber (1804-91),
Carl Friedrich Gauss (1777-1855),
Samuel Finley Breese Morse (1791-1872)**

Early human cultures used drums, smoke signals or fire signals to communicate over great distances. The modern world needed a different solution. One of the first attempts was the telegraph system invented towards the end of the 18th century by Claude Chappe. The electric telegraph was a much more satisfactory solution, once Morse had invented his code for transmitting messages as combinations of dots and dashes.

Claude Chappe was a French engineer and cleric of the late 18th century who set out to provide a visual signaling system between Paris and Lille. His idea was to erect tall poles each within visual range of the next, and each one fitted with two movable arms, the different positions of which would convey the letters and numbers of the message. He called this device a "semaphore," from the Greek meaning "bearing a sign."

The idea of transforming information into electrical signals arose at the beginning of the 19th century as progress in the fields of electricity and magnetism was made. It was necessary to find a way of making the electrical signals visible or audible. It was almost by chance that, in 1833, the German physicist Wilhelm Eduard Weber and the mathematician Carl Friedrich Gauss constructed the first electromagnetic telegraph. The text was coded as electrical impulses and made visible as dots on paper. Both men had been occupied since 1832 with research into the earth's magnetic field, and they saw this device as simply a by-product of their researches. In their eyes it was a rather simple machine that could send information over a distance of about 1 mile.

The real breakthrough in electric telegraphy was achieved by Simon Morse, a professor of drawing in New York. In 1833 his enthusiasm for electrical and chemical experiments led him to work on a telegraph machine that he patented in the United States three years later.

The transmitter of the apparatus was a switch with which an electrical current could be interrupted for a predetermined length of time. The receiver was a pen controlled by electromagnetism that originally drew letters as zigzags on a paper tape.

However, by 1836 Morse had developed a system using signs that were faster and easier to transmit. This was a binary code consisting of just two signals, a short one (a dot) and a long one (a dash). Letters were represented by various combinations of these symbols, the commonest letters having the shortest codes. Samuel Morse's first apparatus could send information over about 20 miles; thereafter the signals became too weak. This problem was solved by installing amplifiers at intervals along the telegraph wires.

The potential of Morse's invention was recognized by American politicians. In 1834 Congress spent $30,000 on the construction of a telegraph line between Washington and Baltimore. Morse sent the first message over this line a year later.

For a long time, Morse code was used almost exclusively in telegraphy but it is still used today in ship radios and by amateur radio fans.

The Morse code consists of only two sounds, short and long, or dot and dash, that are produced with a simple key. This machine prints the signals received on a paper tape.

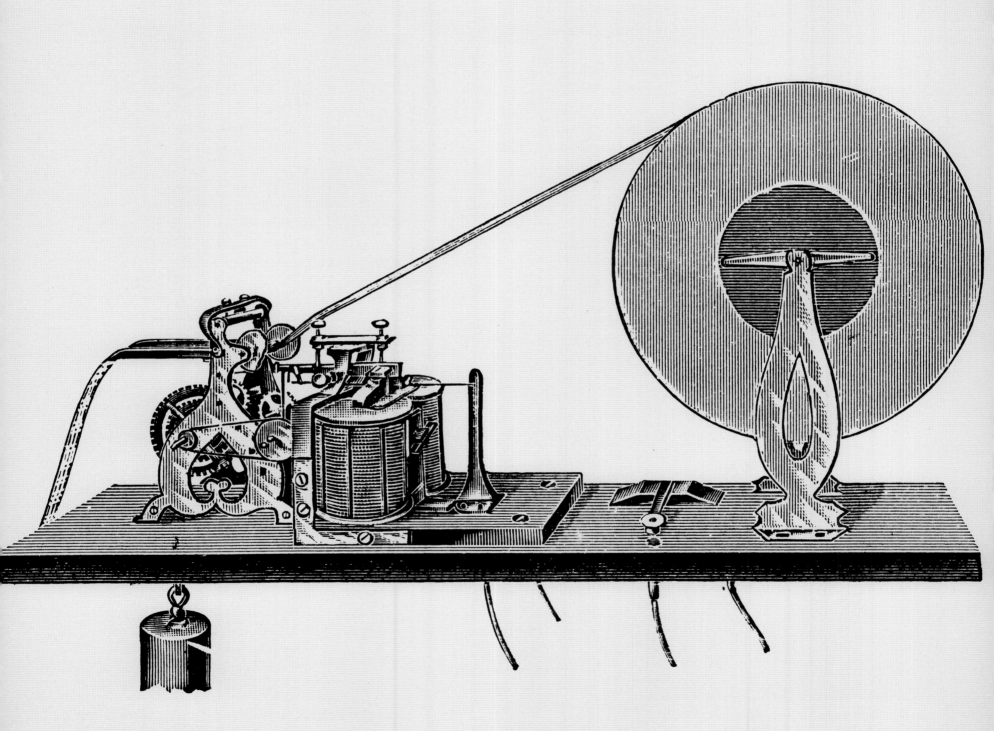

Relays: lower tension when turning the switch

Joseph Henry (1797-1878)

Joseph Henry's invention of the relay was an important step in electrical technology. The device proved indispensable in telecommunications technology and later in early computers.

In the initial phase of electro-technology, switching high voltage cables on and turning them off was expensive and not entirely safe. The high voltages had to be cabled to the switch position, and direct switching of high voltage necessitated massive switches with large contact surfaces. When operated they created massive sparks that damaged the contacts. The presence of high voltage at the switch meant that the operator risked a potentially lethal electric shock.

The physicist Joseph Henry (1797–1878) played a decisive part in the solution of these problems. He is chiefly famous for his discovery of the phenomenon of self-induction, which he observed while working on improving the early electromagnets. He achieved this notably by insulating the wire of the coil so that more turns could be wrapped round the iron core, thus increasing the strength of the magnetism developed. In 1829 he introduced an electromagnet that could lift a weight of nearly one ton. Then, the problem-solver devoted time to the idea of using an electromagnet to switch a circuit reliably and without risk.

In 1835 Henry discovered the solution to this problem: the relay. With this device, a separate, low voltage circuit operates an electromagnet that consists of a coil and an iron core. The switch controlling this circuit can be of lightweight construction since it does not handle high voltages. This also applies to the input to the magnet. When the low voltage circuit is completed, a magnetic field builds up in the electromagnet, which pulls a hinged metal armature to one side. The movement of the armature is used to close a high voltage circuit with substantial switch contacts.

The advantage of the relay lies in the fact that the operator uses the low voltage circuit to switch the high voltage indirectly and without danger. In addition, the installation of the low-power cables can be carried out over long distances easily and inexpensively.

With these qualities, the relay revolutionized the newly emerging technology of telephone communication. Here, the low voltage flowed economically over long distances through telegraph lines, at each end of which the relays of the exchange directed the call to its destination.

The triumphal march of the relay did not slow down until the start of the computer age. The first large computers still carried out switching processes with relays, but the following generations of computers used vacuum tubes and later the more reliable, more compact solid state semiconductor circuits instead of relays. Nevertheless, relays have not yet completely died out. In their modern form (such as the very sensitive reed relay) they are still used particularly in the telecommunications, energy technology and data processing industries.

△ Before solid state technology, mainframe computers used a large number of relays in their circuits.

The invention of the relay made it possible to control high voltage current through low voltage cabling.

The Faraday cage: secrets of electrostatics

Michael Faraday (1791-1867)

1836

IN THE YEAR 1836

> The Mexican state of Texas, in which primarily Americans live, declares its independence. The Mexican troops lose the subsequent campaign against the Texans, and Texas becomes an autonomous republic.

> The London Working Men's Association is established in London. It aims to help achieve more rights for workers.

> Martin van Buren is chosen to be president of the United States.

> Nikolaus Dreyse constructs the first breech-loading needle-firing percussion cap gun.

An automobile is the safest place to be in a thunderstorm. Parents often use this piece of wisdom to calm their frightened children during storms. But why is this actually so? In 1836, Michael Faraday recognized that electrical fields that neutralize those made by bolts of lightning originate on the surface of a housing made of a conductive material, for instance a metal cage. In this way the interior of the so-called "Faraday cage" offers protection from electric shock.

The apprentice bookbinder, Michael Faraday, earned recognition as a natural scientist early in life. He had discovered the laws of induction and invented the first electric motor. His experiments with electrostatics were to make him even more famous. In 1836, he discovered that a person sitting inside an electrified metal cage was in absolutely no danger of receiving an electric shock from lightning, even if he or she touched the cage itself.

The Faraday cage, used today primarily as a protection against bolts of lightning, functions on the following principle. A housing made of a conductive material, for instance a metal cage, shields the interior of the space from electrical or magnetic fields. These are then only present on the surface of the conductor. The electrical field caused by a bolt of lightning produces a so-called "surface discharge" on the outer, conducting surface of the cage. This, in turn, produces a field that precisely equalizes the outer one. The bars of a cage can even be spaced quite widely apart and still achieve this effect.

For instance, during a thunderstorm the occupants of an automobile – even a convertible with the fabric roof closed and a metal roll bar – are quite safe. A bolt of lightning striking the car will divide the current inside the metal bodywork and a field will build up that compensates for that of the lightning. A circuit to earth is created through contact with the road and this conducts the lightning bolt into the ground. Airplanes or rail vehicles are also protected by the mechanism that Faraday discovered. Airplanes are often struck by bolts of lightning when flying through storm clouds without the passengers even being aware of the fact.

Coaxial cables for screening electrical signals from outside interference are constructed on the same principles as the Faraday cage. An outer braided conducting sheath made of metal screens the inner wire from electrical fields that would interfere with a television signal or signals being carried on a computer network. Highly sensitive measurements, such as those of electrical impulses from the brain in medical research, are also carried out in insulated rooms.

The principle of the Faraday cage is not only used for insulating inner spaces from external influences. Often it is the other way around, with an area outside being protected from a field produced inside. The radiation emanating from a cathode ray tube can be caught in this way, by a grounded metal cage built into the interior of the tube. This method has been used as a standard safety precaution for computer monitors for a long time.

Michael Faraday, shown here in his London laboratory, discovered how to give protection from bolts of lightning.

Photography: an image of reality

Louis Jacques Mandé Daguerre (1787-1851), William Henry Fox Talbot (1800-77)

The discoveries of a business-minded French painter and an English physicist marked a milestone in the history of "light picture art." Suddenly it was possible to capture reality on a piece of paper.

The Arabian scholar Ibn al-Haitham (*c.* 965–1039), also known as Alhazen, pioneered the principle of the camera in the 11th century. He made the ground-breaking discovery that if an object reflects rays of light through a tiny hole into a dark room or box, a small mirror image of the object can be seen inside it. This *camera obscura* ("dark room") or "pinhole camera" was used by the painters of the 17th and 18th centuries as a tool when making nature studies. However, the possibility of retaining these "light pictures" permanently remained an elusive wish.

In 1727, the German doctor Johann Heinrich Schulz (1687–1744) made a discovery towards the achievement of this end. He found that certain silver compounds turned black when subjected to light. But retaining an image of light was not possible until 100 years later when the lithographer Joseph Nicéphore Niepce successfully achieved this. He coated a polished plate of tin with a light-sensitive covering of a kind of asphalt, bitumen of Judea. When exposed to light, those parts were bleached. The unexposed asphalt could then be washed off the plate with a solution of lavender oil and turpentine. Niepce heightened the contrast by using iodine vapor. This is how the first photograph in the world was made with an exposure time of eight hours in 1822. It showed the view from the window in the lithographer's workroom. Niepce called this process "heliography," meaning "drawing with the sun."

The ambition of retaining the pictures made in the camera obscura was also shared by the French stage painter and interior decorator Louis Jacques Daguerre (1787–1851). He began to work with Niepce in 1829, but it was not until after Niepce's death that he found a better developing process by accident. He coated a copper plate with silver and made it sensitive to light by treating it with iodine vapor. He then made the exposed image visible by treating the plate with mercury vapor and fixed it with a sodium chloride solution. The first "daguerreotype," a still life, was made in 1837.

In 1839, the English physicist and chemist William Henry Fox Talbot (1800–77) made the first photograph using a negative/positive process, the calotype. He treated paper with silver nitrate and potassium iodine. The actual photographic image, the negative, was then transferred to light-sensitive silver-chloride or silver-bromide paper to make the positive. Talbot's technique greatly shortened the necessary exposure time and made it possible to make an unlimited number of pictures from one negative.

This new invention proved to be of the greatest fascination. People spent hours looking at pictures through a magnifying glass. The images depicted nature in a realistic and detailed way, quite different from that achieved by a painter.

In 1851, the Englishman Frederick Scott Archer (1813–57) invented the wet collodion process. This achieved the greatest light sensitivity so far and reduced the time of exposure from five minutes to between ½ second and 30 seconds. The age of photography for all had begun.

The French graphic artist Honoré Daumier joked about the long exposure times of the first cameras: "Patience is the virtue of donkeys."

1837

IN THE YEAR 1837

> The Russian author Aleksandr S. Pushkin dies after receiving a gunshot wound in a duel.

> The British government puts down a rebellion of independence fighters.

> In Hanover King Ernest Augustus cancels the constitution. Seven Göttingen professors – the "Göttingen Seven" – condemn the measure and are expelled.

> The Viennese government prohibits smoking on public streets.

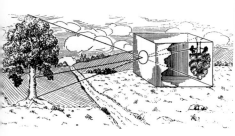

△ Illustration of a tree in a camera obscura.

La patience est la vertu des ânes.

The solar corona: following the light

A vast crowd of astronomers

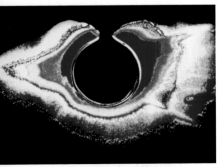

1842

IN THE YEAR 1842

> In Great Britain the Mines Act prohibits women and children working in mines.

> A fire destroys large parts of the old part of the city of Hamburg.

> The Webster-Ashburton treaty fixes the border between the USA and Canada, ending a long-running dispute.

> The premiere of Giuseppe Verdi's opera *Nabucco* takes place in Milan.

Since time immemorial mankind has been fascinated by the sun. What are its rays and how are they produced? Solar eclipses have always been welcomed by astronomers as a natural opportunity for such research. It is only on these relatively rare occasions when the sun is concealed by the moon that the solar corona, the halo or circle of light round the sun, is visible to the human eye.

It is a fascinating fact that many discoveries about the nature of the sun's light have been made when it is concealed by the moon. In the year 1842 there was a total eclipse of the sun that affected a large part of Europe. This rare opportunity to observe the sun attracted a large number of astronomers, who made a number of fundamental findings.

At this time it was not known with certainty whether the corona (the term was coined by the Englishman Francis Baily in 1840) that became visible during an eclipse emanated from the sun or, as had been thought, from the moon. Using spectral research scientists were finally able to identify the corona unambiguously as a solar phenomenon, a finding that gave astronomers a more solid foundation on which to work.

Consequently other discoveries were made, including the structure of the sun, which was found to consist of layers like an onion. From the core outwards, there is first the photosphere, then the chromosphere, and finally the corona, the outer layer that envelops the sun. Because it is diffuse and round as well as a million times less luminous than the surface of the sun, the corona is usually invisible to the human eye. But because of its internal dynamics it is particularly interesting to astronomers. The discoveries of 1842 were therefore an important milestone that prepared the way for further research.

Another phenomenon much studied since then are the solar prominences, great fountains of flaming gas that project from the surface of the sun. These have been meticulously researched since 1942. They are emitted by the sun in the form of red-glowing gaseous clouds that then flow back to the sun's surface in high arcs. This phenomenon is now explained by the knowledge that these glowing gas particles, catapulted up to 250,000 miles away from the surface, travel along the magnetic lines of force of the sun, thus making them visible. But in the 19th century their discovery alone was a significant event.

It was another 100 years before the corona and phenomena round the edge of the sun could be studied at any time, instead of only during solar eclipses. In 1930 the Frenchman Bernard Lyot invented the "coronograph," a telescope in which a diaphragm concealed the solar disc, thus creating the effect of an eclipse at will.

As darkness fell during the eclipse of 1842, the mystery of the corona surrounding the sun was suddenly elucidated. The question "What is radiating thus and above all how?" has now long been answered, but the enduring fascination of the star at the centre of the solar system remains.

The clouds of gas that emanate from the sun are known as solar prominences. They return to its surface in a wide arc.

△ **It is only when the sun is concealed by the moon that the corona becomes visible.**

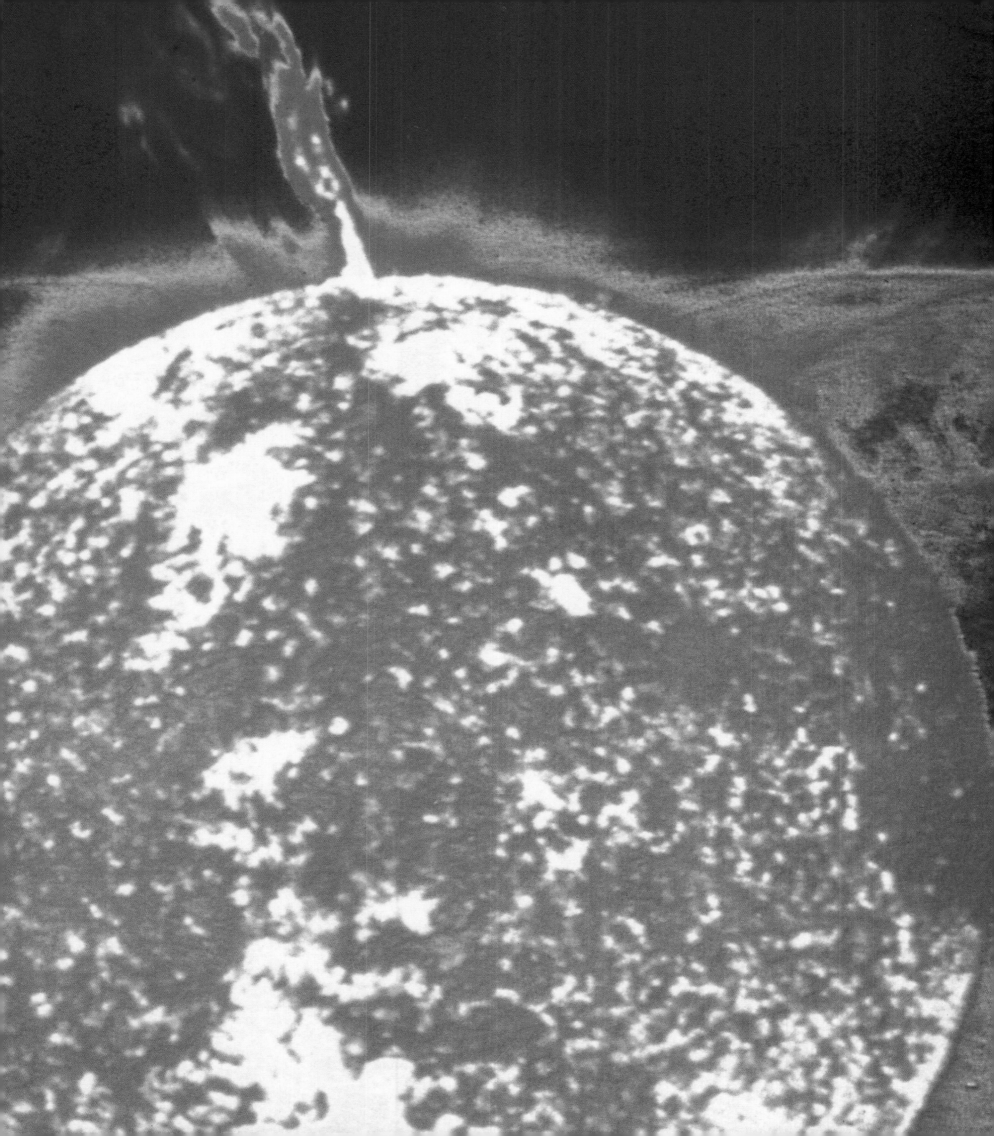

The nervous system: movement at will

Emil Heinrich DuBois-Reymond (1818-96)

How does a specific muscle "know" that it is to carry out an action? In 1843, Emil Heinrich DuBois-Reymond discovered that electrical currents in the nerves and muscles were largely responsible for this activity.

1843

IN THE YEAR 1843

> Robert Koch, the founder of the bacteriology, is born in Clausthal, Germany.

> The London economic newspaper *The Economist* appears for the first time.

> In the USA the Seminole Wars that has been fought since 1835 end. The Seminole Native Americans were fighting back against being compulsorily resettled from Florida to Oklahoma. Now, the tribe is practically wiped out.

> Great Britain takes possession of the South African Boer state of Natal, which originated after the emigration with the "Great Trek."

In the 18th century, by artificially stimulating nerves, physiologists proved that they were sensitive, that is, capable of being stimulated. By the transference of energy they caused the muscle "at the end of the line" to contract. However, they could not determine what kind of energy was being used by the stimulated nerve. They also knew nothing about the origin of this energy. Was it an external mechanical or chemical stimulation, or did the organism create its own energy?

The argument between the two scientists Alessandro Volta (1745–1827) and Luigi Galvani (1737–1798) was characteristic of this debate. In 1780, Galvani connected the muscle and nerve of a dissected frog's leg by two metal conductors. The leg began to twitch. Galvani interpreted this observation as "animal electricity" produced by the muscles, declaring that the organism produced the electricity that triggers the muscle contraction by itself. Alessandro Volta was vehemently opposed to this opinion. He insisted that the jerking of the frog's leg was due to "metallic electricity," that is, the electricity was produced by the contact with metal and was merely discharging into the frog. This dispute divided the scientific world for some time.

The German physiologist Emil Heinrich DuBois-Reymond (1818–96) was instrumental in helping to resolve the problem. As a student he had already written a treatise on electric fishes. The phenomenon of electrical manifestation in the tissues of living creatures continued to fascinate him so much that in 1840 he began to improve the technology of electrical measuring instruments. With these more accurate instruments he hoped to be able to measure low-level electrical currents in nerves and muscles. By 1843 he was able to show that nerve impulses are at least partly of an electrical nature. He recognized that a change in the electrical state of the nerve triggers an impulse. These electrical changes could also be seen along the muscles and not just on the nerves.

Scientists now regarded the electrical impulse as a basic parameter for physiological experiments and were therefore able to begin explaining the mechanism of the successive flow of information along the nerves.

Shortly after this, it was discovered that external stimuli as well as commands of the brain could exert an influence on the nerves. In 1921, Otto Loewi (1873–1961) proved the influence of chemical substances in the transmission of electrical impulses to the nerve endings, or synapses.

The theories of DuBois-Reymond are still recognized today. They make up the foundation of modern electrophysiology and have made possible the later inventions of the electrocardiogram (ECG) and electroencephalogram (EEG), which measure the electrical currents in the heart and brain. The records made by these machines allow pathological abnormalities to be diagnosed. Defining electricity as the actual "nerve fluid" has therefore had an important effect on medical diagnosis.

The nervous system runs through the whole body and is the basis of all transmission of information.

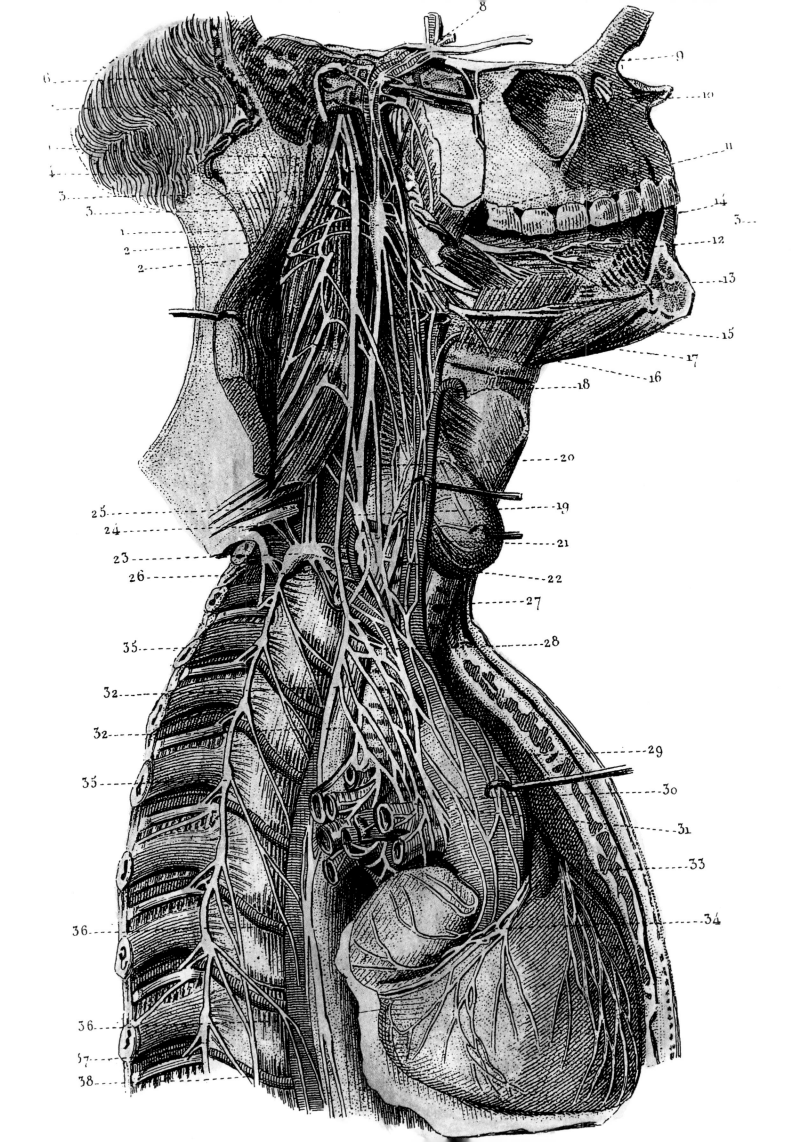

The theory of evolution: the origin of life

Charles Darwin (1809-82)

With his work *On the Origin of Species by Means of Natural Selection*, the English scientist Charles Darwin brought the accepted view of the world of his day crashing down. He forced the "divine humans" to discover themselves as part of a quite unromantic natural history. His theory of evolution exiled the myths of creation forever from the realms of science.

Normally, the antithesis to "revolution" is "evolution." Whereas the former violently overthrows the established order of things, the change through evolution is constant and purposeful. The working hypothesis of evolutionism in natural and cultural philosophy interprets development as something that ascends, from the lower to the higher and more valuable. The philosopher Heraclitus (550–480 BC) expressed evolutionistic theories, and Aristotle (384–322 BC) also believed that lower organisms developed into higher ones, steered by a "driving force."

It was not until the 18th and 19th centuries, however, that philosophers and biologists began to examine the idea of the development of nature in detail. It was the German philosopher Immanuel Kant (1724–1804) who in 1755 first dared to speculate on the origins of planets as a cloud of cosmic mist. Geologists on the other hand could not overlook the increasingly obvious fact that fossils of plants and animals were not exactly similar to living ones. The most celebrated and influential representative of the theory of evolution was Charles Darwin.

As a young man Darwin had taken part in the famous research expedition on the HMS *Beagle*, which had taken him around the world between 1831 and 1836. Studying his collected biological specimens led him to the conclusion that the origin of living things is a historical process. He defined his theory in the phrase "survival of the fittest." Darwin substantiated his opinion by declaring that members of a species pass on various characteristics to their offspring, of which more are born than are actually necessary for the survival of the species. Natural selection ensures that the offspring with the most suitable characteristics are the ones that survive, while the weaker are sacrificed to the process of evolution.

Nevertheless, Darwin was unable to explain how the various characteristics were handed on; the science of genetics did not unravel this mystery until the beginning of the 20th century. He wrote his ideas down in a short essay but did not have it published until 15 years later when a similar work was laid before him for his opinion. In 1859, *On the Origin of Species by Means of Natural Selection* appeared, followed by *The Descent of Man, and Selection in Relation to Sex* in 1871. In this second work, Darwin publicly subscribes to an idea that until then had only been hinted at, which was still unthinkable to many: the evolution of humans from ape-like creatures.

Darwin's theories broke two taboos: the religious idea of a perfect creation, and the rationale of enlightenment that placed people above nature. Darwin forced people to see that they were only a momentary link in the long chain of nature's evolution.

Darwin saw evolution not so much as the fight of single individuals for survival but more as a co-evolution of species.

△ Charles Darwin banished the myth of creation from science.

Neanderthal man: the human being's great uncle

Johann Carl Fuhlrott (1804-14)

As quarrymen blasted open two new caves in the Neander valley near Düsseldorf, they found some curiously thick pieces of bone. At first they thought they had discovered the remains of one of the great cave bears. However, the teacher and natural scientist Johann Carl Fuhlrott from Eberfeld identified the bones as the remains of an early type of human being, until then completely unknown. Later, in 1884, the Irish scientist William King named this prehistoric creature *Homo neanderthalensis*.

There was controversy among the scientists of the time as to the age of the bones. While Fuhlrott assumed they were of "great age," the anatomist Franz Josef Mayer (1787–1865) and the anthropologist Hermann Schaafhausen (1816–93) did not venture to speculate on their age. Rudolf Virchow (1821–1902), an authority in the field, insisted until shortly before his death that they were not prehistoric bones at all but the bones of a modern human who suffered from rickets. Today it is known that the actual age of the skeleton is 50,000 years.

Who was this Neanderthal man? It was 1.7 million years ago that an early species of human being, *Homo erectus*, appeared in Africa. About 800,000 years ago, descendants of this species left Africa to settle in Asia and finally in Europe. From this race, the people known as *Homo heidelbergensis* developed. The emergence of enormous glaciers and far-reaching deserts isolated populations from one another, so that eventually two distinct human types evolved, *Homo neanderthalensis* and *Homo sapiens*.

The forerunners of the Neanderthals pressed on into Europe about 200,000 years ago. During the Ice Age they developed into a small, thickset species of human that was particularly well adapted to the cold climate. Reconstructions have shown that Neanderthals were characterized by a low forehead, a receding chin, a heavy ridge over the brows, and a massive skeleton with a slight bend in the bones of the limbs. Their typical tools were blades, points, and hand axes. These people lived by hunting. They built their shelters in caves or under overhanging ledges and they had mastered the art of making fire. Some tribes of Neanderthals carried out ritual acts, making grave offerings and sacrifices for the dead. These people were the only inhabitants of Europe until 40,000 years ago, when competition appeared on the scene. *Homo sapiens*, indigenous to Africa for the last 170,000 years, began to emigrate to Europe. Several thousand years later, *Homo sapiens* was the only human race to have survived.

Why the Neanderthals died out is a controversial question. Some experts are of the opinion that *Homo sapiens* forced them into the Iberian peninsula, others believe that the two races coexisted peacefully in Europe for many thousands of years and that there were even biological unions between the races. A third theory states that the Neanderthals were not only technologically inferior to *Homo sapiens* but that they also had a lower rate of reproduction.

More will be learned about these distant predecessors of the human race only when further information comes to light. Until then it will not be known for certain why the Neanderthals vanished from the Earth.

The Neanderthal people who inhabited Europe were particularly well adapted to the cold climate.

Genetics: what sweet peas reveal about inheritance

Gregor Johann Mendel (1822-84)

> The Supreme Court of the United States creates a sensation with the Dred Scott decision. This declares that the move of a slave from a slave state into a slave-free state does not make him a free human being.

> A stock market crash in New York precipitates the first world economic crisis.

> New York Irishmen establish a secret society that aims to free Ireland from the rule of Great Britain.

> Sheffield FC is the first association football club in the world.

△ Gregor Mendel experimented with sweet peas and developed the basic laws of heredity.

For thousands of years mankind has experimented with the breeding of domestic animals and cultivated plants in order to "optimize" them according to its wishes. But the criteria by which the desired traits were handed down were unknown. The biologist Gregor Johann Mendel was the first to discover strict laws governing hereditary characteristics.

In 1843 the farmer's son Johann Mendel entered the Augustinian monastery of Altbrünn under the name Gregor. His brother superior recognized Mendel's exceptional scientific talent and allowed him to carry out research in the monastery instead of becoming a preacher. Mendel also continued to teach biology. Soon the processes of heredity attracted his interest. Experiments with breeding in order to produce superior domestic animals and plants that would be more profitable were widespread in the mid-19th century. In the 18th century, the botanist Joseph Gottlieb Kölreuter (1733–1806) had discovered while cross-breeding plants that transfers of pollen from one species to another led to the same result in both directions (reciprocal cross-breeding). The decisive impulse for the development of the study of genetics was the work of Charles Darwin (1809–82) with his theory of variation within species.

Mendel hoped to be able to find order behind this variation. From 1857 he carried out intensive experimentation on sweet pea plants to establish that the hereditary material came only from one parent. He collected the seeds of the plants thus fertilized, planted them, and observed the new generation. Mendel noted that low-growing plants always stayed low-growing over successive generations; therefore their hereditary material was programmed to produce only low-growing plants ("pure line"). Tall-growing plants, though, sometimes brought forth tall-growing plants but could also produce low-growing ones, so their hereditary material could pass down either tall or low growth ("non-pure line"). The only low-growing plants were those that had inherited their low growth from both parents. When crossing a pure low-growing pea with a pure tall-growing pea plant, only tall-growing plants would result. This led to Mendel's first law, the principle of segregation: it stated that the crossing of parents of different pure hereditary lines would result in offspring that were all uniform. In this case usually only the dominant gene is asserted in the first generation, while the recessive gene appears to vanish.

The characteristics of the second generation of offspring led to Mendel's second law, the principle of independent assortment. Mendel bred two offspring of the first generation together and discovered that their cross-breeding resulted in various manifestations of the plant (phenotypes). In the third generation of sweet peas, low-growing and tall-growing plants appeared in the ratio 3:1, marking the reappearance of the recessive gene in 25 percent of the offspring.

Mendel's most important discovery was that hereditary material is built up from independent and consistent hereditary pools. When handed on from generation to generation, these traits are re-grouped and follow strict natural laws. But as the processes of sexual reproduction were then little known, the scientific world took little notice of Mendel's revolutionary conclusions.

Mendel's experiments with plants provided the basis for modern genetics and biotechnology.

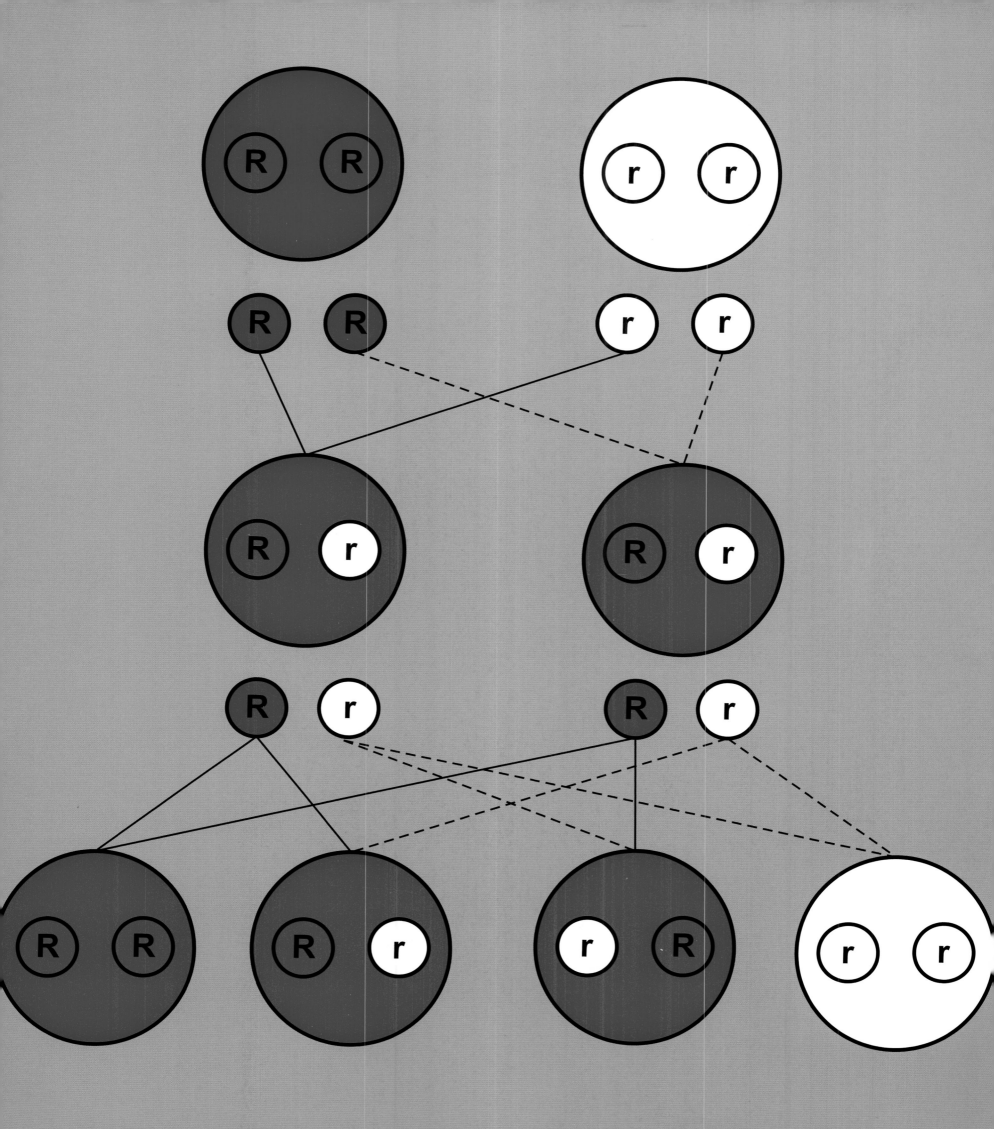

The refrigerator: keeping food fresh for longer

Ferdinand Carré (1824-94)

In the 19th century, the Frenchman Ferdinand Carré built a prototype refrigerator. With it he revolutionized the food industry and private households. This domestic appliance fundamentally changed people's patterns of consumption and nutrition.

1859

IN THE YEAR 1859

> The new Mexican president Benito Juárez García carries out wide-reaching reforms. Civil war breaks out between the conservatives and the liberal forces when he takes away some of the privileges of the military and the Church.

> John Brown, a radical opponent of slavery, raids a weapon depot at Harper's Ferry, Virginia, that belongs to the federal army. After his execution Brown becomes a hero in the eyes of the abolitionists.

> France and Russia sign the Paris Treaty in which the Russian Tsar Alexander II promised Napoleon III his neutrality in the case of a war between France and Austria.

Foods and beverages remain fresh longer and spoil less easily if they are stored in a cool place. Housewives have known this for a long time, even in old China and in ancient Rome, where prosperous citizens used natural ice from the mountains for this purpose. But transport was not only expensive; much of the ice melted before it had arrived at its destination. It was therefore not considered for the long-term preservation of meat, fruit or vegetables. Fresh foods went moldy or quickly fermented, so anyone who could not acquire the costly ice had to forego many foods that are part of a healthy diet.

Before Ferdinand Carré's time, scientists had already devoted time to the problem of refrigerating areas or containers, but without success in practical terms. The doctor William Cullen demonstrated in the year 1748 that when liquid, in this case ether, is evaporated in a partial vacuum it cools considerably. The physicist Michael Faraday (1791–1867) discovered a chilling effect rather by chance when in 1823 he heated a test tube with chlorine during one of his experiments. The chlorine condensed at one end of the tube and the glass cooled noticeably. But since his main interest was electricity, Faraday did not pursue this phenomenon any further.

Almost 40 years later, Carré and his brother Edmond devoted themselves to the problem of a cooling receptacle. They knew of the experiments of Cullen and Faraday and were clear about the basic principle of a cool receptacle: the inside temperature of the heat-insulated receptacle had to be lower than the temperature of the outside environment. According to Carré, a circulation system could achieve this effect: the refrigerant passes through the inside of the receptacle, removes the surplus heat energy and conveys it outside. There, it cools down and is supplied to the inner circulation again. Carré's objective was therefore to find a substance that would absorb heat and divert it in quantity, and that in addition represented no danger to human beings. The refrigerants of earlier attempts – water, air or ether – only partially fulfilled these requirements. Carré chose ammonia and used it to construct the first "refrigerator" in 1859.

He presented his new invention at the 1862 International Exhibition in London, and it immediately aroused great interest all over the world, particularly in North America. During the American Civil War the southern states could no longer expect ice deliveries from the northern states, so the south was an eager market for Carré's refrigerators. But the great breakthrough of the refrigerator took place in the early years of the 20th century, when the industrial manufacture of these appliances began in the USA. By the late 1950s, almost every European household also possessed a refrigerator. Improved models even made it possible to deep-freeze foods. The manufacturers soon replaced the original refrigerant, ammonia, with the better performing fluon/FCKW (fluoride-chlorine-hydrocarbon). However, this substance is no longer used since it destroys the earth's ozone layer, so Carré's refrigerator design has undergone a rebirth: environmentally-friendly models use ammonia once more.

Refrigerators only came into general use 50 years after they were first invented.

Spectral analysis: fingerprints of the elements

Robert Wilhelm Bunsen (1811-99) and Gustav Robert Kirchhoff (1824-87)

The chemistry professor Robert Wilhelm Bunsen and the physicist Gustav Robert Kirchhoff shared a passion for photochemistry. One of their joint discoveries opened the way for completely new possibilities of unraveling the mysteries of a substance: spectral analysis. This was based on the fact that each element emits light on a unique wavelength.

△ Robert Wilhelm Bunsen

Bunsen burners are still used in chemistry laboratories today. The apparatus conducts a mixture of gas and air through a vertical tube until it emerges from a nozzle where it burns with a flame that reaches a temperature of 1,500° C, is almost colorless, and does not give off sooty smoke. Robert Bunsen had originally designed the burner as a heater. However he and Kirchhoff soon realized that with this apparatus they could reveal the electromagnetic spectrum of chemical substances. When salts were evaporated in the flame, they gave off a light that could be split up using a prism.

It was a simple operation to reveal the seven spectral colors of light's visible spectrum. But in the course of this operation Bunsen and Kirchhoff noticed that each chemical element has its own characteristic pattern of spectral lines that, like a fingerprint, is unique. This was true even when an element was chemically combined with other elements, in a compound. Soon the two scientists discovered not only the different color combinations in the spectrum of evaporating substances heated to incandescence, but also the laws that governed these phenomena.

They built the first spectroscope, an optical apparatus that splits up the light produced into the colors of the spectrum. This enabled them to see very small differences in the spectral lines that were invisible to the naked eye. In the same way that the prism is the simplest part of a spectroscope, the seven colors of the spectrum represent only a small segment of the spectrum's electromagnetic waves. A modern spectroscope is a highly sophisticated device with a wider range and an integrated computer.

Spectral analysis enables scientists to detect the existence and concentration of chemical elements in a substance. It has even enabled them to discover unknown elements in this way; Bunsen and Kirchhoff themselves discovered cesium and rubidium two years after their pioneering invention.

Because the distance between the source of light and the spectroscope is irrelevant, spectral analysis has also found an application in astrophysics. Helium, for instance, was discovered in the spectrum of the sun long before scientists were able to detect its existence on the earth.

Such spectroscopic studies of the stars provide important information about chemical reactions under specific conditions such as extreme heat, extreme cold, or in a vacuum. For instance, the spectra of elements changes under the influence of external circumstances. Changes in the spectral lines caused by the movement of the source of light have enabled scientists to draw conclusions about its speed. A similar alteration in the spectrum of galaxies led to the theory of the expansion of the universe.

Gustav Robert Kirchoff and Bunsen discovered the spectrum of chemical elements, resulting in the invaluable study of spectral analysis.

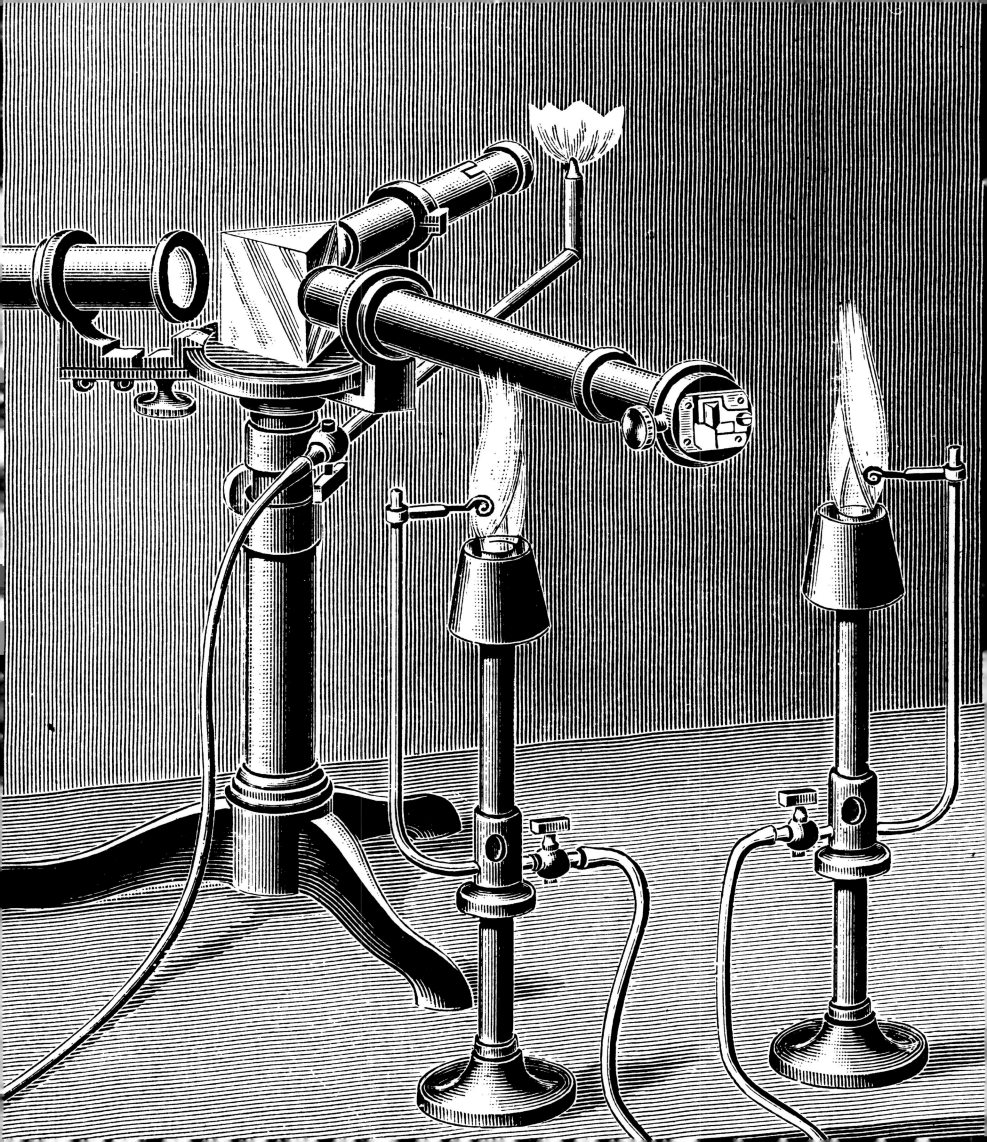

Biology: Searching for the secret of life

What are the questions?

Life in itself is a multilayered phenomenon, and recognizing this variety in all its guises is a characteristic of all the sciences appertaining to it. Investigating living nature in general and discovering her natural laws in particular falls to the discipline of biology among the natural sciences. This is why the areas of research are so varied and the gains in knowledge so wide-ranging.

Today it is easy to lose one's bearings in the sheer amount of data relating to plants, animals, and human beings that has been collected. The world opened up by the science of biology has proved to be increasingly complex. Botany, zoology, anthropology, the study of unicellular organisms, and genetics—all these have contributed (and are still contributing) to the treasure hoard of knowledge. However, even though fathoming the secret of life leads in so many different directions, the pioneering questions underlying scientific inquiry in the field of biology are fundamentally the same.

The question of what is

In ancient times, natural scientists using scientific criteria had already begun to

Botanical studies led to an increasingly detailed classification of plants. This is a representation of a summer landscape dating from the 13th century.

In the late 19th century the observation and breeding of animals in zoological gardens gave people an impression of the exoticism of foreign lands.

observe, order, and name the plants and animals of the earth. The first known botanical studies with an encyclopedic character were made by Theophrastus, a pupil of Aristotle. In his work he laid the foundation of the systematic cataloging of living things as well as determining and differentiating their characteristics.

However, it was not until the 16th century that the classification of species took place on a large scale. One of the reasons for this was that knowledge of the various species of plants and animals had grown constantly, mainly as a result of the geographical explorations of the time, and another was that, due to the general trend towards specialization, it was now possible to make more detailed classifications within the biological systems. This "inventory of living things" reached a temporary conclusion with the work of Carolus Linnaeus in 1735. In his classification system for plants and animals he established the use of the binomial descriptive label.

The question of composition

What is an organism made of? What structures go together to compose a living body? As a result of the anatomical studies of Galen of Pergamon, the first definite clues in this direction were forthcoming at the beginning of the 2nd century, at least with regard to plants and animals. The anatomy of the human body was only scientifically studied when autopsies (the dissection of corpses) became possible in relatively modern times. It was Andreas Vesalius in particular who blazed the trail for further decisive research. His recording of the individual parts of the vascular system in 1543 laid the foundation for the discovery of William Harvey, who mapped the complete circulatory system of the blood in 1628.

Apart from autopsy, it was the invention of the microscope (c. 1590) that gave a decisive boost to research. In 1665 scientists were able to track down the elementary unit of life, the cell, using this instrument's power of magnification. The discovery of the cell nucleus in 1831 was a further stage in the search for the still "invisible" dimensions of life.

The question of sequence

Before the life processes found in the cell became the focus of interest, attention was mainly directed towards the observation of functional aspects, particularly that of the nerves. Their structure had been discovered by anatomists relatively early on. However, it was not until the advent of electrophysiology that the phenomenon of information being carried along them by electrical impulses could be observed. The development of electrophysiology in the 19th century was the beginning of the gradual process that would successively help disclose the circuits between the brain and the organism. Thus the body's own communication system as a component of the living organism was recognized. This was a significant step forward.

Great steps were also made in other directions, especially in the rapidly expanding understanding of the physiology of metabolism. By 1827 scientists recognized that sugar, fat and protein were essential to human nutrition. In 1878 enzymes and in 1906 vitamins were added to this list, knowledge of both of them helping towards a greater understanding of the sequences of organic processes. Hormones too were discovered in 1901. Light was shed on a metabolic achievement of a particular kind by the complete analysis of photosynthesis, the "breathing" process of plants. Staying alive by generating energy is a characteristic of all living things.

The question of origin

The scientific interpretation of the phylogenic and developmental history of different forms of life is bound together in the first instance with the name Charles Darwin and the basic principles of his theory of evolution. His main work, *On the Origin of Species*, published in 1859, had far-reaching and profound consequences for biology and also for the whole scientific view of the world. With his theory of the common origin of organisms and his concept of gradual evolution, mankind had forever to climb down from the biological pedestal on which it had placed itself.

Although Carolus Linnaeus had grouped human beings as a species within the animal kingdom, for most people there was still at least an emotional distance between *Homo sapiens* and the animal world. Darwin put an end to that. The direct connection between humans and animals was clearly demonstrated in his teaching of evolution. This therefore became an important issue in anthropology. In particular the Darwinian theory of natural selection resulting in the survival of the fittest was an encouragement to further research. For instance, the study into animal behavior and ethology were developed from this in the 20th century.

The question of development

A decisive step towards more knowledge of how life develops after conception was the discovery of the function of the egg. In about 1600, Girolamo Fabricius founded an early form of embryology on the basis his investigations into chickens' eggs from fertilization to the hatching of a fully formed chick.

The second and more decisive step, however, was the examination of the processes within the the cell itself, that is, the realization that every cell has to begin with a fertilized egg (in the case of

Botanic gardens, such as this one in London illustrated in 1852, were a valuable resource of information for botanists as well as a source of great enjoyment for the public.

humans and animals) or seed (in the case of plants). It was Wilhelm Roux in particular who, with the foundation of experimental embryology in 1885, set revolutionary standards for this. The study of the configuration of cell division as well as the parallel study of differentiation in each living being brought science much closer to a greater knowledge of the development of the embryo and also to a better understanding of the essentials of the cell itself.

At the beginning of the modern era little was known of the more exotic animals. These imaginary sea creatures and rare beasts are from a image dating from 1550.

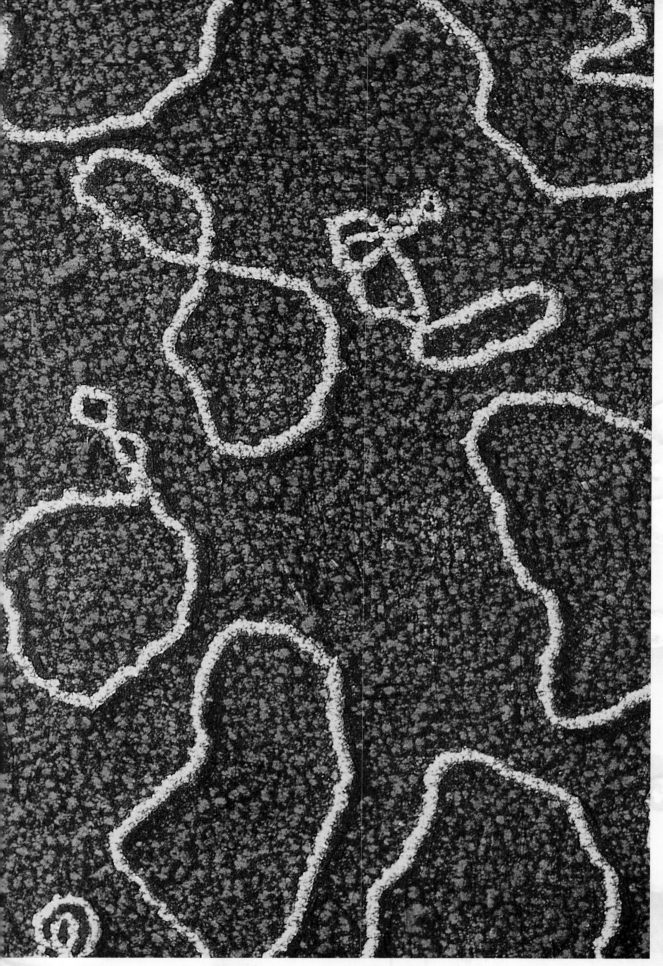

The question of heredity

Fundamentally, genetics is a science of the 20th century. The explosive development of this branch of biology was largely stimulated by the rediscovery of the laws of heredity stated by Gregor Johann Mendel in 1865. Further research followed at a breathtaking rate. In 1910 the first chromosome theory of heredity was put forward. Then in 1926, once the hereditary factors in the genes had been located, this developed further to become the foundation of the theory of genetics. In 1944 the genetic material DNA was discovered. Then in 1953 the double-helix structure was uncovered by the researchers Watson and Crick. In 1966 the genetic code was investigated, and in 1977 for the first time it became possible to identify and analyze DNA sequences. Since then the goal has been to decipher the code of the genetic language–an aim which was at least partly realized in the year 2000. The complete sequencing of the human genome has now been achieved. The sequence of "letters" is now known, but the "words" are still not understood. Life is perhaps no longer such a riddle to biology, but it still contains its mysteries.

Genetics, the science of the 20th century, has opened up hitherto undreamed-of possibilities in the field of biology but also poses new ethical questions.

The telephone: "Do horses eat cucumber salad?"

Johann Philipp Reis (1834-74)

In 1861 when Philipp Reis presented his "apparatus for transfer of sound over distance" to the Frankfurt Physics Society, the public had little need for gadgets of this kind. Today the telephone is an integral part of modern life and the most used means of communication throughout the world.

The basic elements of the telephone are the mechanism of communication and transmission, and the telephone apparatus at each end that converts the acoustic vibrations of words into electrical signals, and then converts these electrical signals back into audible words.

It was an experiment by the lecturer Johann Philipp Reis (1843–74) that marked the birth of such a "distance speaking machine." Reis wanted to demonstrate the conversion of sound waves into electricity to his students by using a wooden earpiece. First he built a "speaking shell" or mouthpiece. Reis attached a platinum strip to a membrane stretched across the opening of the wooden earpiece, and on the back of the "ear" he mounted a feather. Both parts had a metal contact point and were connected to a battery. When Reis produced sounds in front of the wooden earpiece, the membrane vibrated, touching the feather and then moving away from it again. Thus the electric circuit opened and closed to the rhythm of the vibrations. Reis placed this instrument, the sender, in a small wooden box with a glass plate and a tube. Using a linking cable he then directed the vibrations produced into the receiver, another small open wooden box that contained a coil on two bridges. When the electric impulses reached the coil, it produced an alternating magnetic field. In turn the magnetic field caused a knitting needle mounted in the box to produce vibrations that were reinforced by the wooden box, which acted as a sound box. Reis sent a colleague into another room with a transmitter and asked him to speak a sentence of his own choice into the mouthpiece. "The horse does not eat cucumber salad" were the words that he heard in the receiver. The experiment had succeeded, but the quality of the speech transmission could still be improved, since the rapid turning on and off of the current distorted the sounds.

In 1876 Alexander Graham Bell (1847–1922) applied for a patent in the United States for "an apparatus that transmits sounds by producing electrical waves." Inside the second wooden receiver was a bar magnet with an induction coil, with an iron membrane in front of it. When the sound waves caused the membrane to vibrate the magnetic field of the bar magnet changed, and analog current corresponding to the acoustic vibrations was induced in the coil. As a result Bell's apparatus did not interrupt the current but modulated the frequency of the vibrations. As well as providing sound of higher quality, it had the further advantages that the sender and the receiver were similar constructions, and the apparatus was easier to handle.

The telephone spread rapidly throughout the world. Subsequent development of communication and transmission techniques led to the digital controls that are commonly used today. As a result of the enormous progress made in electronics today, the telephone has become increasingly easy to use and more mobile. The invention of the telephone as a means of immediate communication over distances great and small marked the beginning of a new era for industrial countries.

Feature dated October 6, 1877 concerning Alexander Graham Bell's new telephone device.

△ The knitting-needle receiver used by Johann Philipp Reis.

SCIENTIFIC AMERICAN

A WEEKLY JOURNAL OF PRACTICAL INFORMATION, ART, SCIENCE, MECHANICS, CHEMISTRY, AND MANUFACTURES.

Vol. XXXVII.—No. 14. [NEW SERIES.]   NEW YORK, OCTOBER 6, 1877.   [$3.20 per Annum. [POSTAGE PREPAID.]

THE NEW BELL TELEPHONE.

Professor Graham Bell's telephone has of late been somewhat simplified in construction and also arranged in more compact portable form. It consists now of but three metal portions and is contained in a casing of wood or light hard rubber, but five and five eighths inches in length and two and seven eighths inches in diameter at the enlarged end. It will be remembered that this telephone differs from all others in that it involves the use of no battery nor of any extraneous source of electricity whatever. The only current employed is that generated by the voice of the speaker himself.

The simplicity of the construction is clearly shown in Fig. 1 of our engravings, in which both sectional and exterior views of the device are given. Referring to the sectional view, A is a permanent magnet, held by the screw shown in the rear. Around one end of this magnet is wound a coil B of fine insulated copper wire (silk covered), the ends of which are attached to the larger wires C, which extend to the rear and terminate in the binding screws D. In front of the pole and

coil B, is a soft iron disk, E. Finally the whole is inclosed in a wooden casing having an aperture in front of the disk and which, besides serving to protect the magnet, etc., acts somewhat as a resonator.

The principle of the apparatus we have already explained in some detail but it may be summarized here as follows. The influence of the magnet induces all around it a magnetic field and the iron diaphragm, E, is attracted towards the pole. Any alteration in the normal condition of the diaphragm produces an alteration in the magnetic field, by strengthening or weakening it and any such alteration of the magnetic field causes the induction of a current of electricity in the coil B. The strength of this induced current is dependent upon the amplitude and rate of vibration of the disk, and these depend in turn upon the air disturbance made by the voice in speaking, or in any other similar source. Therefore, first, a wave of air throws the diaphragm into vibration, second, each movement produces a change in the magnetic field, and third, an induced

[Continued on page 212.]

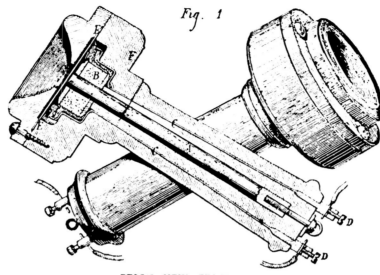

Fig. 1

BELL'S NEW TELEPONE

Plastics and synthetics: materials of the modern world

Alexander Parkes (1830-98)

> The Prussian king Wilhelm I. appoints Otto von Bismarck prime minister. In his famous "blood and iron" speech, Bismarck aims to persuade the parliament, which has refused army reform and funding, of the importance of the military for German unification.

> The Confederate States of America established in the previous year, which are at war with the Union, appoint General Robert E. Lee as the commander-in-chief of its armed forces.

> The French physicist Léon Foucault is the first scientist to measure the speed of light.

> With the Emancipation Proclamation the American president Abraham Lincoln announces that all slaves in the Confederate States are free from January 1, 1863.

PVC, nylon, and silicone, the descendants of the original synthetic material, are today some of the most widely used materials in the world. Alexander Parkes first presented this new synthetically produced material in 1862 in London. The little "masterpieces" made from Parkes's synthetic material at the time are now much sought-after collector's items. But Parkes' contemporaries did not appreciate the new material very much.

Alexander Parkes had no special training in either chemistry or physics. He nevertheless acquired an impressive specialist knowledge on these subjects and carried out many experiments with substances such as natural rubber. The mass-production of industrial and consumer goods required increasing quantities of stable, less expensive raw materials, and it therefore occurred to Parkes to try and produce such materials synthetically.

In his experiments Parkes heated nitrated cotton, previously soaked in sulfuric acid, and made the fabric soft and elastic with oil and camphor. The end product was an ivory-colored material that became distorted when subjected to heat. Named "Parkesine," it was the first synthetically produced material. Parkes presented the first product made from this synthetic material at the 1862 Great Exhibition in London. An advertising poster described this material as a true wonder substance: it was usable in solid, malleable, and liquid form, it was sometimes hard like ivory, sometimes lightproof, sometimes flexible, and always waterproof, or it changed color. It was possible to work the new material in the same way as metal: it could be cast, pressed, stamped, or rolled using tools. The medallions, combs, knife handles, little boxes, and fountain pens presented by Parkes at the exhibitions were all beautifully decorated, and today surviving examples fetch extremely high prices. But at the time people were not very keen on this alternative to natural substances such as horn. The objects made from Parkesine, later also called Xylonite, remained unsold in the shops. Many people complained that the products made from the new synthetic material easily lost their shape or even tore. Nevertheless, six years later, in 1868, factories began manufacturing Parkesine products.

Parkes's formula for a synthetically produced material laid the foundation for the development of plastic as a universally used material. As early as 1863 the American John Wesley Hyatt developed Parkesine further and called his new material "Celluloid" after its basic component cellulose. In 1920 Hermann Staudinger (1881–1965), director of the Freiburg Institute for Chemistry, made an important step forward in the processing of synthetic materials when he developed thermoplastic synthetics that were stable in themselves. This was to prove decisive for the present-day manufacture of synthetics, since it made them easy to form into shape.

Today the concept of "plastic" or "synthetics" is applied to a number of substances produced artificially in chemical laboratories, namely the polymers. Depending on its composition, the synthetic substance has different properties. Packaging, clothes, electrical apparatus and many parts of motor vehicles consist mainly of synthetic substances similar to the one first developed by Parkes in 1862.

Synthetic materials are used in the mass-production of consumer goods but are also widely used in industry.

Dynamite: an explosive mixture

Alfred Nobel (1833-96)

Few inventions illustrate the mixed blessings of technological progress as well as dynamite. On the one hand it freed the miners from the most terrible drudgery and made possible the great canal and tunnel building of the 19th century that helped to link nations. On the other it has brought destruction and death to many people.

△ The Suez Canal. Dynamite allowed much wider and deeper canals to be built.

Dynamite is the "big brother" of gunpowder, which has been known in Europe since the 13th century. Its appearance on the scene radically changed mining methods and the way wars were fought. Underground blasting enabled three times more ore to be mined than was possible by using muscle power alone. However, dynamite hit the world like a bomb. In contrast, the changes that gunpowder had brought with it were relatively insignificant.

When Alfred Nobel was born in Stockholm in 1833, gunpowder was the only explosive in use for artillery and blasting in mines. Nobel's father manufactured weapons of all kinds, which were used mainly in the Crimean War (1853–56). In 1853, he and Alfred first witnessed the great explosive power of the new substance nitroglycerine that the chemist Ascanio Sobrero (1812–88) had manufactured. In 1864, Nobel discovered that detonating the highly explosive nitroglycerine could be controlled by a small capsule of slowly burning gunpowder. This idea of an "initial trigger" forms the basis for modern explosives technology.

However, before this, Nobel had some problems with his research procedures. Since nitroglycerine was so highly explosive, catastrophes were always happening. Nobel discovered that by mixing the nitroglycerine with diatomite, a natural soil composed of decayed deposits of diatoms – unicellular algae – he could avoid this danger.

In 1867, Nobel applied for a patent for the new explosive under the name of Dynamite (Greek *dynamis* = power) or "Nobel's safety powder." The armies of the world powers could not buy it fast enough. In the Franco-German war of 1870–71, dynamite was used by the military for the first time in large amounts, with Nobel supplying the German as well as the French side. Within a very short time he had built up an international business emporium. The dynamite production of the Nobel factories rose 450-fold in just nine years, from 11 tons in 1867 to 5,000 tons in 1876.

Mine owners and tunnel builders were also eager to buy the new explosive, which could increase mine output by four or five times. The great number of railway tunnels that were built in the 19th century would hardly have been possible without dynamite. In the case of the Saint Gotthard Tunnel in Switzerland, the engineers blasted their way through over 9 miles (15 km) of solid rock in just eight years. In the next 30 years, blasting experts made Swiss cheese out of the Alps. An Italian newspaper called the engineers the "generals of a peaceful bombardment of an immense natural barrier between peoples." During the building of the Panama Canal, which was opened in 1914, 30,000 tons of dynamite were exploded, another great achievement made possible by the new explosive, dynamite.

Alfred Nobel built up an international business empire after inventing dynamite.

The periodic table: the inner logic of the elements

**Dmitry Ivanovich Mendeleyev (1834-1907),
Julius Lothar Meyer (1830-95)**

1869

IN THE YEAR 1869

> The railroad between Boston and Oakland connects the American east and west coasts.

> The Suez Canal is opened, connecting the Red Sea and the Mediterranean.

> The German Alpine Club is established in Munich.

> Napoleon III grants the French parliament more rights, including budget approval.

In the 19th century an increasing number of chemical elements were identified. At the same time scientists also established similarities in their chemical properties and defined the atomic weights of the different elements. This seemed to imply that there was a higher order among them.

In 1829 the German chemist Johann Wolfgang Döbereiner divided related elements into triads. In doing this he recognized the close relationship between calcium, strontium, and barium, or chlorine, bromine, and iodine. In 1850 Max von Pettenkofer drew up similar "chemical families" with groups of four, such as nitrogen, phosphorous, arsenic, and antimony. Ten years later the Russian scientist Dmitry Ivanovich Mendeleyev of St Petersburg was studying molecular cohesion at Heidelberg, when he heard the Italian scientist Stanislao Cannizzaro give an inspiring lecture at the first International Chemistry Conferrence in Karlsruhe.

Cannizzaro explained in his paper that most gaseous elements appeared as two-atom molecules. As a result he proposed that chemical elements should be classified according to their atomic weight. The British scientist John Newlands arranged the elements in a linear sequence according to this principle, and in 1864 he observed a "periodicity of octaves" in which after every seven elements an eighth followed whose properties resembled those of the first element. Five years later Mendeleyev and the German scientist Julius Lothar Meyer, independently of each other, systematically classified all the chemical elements in relation to each other in a chart, known as the periodic table.

In the periodic table, the elements are classified by increasing atom mass and by similar regularly recurring chemical and physical characteristics, or periods, from which the table takes its name. By arranging the periods above each other, a table is created in which related elements are grouped in vertical columns. In the horizontal rows the atomic numbers increase and the properties change. There are certain regularities between the elements in the horizontal rows and vertical columns.

The importance of the periodic table lay in the fact that it enabled scientists to identify theoretically in advance elements that had not yet been discovered, thus filling in the gaps in the table. This is how Mendeleyev was able to predict the existence of elements such as gallium, germanium, scandium, and rhenium. These were only positively identified in 1925 after prolonged research by analyzing radio spectra. Some irregularities in Medeleyev's table were resolved by other scientists after him when elements were classified not by atomic weight but according to the number of protons in the atomic nucleus.

Today the periodic table consists of 115 chemical elements, while the places numbered 113, 115, and 117 are still unoccupied. The transuranic elements from number 92 onwards have, with the exception of uranium, been produced synthetically and they do not occur in nature. Element 101, mendelevium, was named after Mendeleyev, the man who predicted it. The attempt to explain the irregularities in Mendeleyev's periodic table finally led to quantum theory.

The periodic system enabled scientists to predict the existence of elements that had not yet been discovered.

Wasserstoff 1.

Wertigkeit	0	1	2	3	4	3 (5)	2 (6)	1 (7)
I. Periode	He 4	Li 7	Be 9	B 11	C 12	N 14	O 16	Fl 19
II. Periode	Ne 20	Na 23	Mg 24	Al 27	Si 28	P 31	S 32	Cl 35

Wertigkeit	0	1	2	3	4	3 (5)	2 (6)	1 (7)	6	4	2	0	1	2	3	4	3 (5)	2 (6)	1 (7)
III. Periode	Ar 40	K 39	Ca 40	Sc 44	Ti 48	V 51	Cr 52	Mn 55	Fe 56	Co 59	Ni 59	—	Cu 64	Zn 65	Ga 70	Ge 72	As 75	Se 79	Br 80
IV. Periode	Kr 83	Rb 85	Sr 88	Y 89	Zr 91	Nb 94	Mo 96	—	Ru 102	Rh 103	Pd 106	—	Ag 108	Cd 112	In 115	Sn 119	Sb 120	Te 128	J 127
V. Periode	X 130	Cs 133	Ba 137	La 139	Ce 140	—	—	—	—	—	—	—	—	—	—	Er 167	—	—	—
VI. Periode	—	—	—	Yb 172	—	Ta 181	W 184	—	Os 191	Ir 193	Pt 195	—	Au 197	Hg 200	Tl 204	Pb 207	Bi 208	—	—
VII. Periode	—	—	Ra 226	—	Th 232	—	Ur 238	—	—	—	—	—	—	—	—	—	—	—	—

Bacteriology: study of the microcosm

Ferdinand Julius Cohn (1828-98)

Bacteria can be found everywhere: in the soil, in water, in the air. These micro-organisms had already been studied in the mid-17th century, but it was Louis Pasteur who showed that bacteria caused diseases, and Ferdinand Julius Cohn who succeeded in classifying them.

1872

IN THE YEAR 1872

> Great Britain abolishes public polls and introduces secret ballots.

> The first international football match between Scotland and England takes place in Glasgow. It ends in a goalless draw.

> The Japanese emperor Tenno refuses to set up a parliament.

> In the Ruhr area 15,000 miners strike for better working conditions.

"Bacteria" (from the Greek *bakterion* = stick or rod) are microscopic small unicellular organisms without a clearly marked cell nucleus. They generally propagate through cell division and are divided into three basic shapes: spherical (coccus), rod-shaped (bacterium), and spiral (spirillum). Many bacteria are sporogenous (bacilli), which means that they produce a kind of seed. The occurrence and multiplication of these microscopically small organisms depends on the ambient temperature; there are bacteria that exist in extreme cold or heat and others that prefer a normal temperature of 50–122° F. All bacteria die at a temperature of 176–212° F, with the exception of spores, which only die when the temperature reaches about 248° F.

One of the first scientists to speculate that such pathogenic organisms existed which could cause malaria, for instance, was Caesar's librarian, Marcus Terrentius Varro in 35 BC. However, these micro-organisms were invisible without a microscope. In 1676 the Dutch amateur scientist Antonie van Leeuwenhoek (1632–1723) examined bacteria under a microscope he had made himself. Later the chemist Louis Pasteur, a specialist in the field of micro-organisms, put forward the "germ theory," describing bacteria as disease-causing germs that caused the human body to produce antibodies. This theory prepared the way for the research into immunology. The science of bacteriology was based on Pasteur's discoveries.

The first classification of bacteria dates from 1872 and was the work of the German biologist and botanist Ferdinand Julius Cohn. In his three-volume work *Über Bakterien, die kleinsten lebenden Wesen* ("On Bacteria, the Smallest Living Organisms") he arranged bacteria genera and species on the basis of their morphological characteristics, that is, by their form and structure. Cohn also described how to produce bacterial cultures. Cohn encouraged the young German physician Robert Koch (1843–1910), who was responsible for significant developments in the science of bacteriology. In 1876 Koch succeeded in isolating the anthrax bacillus by culturing it in a laboratory on a solid nutritive medium such as gelatin rather than in a bacterial culture broth. The scientist assumed that the poisonous metabolic products produced by the bacteria killed the animals affected with anthrax. In 1882 Koch discovered the tubercle bacillus, the tuberculosis pathogen. In 1884 the Danish bacteriologist Hans Christian Gram (1853–1938) developed a method of dyeing bacteria, thus making it possible to identify them more easily.

After these important discoveries, one mystery remained unsolved: why did people fall ill with infections whose pathogens they had not been in direct contact with? The explanation was that infection was carried from one patient to another by third parties. The discovery of this missing link in the chain of evidence was an important step forward for medicine. In spite of initial protests, it became a requirement in hospitals that doctors and nurses had to wash their hands before coming into contact with any patient.

Scientists in antiquity suspected that micro-organisms were the cause of disease, but it was only around 1800 that their existence could be proved.

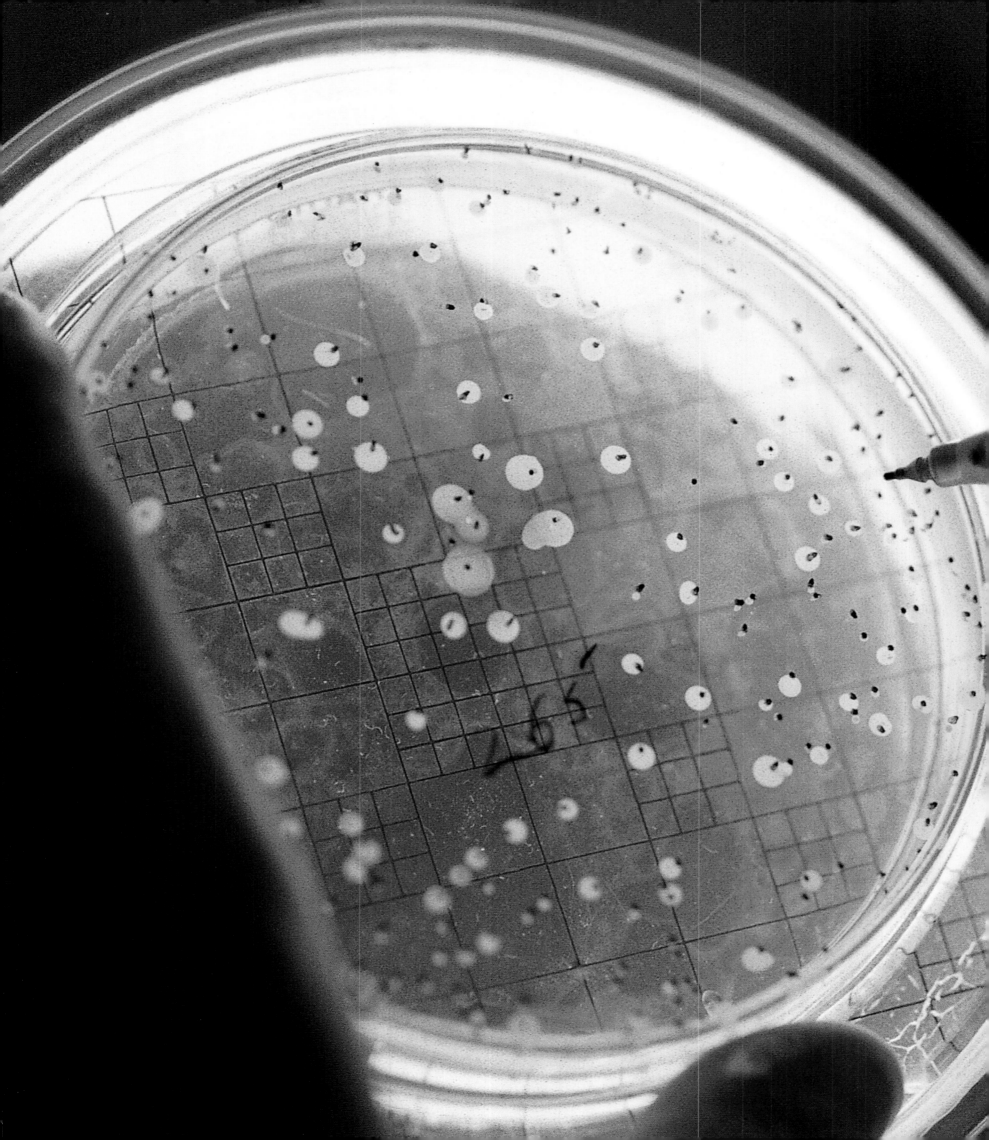

The contraction theory: how mountains were created

James Dwight Dana (1813-95), Eduard Suess (1831-1914)

1873

IN THE YEAR 1873

> In the struggle between the state and the Catholic Church, Prussia introduces the May laws, which subject the Catholic church to state supervision.

> The German archaeologist Heinrich Schliemann discovers Priam's treasure in his excavations in Troy.

> Italy begins begins secularizing its monasteries.

> The USA introduces the gold standard in order to support the dollar.

"It is the collapse of the Earth that we are witnessing!" This is how the Austrian geologist Eduard Suess summed up the theory that mountains are caused by the cooling and shrinking of the Earth. The theory marked the beginning of the study of global tectonics.

In the 18th century, some natural scientists such as Johann Scheuchzer (1684–1738), Horace-Bénédict de Saussure (1740–1799), and the abbot Antonio Lazzaro Moro (1687–1764) began to investigate the geology of the Alps. There they discovered that the layers of rock were thrown about in all directions, lying diagonally, up-ended, bent, and folded. They had difficulty in explaining this disorder. Scheuchzer suspected it was due to the Biblical flood while Moro ascribed it to volcanic activity.

In 1829, the geologist Jean Baptiste Élie de Beaumont (1798–1874), who had been working on a comprehensive geological map of France since 1825, presented a new theory dealing with the origin of mountains. According to him, the mountain ranges of the earth were of different ages, and one could also distinguish different elevating systems. Élie de Beaumont believed that the cause of the elevation and folding of mountains to have been caused by a slow contraction or shrinking of the earth. Since the inner core was slowly cooling from its original red-hot, molten state, the globe was contracting.

With this theory, the French geologist founded the science of tectonics, the study of the composition and formation of the earth's crust. Almost 30 years later, the geologist James Hall (1811–98) took a second and decisive step into this rocky field. In 1858, he made an interesting discovery in the Appalachians, the low mountain range in the eastern United States. He found that the extent of sedimentary layers – the deposits of prehistoric oceans – was ten times as large as it was outside the area. From this he deduced that the origin of mountains lay in basins of sediment that, due to the great weight of the deposits, had sunk over the course of the earth's history. In 1873, the geologist James Dwight Dana (1813–95) used the term "geo syncline" for this basin, which means more or less "earth crust trough." He combined this with Élie de Beaumont's theory and arrived at the conclusion that the sedimentary basins originated from horizontal pressure caused by contraction of the earth.

However, the real "prophet" of the contraction theory was Eduard Suess. Between 1883 and 1888 he published a work in several volumes, *The Face of the Earth*, in which he developed the shrinking hypothesis to its conclusion. Due to the conspicuous correspondence of species from the ancient plant and animal world on different continents, he deduced the existence long ago of a large southern continent, "Gondwanaland," that included South America, Africa, India, parts of Australia and the Antarctic. These countries would have been connected by land bridges that later sank into the sea. Although the polar explorer Alfred Wegener (1880–1930) contradicted this hypothesis in 1912 with his theory of continental drift, the contraction theory is still at the forefront of modern global tectonics.

James Dwight Dana believed that mountains were created over the course of time by sedimentation basins subsiding under the weight of deposits.

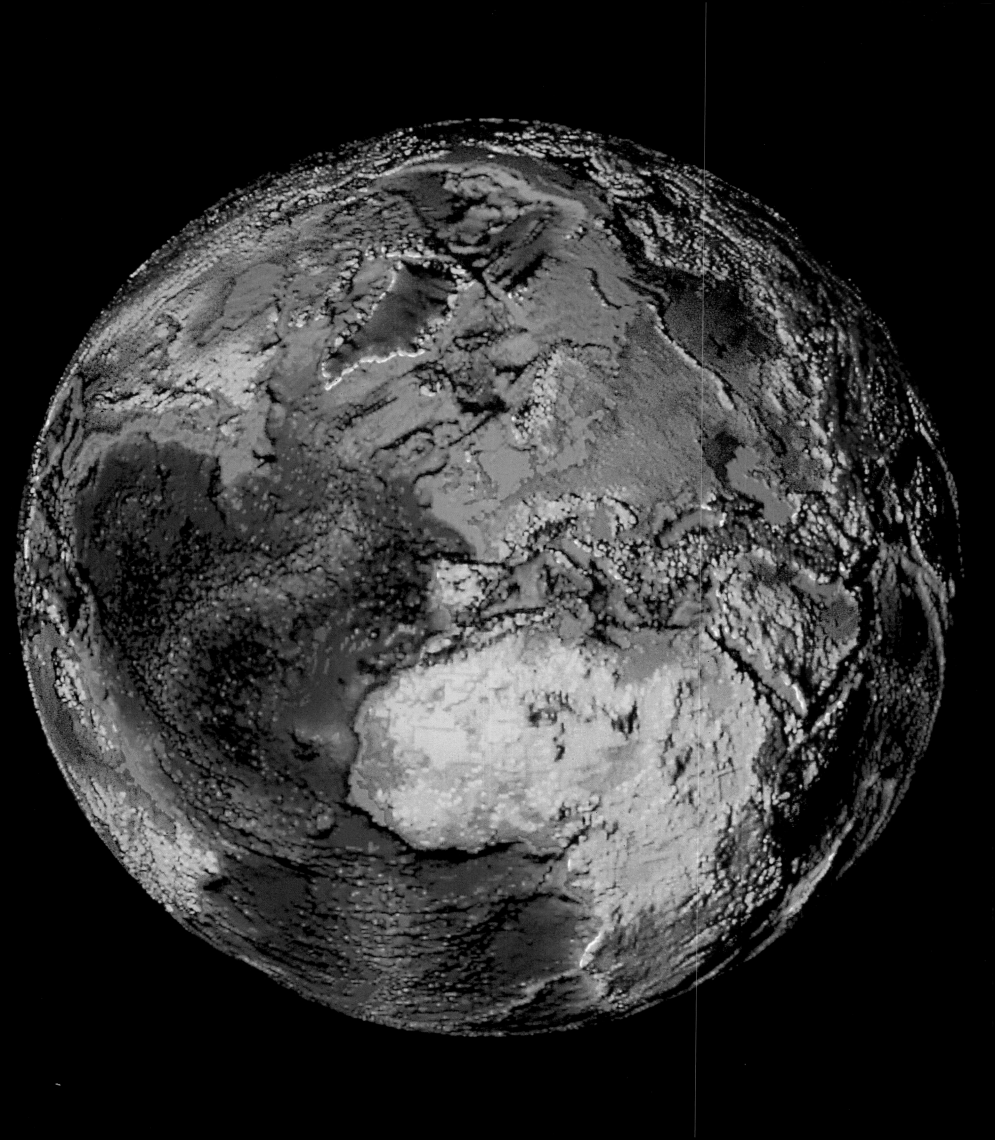

The Otto engine: a brilliant idea for a drive

Nikolaus August Otto (1832-91)

The invention of the steam engine by James Watt triggered the beginning of the industrial revolution. More and more powerful engines were developed, but only big businesses could afford them. Small businesses and workshops were threatened with being passed over by technological progress unless less expensive engines could be built.

In 1862 the French engineer Alphonse Beau de Rochas described the principle of a four-stroke engine in which the fuel/air mixture was compressed before being ignited, but this engine was never built. Independently of Beau de Rochas, the German engineer Nikolaus August Otto was working on the development of a similar engine powered by gasoline. Three years after he had founded the first engine factory in the world, Otto constructed an atmospheric gas engine in 1867 and exhibited it at the World Exhibition in Paris. The Otto engine, a four-stroke internal combustion engine that became a reality in 1876, was the prototype for all later combustion engines.

In contrast with the steam engine, where the energy source is external, the power of an internal combustion engine is produced by the ignition of a fuel/air mixture in a combustion chamber. The combustion chamber consists of a cylinder closed at one end in which the tightly fitting piston moves up and down. A crankshaft is connected to the piston by a connecting rod, which converts the up-and-down reciprocating movement of the piston into a four-stroke rotation. First the piston descends in the cylinder head, opening the inlet valve through which the fuel/air mixture is sucked in. Secondly it compresses it with the next movement upward in the cylinder head. At the end of this sequence the mixture is ignited. Thirdly the expanding ignition gases drive the piston down again. With the fourth movement, once again upwards, the exhaust gases are forced out of the combustion chamber through the exhaust valve. The sequence is then repeated.

Otto's first engine was ignited by a gas flame that was introduced into the cylinder at the end of the compression phase. It took 17 years for a gasoline-powered engine with electrical ignition to be developed, resulting in the construction that is still being used today.

The inventor of the prototype combustion engines was never granted a patent, since Beau de Rochas had already patented his theoretical design. Nevertheless, the practical Otto gasoline engine, followed by diesel engines and electric motors, introduced a second industrial revolution in which smaller businesses could afford the new motive power.

The engineer Gottlieb Daimler was a great admirer of Otto's new invention. Daimler had already worked in various large engineering works and he was interested in the gasoline engine as an alternative to the steam engine. As the technical director of the Deutz engine factory founded by Otto, he developed the Otto engine further and started to produce it commercially. In 1883 he patented a lightweight single-cylinder engine that he used in two-wheeled vehicles, then in boats, and eventually in a carriage. At the same time as Carl Benz, but independently of him, he had invented the automobile.

The Otto engine led to the development of the automobiles that began to appear on the streets at the end of the 19th century.

The phonograph: an invention that speaks for itself

Thomas Alva Edison (1847-1931)

IN THE YEAR 1877

> The first nationwide strike in the USA quickly spreads from the railway workers to become a general strike.

> Queen Victoria is crowned Empress of India.

> After the explorer Henry Morton Stanley has traveled along the Congo to the estuary, it is possible to map the course of the river.

> The federal patent office opens in Berlin.

When Thomas Alva Edison invented the phonograph in 1877, it was a tremendous attraction. For the first time sounds, whether talking, music, or songs, could be recorded and played back. Everything was stored in just the thin groove of the recording medium, first a cylinder and then a disc.

Thomas Alva Edison was a versatile inventor who in the course of his life registered 1,093 patents, including such epoch-making inventions as the telegraph, the phonograph, the electric light bulb, and the tramcar. He also set up dozens of companies, including General Electric.

The idea of building a phonograph or "sound-writer" came to Edison during his work on telegraphy. After the invention of the electromagnetic telephone by Alexander Graham Bell (1847–1922) and the carbon microphone by David Edward Hughes (1831–1900), the technical possibilities already existed for sending and receiving sound waves. A device also existed for recording sound, but it could not play them back. Edison combined all these devices in the prototype of the phonograph. The first words that he recorded on it went down in history: the first verse of the well-known nursery rhyme *Mary had a little lamb*.

How did this sound recorder work? A funnel-shaped horn guided the sound to a receiving membrane, to which a sharp needle was attached. The end of this needle pressed on a copper cylinder wrapped with tin foil that was rotated by a crank, along which the needle moved. When the sound waves caused the membrane to vibrate, the needle left a groove – the sound track - on the rotating cylinder with a depth varying according to the amplitude of the vibrations. When the cylinder was run again, the needle was moved by the recorded groove, causing the membrane to make the same vibrations that it had received when recording.

Amplified by the horn, the sounds recorded earlier were heard again.

Edison saw the benefit of his invention particularly in the educational and professional fields – he was not interested in the millions of people who wanted simply to be entertained. Wanting to record the voices of famous people for posterity, he made records of lectures and speeches, and with his invention blind people would be able to hear literary works. Recording music was initially only incidental as far as Edison was concerned. At first many interpreters of classical music even refused to have be recorded by such a "toy."

Edison continually improved his favorite invention, which he once said jokingly should pay for his old age. A later model had two needles and two membranes, one for recording and the other for playing back, and longer-lasting cylinders, needles, and membranes were developed and manufactured. For the commercial exploitation of the device, the inventor established the "Edison Speaking Phonograph Company" in 1878. This had an initial annual turnover of $25,000 dollars a year, which by the end of the 19th century had increased to $250,000 dollars a year. Only in 1907 did the turnover start to fall, as a result of the development of a rival article. Emil Berliner's phonograph was admittedly "only" a sound player, but this was sufficient for most customers since they hardly ever used the recording function of Edison's invention.

The phonograph became a commercial success very soon after it was invented.

WHAT WILL YOU DO

IN THE

LONG, COLD, DARK, SHIVERY EVENINGS,

WHEN YOUR HEALTH AND CONVENIENCE COMPEL YOU TO STAY

INDOORS ?

WHY !!! HAVE A PHONOGRAPH, OF COURSE.

It is the FINEST ENTERTAINER in the WORLD.

There is nothing equal to it in the whole Realm of Art.

It imitates any and every Musical Instrument, any and every natural sound, faithfully :

the **HUMAN VOICE**, the **NOISE OF THE CATARACT**, the **BOOM OF THE GUN**, the **VOICES OF BIRDS OR ANIMALS**.

From

£2 2s.

THE GREATEST MIMIC.

A Valuable Teacher of Acoustics. Most Interesting to Old or Young. A Pleasure and Charm to the Suffering, bringing to them the Brightness and Amusements of the outside World by its faithful reproductions of Operas, New Songs, Speeches, &c.

EVERY HOME WILL sooner or later have its **PHONOGRAPH** as a **NECESSITY.**

HAVE YOURS NOW; you will enjoy it longer.

Brought within the reach of every family by Mr. Edison's last production at **£2 2s.**

Send for our Illustrated Catalogues to

EDISON - BELL CONSOLIDATED PHONOGRAPH CO., LD.,

Or to our Licensees—

39, Charing Cross Road, W.C.

EDISONIA LD., 25 to 22, Banner Street, and City Show-Rooms, 21, Cheapside, E.C., LONDON.

Vaccines: a milestone in the history of medicine

Louis Pasteur (1822-95)

> The Republican Jules Grévy is chosen to be president of France.

> Like many other industrial nations, Germany also decides to raise protective tariffs.

> Germany and Austria form a defensive alliance against Russia.

> The artificial sweetener saccharin is first produced.

Everyone knows what pasteurized milk is. Pasteurization kills the micro-organisms such as bacteria that are found in foodstuffs, thus helping to preserve the food. For this process to be used successfully, the man after whom it was named, Louis Pasteur, had first to identify bacteria as carriers of decay or disease. His experiments were successful in developing vaccines for inoculation against several serious diseases.

The basic principle of active vaccination, the strengthening of the immune system by the introduction of the disease-causing pathogen, had been known since the 18th century. But the actual cause of the disease, the causative agent was not then known. In 1850 a micro-organism, the anthrax bacteria, was first found in the blood of animals. In the 1870s and 1880s research into vaccination made speedy progress; in rapid succession scientists found the pathogens causing leprosy, malaria, tuberculosis, cholera, diphtheria, tetanus, and syphilis.

A pioneer in the search for such disease pathogens was the chemist and physicist Louis Pasteur who saw his life's work as the fight against disease and death. His interest in micro-organisms was awakened when he became interested in the process of fermentation. It was Pasteur, who proved for the first time that the process of decay and fermentation was the result of the influence of micro-organisms. This observation led him to heat foodstuffs in order to kill off the heat-sensitive bacteria. He was correct in thinking that this procedure would help to preserve food from going bad. Since that time it has been called "pasteurization."

It was not until later that Pasteur enlarged his field of experiment to include human diseases. With the conviction that many sicknesses were caused by bacteria, in 1879 he turned to immunization using weakened forms of the bacteria.

This led him to carry out a ground-breaking experiment in 1881. He vaccinated several sheep from a test herd with weakened anthrax bacteria. After a time, he subjected the whole herd to the usually fatal pathogen. The immunized sheep survived the disease with no harm while all the others died. Following from this, and using similar experiments, he developed vaccines against chicken cholera, anthrax and in particular against rabies.

These fundamental discoveries by Pasteur led to the founding of bacteriology, the science of bacteria. They are named after the Greek word *bakterion* meaning "little stick," which was the shape of the first of these tiny creatures to be observed. Quite soon this new branch of research would chalk up more successes in the field of immunization.

Pasteur's "germ theory of disease," according to which disease-causing agents were carried from the sick to the healthy via their doctors and nurses, had far-reaching consequences. Until the mid-19th century, poor hygiene in hospitals was responsible for a high mortality rate. With the introduction of asepsis, whereby the pathogens were sterilized either by physical methods such as heat or by chemical substances such as formaldehyde, the situation and survival rate of the patients improved substantially.

Louis Pasteur experimented with weakened germs so as to develop vaccines against various diseases.

The light bulb: a flash of inspiration that lights the dark

Thomas Alva Edison (1847-1931)

In 1879 Thomas Alva Edison presented the electric incandescent lamp, the latest product developed in his "inventor's workshop." The people who saw his demonstration were overcome with excitement. Simply by pressing a button, Edison was able to illuminate a whole room, producing a light that had never been possible with candles, oil lamps or gas lamps.

In the 19th century there were candles, paraffin lamps, and gas lamps that brought light into darkness. But all these types of lighting were hazardous because of the risk of fire, and the rooms in which they were used became too hot in warm weather. There were electric lamps that produced a bright arc of light from the current between two carbon electrodes and the ionization of the air, but these were very expensive and not many people could afford them. They were mainly used for street lighting and the illumination of public places. The main problem in the search for a means of electrical illumination was finding the right material to produce it. It had to conduct current while withstanding the very high temperatures that were needed to produce as bright a light as possible, and it had also to be durable as well as inexpensive. The observation that the glowing material burnt less quickly in a vacuum glass bulb was a helpful step in the right direction.

In 1878 Thomas Alva Edison and his team began searching for a solution to this problem. Although carbon had the highest melting point, it burned too quickly, while platinum only produced a bright enough light when it had almost reached its melting point. Edison eventually found a better material in a carbonized cotton filament, treated in carbon powder at a high temperature. These lamps glowed for 13 hours before failing. Edison and his team tried every material they could lay their hands on in order to find a better filament, including strips of playing cards, human whiskers and beard hair, and vegetable fibers. In 1880 they finally discovered a Japanese bamboo fiber that passed the test. Its burning duration was an amazing 1,200 hours. Edison immediately developed this successful discovery and produced a whole lighting system that included a power station with generators, cables, wires, screw-threaded incandescent lamps, and accessories such as sockets, awitches, joint boxes, fuses, and electricity meters.

Edison attracted the public's attention with his impressive installations as, for instance, at the International Electrical Exhibition of 1881 that was held in Paris. Edison's "brainwave" solved all the problems associated with gas lighting. The incandescent lamp could be used in smaller rooms and it was also clean and easy to use. The development of a network of electricity supply led to a reduction in the price in electric lighting. This in turn led to the mass-production of incandescent lamps. In order to make them burn even brighter and longer, manufacturers returned to using metal filaments again. Today lamps usually consist of a tungsten filament in a glass bulb filled with argon and nitrogen.

Nowadays electric lighting is everywhere and completely taken for granted. However, the originally extravagant use of electricity has now given way to a more thrifty, environmentally conscious approach.

The electric incandescent lamp has developed into an omnipresent product that has become an indispensable item in every household today.

Das ist die richtige Lampe!

AEG

Metalldraht-Lampe

The discovery of malaria pathogens

Charles Louis Alphonse Laveran (1845-1922)

1880

IN THE YEAR 1880

> Construction of the Cologne cathedral is finished after 600 years.

> The Irish nationalists, organized in the Home Rule party, decide to force agrarian reform by a strike of the workers against the English landowners.

> France annexes the South Sea island of Tahiti.

In the tropical regions of the earth, malaria has always claimed many victims among the native populations. In the period of exploration and colonization of the 18th and 19th centuries, the illness was the fearsome enemy of Europeans who had gone to live in Africa. Nobody knew where "swamp fever" came from; it was suspected that the putrefying gases in tropical swamps were the trigger.

The symptoms of malaria have been known to people in the affected areas since antiquity. Today, doctors distinguish three variations of malaria with different courses of illness. Malaria tertiana and malaria quartana are marked by vehement attacks of fever that are cyclically recurrent. The most dangerous form, malaria tropica, appears as a continually rising fever and damages the function of the brain or kidneys. Usually it results in the rapid death of the patient.

The earliest record of a case of malaria is about 4,000 years old and comes from Thailand. The health handbook of the Chinese Emperor Huang-Ti (c. 2700 BC) tells of three malaria demons, whom the people torment with a hammer, a pail of cold water, and a stone. These instruments of torture symbolize the typical symptoms of malaria: headache, cold chill, and fever. The conquests of the great rulers such as Alexander the Great also had the effect of carrying the illness into areas that were not previously endangered.

The Dutch naturalist Antonie van Leeuwenhoek was the first to suspect that the pathogen of the illness was a living organism that he named an "animalcule." In 1717 the doctor Giovanni Lancisi put forward the hypothesis that malaria was transferred by mosquitoes, but he could not prove this theory. Until late in the 19th century scientists continued wrongly to believe that malaria (from the Italian *mala aria* = bad air) was caused by tropical marsh gas. In 1880, the military doctor Charles Louis Alphonse Laveran, stationed in Algeria, found the pathogen plasmodium in the blood of a soldier suffering from malaria. This pathogen is a type of unicellular organism that lives as a parasite in the blood of living creatures. According to Laveran, plasmodium was passed to the human being by the sting of the anopheles mosquito and caused the various forms of malaria and other tropical diseases.

When the doctor presented his findings at the medical academy in Paris, he caused controversial discussion throughout the world. Although another French military doctor had made similar observations, doctors outside France resisted the explanation as a result of entrenched, anti-French nationalistic motives. Even among his French colleagues Laveran found few comrades-in-arms, and in the army itself his performance was not recognized with promotion. Laveran therefore gave up his military career in 1896 and went to the Institut Pasteur, which received him with open arms. In 1907 he was awarded the Nobel Prize for Medicine, finally achieving recognition for his discovery.

Laveran's findings spurred medical science in its search for pathogens and an effective vaccine against infections. Nevertheless, malaria is still widespread in the tropics and someone dies of the disease every 15 seconds.

In the 18th and 19th century malaria was greatly feared by European scientists and colonial occupying forces in Asia and Africa, including the British troops in Burma shown here.

Skyscrapers: right up to the sky

Metropolitan North America

> 1881: The gunman William H. Bonney, known as Billy the Kid, is shot in Lincoln County, New Mexico.

> 1882: The Chinese Exclusion Act forbids any Chinese immigration into the USA for ten years.

> 1883: The Brooklyn Bridge, New York, is opened. It is the longest suspension bridge in the world.

> 1884: Germany enters the stage of colonial power. South-West Africa becomes the country's first protectorate.

Towards the end of the 19th century industrialization was booming, particularly in the United States of America. Companies needed more and more space for their administrative buildings, and the brisk growth in banking, transport, and the insurance business led to an increasing demand for offices and therefore for land. The result was that the cost of land in city centers rose dramatically. Entrepreneurs coped with the soaring price of land by making the best use possible of it, by building skyscrapers.

But these high rise buildings necessitated the use of entirely new inventions and technologies. These new technologies found their application in the foundations of the building, since high-rise buildings were real heavyweights. If the building had more than 16 floors it required reinforced piers that had to be anchored in the rocky subsoil. This construction work took place mostly below the level of the water table, so pumping machinery had to be used to pump the water from the deep building sites.

By 1884 building techniques were sufficiently developed to meet these (literally) fundamental requirements. At the same time static equilibrium had also made great progress. Steel skeleton construction made possible the erection of much taller buildings. The Home Insurance Building built in Chicago between 1884 and 1885 was the first building to be constructed using a steel frame. Such a steel framework is quick to build, strong, and will not catch fire.

Progress was not restricted to the building methods. Other new inventions resulted in new standards of comfort, utility, and economic viability. The American Elisha Graves Otis (1811–61) developed the first safe elevator in 1852. Rails fitted in the elevator shaft prevented the lift cage from falling if the supporting cables failed. These early steam-operated elevators were succeeded by hydraulic and later electric versions. People and goods could now reach the upper floors of skyscrapers reliably and quickly.

By the turn of the century North American cities were dominated by increasingly tall buildings. But it was New York's Woolworth Building, built in 1913, that was the first true skyscraper. This office block dominated the surrounding streets from its dizzy height of 791 ft. With its concrete pillars anchored into the rocky subsoil, steel frame construction, and high-speed elevators, the Woolworth Building combined all the features of the modern skyscraper. Its rational use of floor space was also exemplary. As well as the Woolworth headquarters and other offices, there were also stores, health institutions, a barber shop, and a restaurant.

In the course of the 20th century skyscrapers became the symbol of modernism, prosperity, and economic success throughout the world. Since the unimaginable destruction of the World Trade Center on September 11, 2001, high rise buildings have also come to symbolize the vulnerability of civilization when threatened by terrorism. Nevertheless, skyscrapers continue to fascinate because of their breathtaking height. Today the tallest buildings in the world are the Petronas Twin Towers in Kuala Lumpur, 1,483 ft high.

The construction of high-rise buildings has always enabled architects to make the best use of the smallest area.

△ **The highest buildings in the world, the Petronas Twin Towers in Kuala Lumpur.**

From hand ax to atom bomb

The tools of mankind

It is not without justification that in 500 BC the Greek philosopher Heraclitus of Ephesus (544–483) wrote the much quoted sentence "War is the father of all things." This statement has proved correct over and over again in the course of history. The ability to smelt bronze and iron not only enabled man to produce agricultural tools, it also enabled him to forge ever more effective weapons. People then used these weapons for defense or attack. The development of a civilization has always gone hand in hand with this ability to defend itself and extend its own sphere of influence. To do this the community needed a well-organized administration and well-equipped army. This required money, so it had to raise taxes. Consequently, military power became the driving force behind modern state systems, shaping the entire civilian and political culture of a state.

Stone Age weapons

Stone Age man invented the bow and arrow, spears, and daggers, which were a natural development of the hand ax. These weapons could used both for hunting and for fighting hostile "creatures of the same species." The bow and arrow in particular proved a remarkably successful invention, being used for military purposes into the modern era. In the Hundred Years War (1339–1453) between England and France the longbow gave the English the decisive

edge on its enemy. This was because the longbow could shoot arrows 12 times a minute and the crossbow (used by the French) only two to three times. The spear also survived from the Stone Age. It was continually improved technically and retained its military usefulness until the invention of the gunpowder. As a throwing, striking, and thrusting weapon, it was an important part of the ancient medieval armory. The halberd, a wooden spear 6 ft 6 in long with a metal blade at the end, was a particularly successful weapon, used by infantry troops in the late Middle Ages.

Bronze and iron

The invention of bronze in 3600 BC marked a real breakthrough in the history of weapons. Bronze is an alloy of zinc and

copper whereby copper is added to zinc during the melting process. Compared to pure copper the new alloy was far superior, being harder and sharper. Now it was possible to use metal swords in addition to stone daggers. The sword's long metal blade made it a much better striking and thrusting weapon. Bronze was also excellent for manufacturing of defense weapons including metal shields and armour, which only lost their military importance at the very end of the late Middle Ages.

A further milestone in the history of weaponry was the beginning of the Iron Age in about 1500 BC. Blacksmiths learned to smelt iron using charcoal to bring iron ore to a temperature of 2,100° F. This gave Iron Age man a new material suitable to make weapons. Initially iron was still a relatively soft metal but a few centuries later people had developed the skill of hardening iron by hammering and forging iron in a charcoal fire, then plunging it into cold water. This made iron superior to bronze which had been used until then, in that it was harder and could take a sharper edge. In antiquity iron weapons played a decisive part in the sruggle between Celts and Romans: when the Celts sacked Rome in 387 BC this technical advantage played a major part in the outcome.

Late antiquity saw the advance of the horsemen from the East. In order to defend themselves against their enemies

Towards the end of the Middle Ages flexible ground troops armed with lances and halberds became more important than troops on horseback.

Motorization and automation gave modern weapon technology a decisive increase in scale and power, culminating in the mass destruction of World War I and World War II.

on horseback, the Romans began to use longer swords from the 3rd century AD. The traditional short sword was increasingly useless in this new warfare, particularly since the invention and development of the saddle also increased the striking power of mounted troops. Armed with lances or swords, the cavalry was superior to the infantry, and for several centuries mounted troops remained the military backbone of the European powers, influencing the whole culture of the Middle Ages.

To the modern age

The transition from the Middle Ages to the modern age in about 1500 represents a decisive military revolution. The reason for this was the invention of gunpowder, a mixture of saltpeter, charcoal, and sulfur. Gunpowder changed the kind of weapons used, and hence the tactics and strategy of war, since "man to man" combat at close quarters became less important. Technical developments led to a continuous improvement in guns and artillery, which became more durable, reliable, and accurate. The invention of the flintlock in 1640 was a major improvement since the use of flint for igniting the powder made guns more reliable and shortened the loading time. Improved gunpowder also increased the weapons' explosive power.

The 19th and 20th century saw the beginning of a new phase in warfare, the arms race. The first arms race was prompted by two developments in Europe: emerging nationalism and industrialization. Johann Nikolas Dreyse invented the "needle-firing

gun" in which a pin pierced a percussion cap to detonate the powder. The Prussian army introduced this rifle in 1841. It was a reliable breech-loader that fired twice as fast as the traditional muzzle-loader. Soldiers could now load their guns in the prone position so that they could shoot while staying under cover. These guns played a decisive part in the Austo-Prussian war of 1866. Gunpowder continued to be improved and new explosives were invented; Alfred Nobel discovered dynamite in 1867. A little later gunpowder was produced without saltpeter making it smokeless when fired and also increasing the range.

At the beginning of the 20th century military technology benefited considerably from developments in motor power, which also led to the development of the tank. While tanks played only a small part in World War I, they were decisive in the early campaigns of World War II. In the early 20th century the possibilities resulting from the progress made in aviation were also recognized.

Mass destruction

These technical developments eventually made the "total war" envisaged by Clausewitz a possibility, as the German propaganda minister Joseph Goebbels declared in his notorious Sports Palace speech of February 18, 1943. Concentrated efforts by scientists would lead to the invention of "wonder weapons" in order to avoid the threat of defeat in World War II. For instance, the V-1 and V-2 rockets that were used against Britain were the precursors of the cruise missiles and medium distance rockets of today.

But the undoubted peak of technical development was the first atom bomb dropped by American forces on Hiroshima on August 6, 1945. The atom bomb was the result of the Manhattan Project that had involved 150,000 men working under the leadership of Robert Oppenheimer. The capability of splitting the atom released vast amounts of energy—and gave mankind the capability of destroying itself entirely.

Punch cards: the end of data chaos

Hermann Hollerith (1860-1929)

1886

IN THE YEAR 1886

> Ludwig II drowns under mysterious circumstances in the Starnbergersee. His ministers had already declared the Bavarian king incapable and deposed him.

> The Apache chieftain Geronimo surrenders after a long fight against American troops. With it the Indian resistance against the settling of their country by the white man is finally broken.

> The pharmacist John S. Pemberton develops the recipe for Coca-Cola in Atlanta, as a syrup against tiredness and headaches.

> The Statue of Liberty In New York is unveiled. France had given it to the USA.

Managing the flood of data is not a problem unique to the computer age. Already in the 19th century administration, trade, and industry produced enormous quantities of data. Handling and organizing all this information demanded an enormous expenditure of time and calculation. For example, seven years passed before the results of the 1880 United States census became available. So it was a real sensation when the American engineer Hermann Hollerith found a solution to this problem.

Hermann Hollerith took part in the evaluation of the 1880 census and he had direct experience of how lengthy and difficult this procedure was. In thinking about the possibility of appraising such records mechanically, he came to consider a machine from the textile industry. In 1805 the inventor Joseph-Marie Jacquard (1752–1834) had developed a loom that wove complicated patterns controlled by a pack of punched cards. Until then, weavers made patterned fabrics by selecting which warp threads to raise by hand. In the Jacquard loom cards punched with holes in a particular order were sensed by metal pins. When a pin encountered a hole, it allowed a lever to move that lifted the relevant thread.

Hollerith's invention of 1886 was based on this principle. He divided the cards into fields, each of which represented one detail of the census. The answers were then entered into these fields, punched holes signifying "yes" and unpunched fields "no." Data entry, that is, the transfer of data to the cards, was carried out by punch machines. The Hollerith tabulator then sorted the punch cards and processed the data by counting the holes in each field.

Hollerith tabulators came into use with the American census of 1890, with dramatic success. Instead of the anticipated processing time of 12 years, the data was appraised after two years, although the number of pieces of information handled had increased since the previous census. In the following years, other administration-intensive organizations such as the military, insurance companies, banks, and industrial businesses adopted punched card systems.

Data processing had now become simpler, but with this benefit came the danger of misuse. For example, the recording of census information such as religious affiliation and national origin was used by the Nazi regime to find all so-called "enemies of the state." Nevertheless, the growth of punched card systems continued triumphantly after World War II. Whether in the search for criminals, the administration of accounts or the preparation of wage bills, the punched card played an important role in the economy of the 1950s and 1960s.

Soon, faster, more reliable sorting and tabulating machines were developed, but the heyday did not last for ever. Mechanical data-processing machines were gradually displaced with the development of new technologies. During the 1970s years more efficient and more flexible storage media such as magnetic drives and diskettes ousted punched cards from data processing, and today they are virtually only used in a few surviving old-fashioned time clocks recording workers' hours.

Punched card data systems have gradually been replaced by modern digital technology.

Phonograph and discs: music for everyone

Thomas Alva Edison (1847-1931), Emil Berliner (1851-1929)

Since ancient times, the spoken word and music had been regarded as "ephemeral arts" that cannot be preserved, except in the incomplete forms of writing or musical notation. Only when the phonograph and discs appeared in 1887 was it possible to "preserve" sounds. The fledgling music industry used this new invention to make music available to the public.

1887

IN THE YEAR 1887

> In Milan Guiseppe Verdi's opera *Othello* is premiered and enthusiastically received.

> Great Britain annexes Zululand in South Africa. As a result the South African Boer republic of Transvaal has no access to the sea.

> Pope Leo XIII ends the cultural war between Prussia and the Catholic Church with an appropriate explanation.

> The US Congress alters the status of the Native Americans. The Dawes General Allotment Act declares that tribes are henceforth no longer legal bodies but individuals. The Indian lands are nationalized.

In 1887 Thomas Alva Edison (1847–1931) handed the blueprint of a machine for recording and playing sound to his Swiss precision engineer. This apparatus collected sound waves through a funnel terminating in a membrane with a needle attached, which imprinted them onto a cylinder covered with foil. In 1878 Edison demonstrated this "phonograph" to the public and caused the sensation of the year. But it was not until 1903 that Edison found a method of copying the cylinders so that they could be produced in quantity. Until then, hired singers had to record each cylinder individually.

Emil Berliner (1851–1929) replaced the cylinder with a disc. He was a bookkeeper who had emigrated to the USA and occupied himself in his spare time with science and technology. On November 8, 1887, he applied for a patent for his "Gramophone," which used the same principle as the phonograph. In contrast to Edison's apparatus, the needle of the gramophone moved horizontally from left to right rather than vertically. Under a magnifying glass the groove could be seen as a wavy line with varying amplitude. Berliner also used tin plates coated with wax for his recordings. From one of these masters, a negative was made from which a large number of copies could be pressed. These were the first discs.

In 1889, the German toy company Kämmer and Reinhard offered an "Original Berliner Phonograph" for sale. Six celluloid discs were included with each one. Music was recorded on one side and on the other the lyrics of a suitable children's song. Among Berliner's singers was Enrico Caruso (1873–1921), who sang ten arias for $100. The conditions under which the first acoustic recordings were made were difficult. There were no microphones and no electrical amplifiers. Until the beginning of the 1920s, the sound had to be recorded purely mechanically and huge funnels for "collecting" the sound were installed in the studios and concert halls where recordings were made.

Mass production started with the development of the shellac record, which was industrially produced from 1897 onwards. The famous "78s," discs that revolved 78 times per minute, survived for decades in the music industry. In 1904, the firm "Odeon" in Berlin introduced a record that could be recorded on both sides. The chief technical development was the replacement of acoustic with electric technology. The needle now transferred its vibrations to a moving coil or a piezo-electric crystal, which converted the vibrations to electric currents. These were amplified electronically and made audible through a loudspeaker. The 1950s saw the invention of the long-playing microgroove vinyl disc rotating at 33 rpm, and stereophonic recording was introduced.

The fate of the disc was sealed with the invention of digital sound recording on compact discs (CDs). Today, shellac and vinyl records are the province of collectors and audio connoisseurs.

The invention of the phonograph led to the development of discs and the mass production of sound recordings.

Radio: fascinating waves from the ether

Guglielmo Marconi (1874-1937)

In spite of many prophecies of doom, radio has successfully managed to withstand the competition of television, and more recently the Internet. The golden age of radio was instigated by the young physics enthusiast Guglielmo Marconi in a villa near Bologna.

△ Radio became a mass medium. In the 1930s it was used to propagate National Socialist propaganda in Germany.

The principle of radio or rather of broadcasting lies in the sending of an acoustic message by means of electromagnetic waves. The sounds are picked up live in a studio by a microphone and converted into electromagnetic waves. In the transmitter, an oscillator produces a carrier wave of a high frequency. A transmitting antenna sends out the high-frequency waves as electromagnetic waves to the receiving aerials of individual radio sets.

The physicist Heinrich Rudolf Hertz proved the existence of electromagnetic waves in 1887. A year later, Hertz built a transmitter, the "resonator," with which he produced electromagnetic waves and transmitted them for the first time. In 1888, the physicist Édouard Branly discovered how to convert radio waves into electrical current. Branly then built a radio-wave conducting tube (detector) with which he could pick up waves over a distance. The detector could detect waves even through solid walls. This invention was used by Alexander Popow (1859–1906), an assistant at the torpedo boat school in Kronstadt, Russia. Using the detector, he received electric air discharges from thunderclouds. In this way he was able to give advance warning of distant thunderstorms. Popow also noticed that the receptivity of the receiver was increased when he connected it to a long vertical wire. With this "antenna" he achieved a Morse code connection without wires, sending the words "Heinrich Hertz" over a distance of about 270 yards.

The real pioneer of radio, however, was Guglielmo Marconi (1874–1937). A neighbor of his in Bologna who was a professor of physics aroused his spirit of invention and introduced him to the work of Heinrich Hertz. In 1894, Marconi began experimenting in the courtyard of his father's villa. A year later, he was able to transmit electrical impulses over a distance of 2,600 yards. Marconi then emigrated to England since his work seemed to be of no interest to anyone in Italy. After successful demonstrations in London in 1896, Marconi received a patent and founded the Wireless Telegraph and Signal Company Ltd.

The physicist Karl Ferdinand Braun (1850–1918) dramatically increased the range with his invention of the sparkless antenna circuit, which he patented in in 1899. In the same year Marconi set up a connection of over 30 miles between Dover in England and Wimereux in France. In 1901, he made the first "wire-less" connection across the Atlantic between Cornwall in southwest England and Newfoundland – a distance of 2,100 miles. In 1909, Braun and Marconi were jointly awarded the Nobel Prize for Physics for their contribution to the development of wireless telegraphy.

With the development of an apparatus that could record sound and the improvement of transmitting and receiving devices, the triumphal march of radio towards being a mass medium had begun. Music, plays, and news could now be heard in every home that owned a radio. In 1898, the world's first radio factory opened in Chelmsford, England.

In 1909 Guglielmo Marconi was awarded the Nobel Prize for Physics for his part in inventing wireless telegraphy.

Motion pictures: movie premiere in Paris

Auguste Lumière (1862-1954), Louis Lumière (1864-1948)

Motion pictures! The long-awaited "living photography" became a reality in 1895, first of all as an attraction in cafés and then for the mass public. The "other world" on 35-millimeter film could entertain an audience and enchant people – and it could also manipulate them.

A movie is actually nothing more than a series of many still photographs. The optical effect of movement is based on the phenomenon of persistence of vision. When the observer sees a series of pictures at a fast enough speed, the individual pictures merge together in the eye to make a moving picture. Precursors of movies, such as flicker books or photograph sequences, were based on this principle. There were also devices in which a rotating sequence of individual pictures was illuminated by short flashes of light, giving a moving image almost free of flicker.

The Lumière brothers, sons of a photographic paper manufacturer in Lyon, France, are regarded as the real inaugurators of the modern motion pictures. The breakthrough in constructing a film projector was achieved by Louis Lumière with the development of the "cinematograph," which the brothers patented on February 13, 1895. The first public showing took place on December 28 of the same year, in the Grand Café on the Boulevard des Capucines in Paris.

The Lumière Cinématographe was a combination of a photographing and a projecting device. The technical equipment of the apparatus was very advanced. The film was held still while being exposed or projected, a shutter covered or darkened it while the next frame was being moved into place, and the frame rate was sufficient to give the illusion of movement. The first demonstrations in fair booths, music halls and cafés showed a colorful mixture of short films documenting daily life as well as special events. The Lumière brothers made more than 1,000 such films with subjects such as a train driving into a train station, scenes from family life, parades, or a Spanish bullfight.

Two years earlier, in 1893, the American inventor Thomas Alva Edison (1847–1931) had presented a "kinetoscope." This he set up at fairs, where a short film could be watched on payment of a nickel. Technically, the apparatus was inferior to that of the Lumière brothers, but parts of Edison's invention survived in the form of perforated celluloid film, about 1.4 inches wide, and the name "movie."

The step into the entertainment industry came after the turn of the century. By the start of World War I, there were 15,700 movie theaters in the USA. The most popular genres had been established by the French and American film industry before 1910: detective and adventure stories, science fiction and horror, monumental epics, and westerns. Science fiction was the province of Georges Méliès (1861–1938), who created highly imaginative animated films such as *The Journey to the Moon* (1902). The golden age of silent movies began in about 1910. Then in the early 1930s silent film productions were superseded by sound movies. Although the word "movie" is often thought to be synonymous with the studio system of Hollywood and full-length "blockbusters," over the years many other nations have developed their own characteristic film language and subjects that have had their impact on the history of cinema.

The Lumière brothers created the technology that led to the development of the cinema.

X-rays provide a look inside

Wilhelm Conrad Röntgen (1845-1923)

The discovery of X-rays by the physicist Wilhelm Röntgen rang in a new era of medicine. Using X-rays, doctors could "see inside" a patient without having to make incisions with a scalpel. The X-ray is indispensable today in many other areas apart from medicine, particularly in the field of materials testing.

Towards the end of 1895, Wilhelm Conrad Röntgen, a physics professor at Würzburg University, was experimenting with cathode rays, the electronic rays that discharge themselves in electron tubes. On the evening of November 8, he observed a mysterious phenomenon. He noticed that a glass plate with a fluorescent coating of barium platinocyanide gave off light when it was near a vacuum tube, even though the tube was wrapped in black paper. According to the physical knowledge of the day, such a phenomenon was inexplicable.

Röntgen quickly realized that it was not the cathode rays themselves that were causing the mysterious illumination, but rather a new kind of ray that originated when the cathode rays struck the glass wall of the tube. As well as paper, these new rays could penetrate wood and metal, revealing a photographic image of the inside. Images of the hands of Röntgen and his wife Anna Bertha (1839–1919) were among the first X-ray pictures. In naming the phenomenon, Röntgen chose an "X" on account of the still unknown physical properties of the rays. They are still known as X-rays internationally, except in Germany where they are called Röntgen rays after the man who discovered them. In 1901, Röntgen was awarded the first Nobel Prize for Physics for his ground-breaking discovery.

He himself did not concern himself much longer with the new rays. He left their study to younger colleagues, but he did suggest ways in which they might be used. By the beginning of 1896,

only a few weeks after his first observation, doctors in many countries were using X-rays in their daily practice, despite inadequate technical resources. Suddenly it was easy to set a broken bone correctly. Today X-rays play a fundamental part in diagnostic medicine, not only for fractures but also for the location of foreign bodies, and the examination of the various organs of the body. They are also used therapeutically in radiotherapy for treating malignant disease.

After medicine, the second major field of application of X-rays was in materials testing technology. Testing to see if seams and metal parts are sound is an integral part of safety technology today. Röntgen had anticipated this application. He made photographs of four soldered strips of zinc, the first modern testing of metal joints. Non-destructive testing with X-rays is now widely used, for instance in laying cross-country pipelines for oil or gas.

Air travelers come into indirect contact with X-rays with every flight, when the passenger's baggage is examined for concealed weapons by X-ray equipment.

Wilhelm Conrad Röntgen never patented his revolutionary discovery, since he wanted every doctor and scientist to be able to work with X-rays without hindrance. He died in complete poverty in 1923.

Wilhelm Conrad Röntgen. Among the first photographs he produced with the X-rays he discovered were images of his own hand.

1895

IN THE YEAR 1895

> Herbert George Wells publishes his first science fiction novel *The Time Machine*.

> Islamic Kurds massacre Christian Armenians in the Ottoman empire. 200,000 people die.

> Robert Gascoyne-Cecil becomes prime minister of Great Britain. He opposes Irish endeavors after Home Rule has been determined.

△ The X-rays discovered by Röntgen heralded a new era in the history of medicine.

Oedipus complex: psycho-analysis and the unconscious

Sigmund Freud (1856-1939)

Mental illness posed a riddle to medicine for a long time. How could a doctor diagnose the cause of an illness and cure the patient if the body was perfectly healthy? Towards the end of the 19th century, Sigmund Freud developed forms of psychoanalysis and psychotherapy that recognized the subconscious as the trigger for neuroses.

"Results: negative." This diagnosis was a quandary for doctors in the 19th century. Many mental illnesses were difficult to pin down. In most cases, knowledge of classical psychology as well as of medical neuroanatomy was lacking, and the patient could not be successfully treated. In his practice in Vienna, Austria, the neurologist Sigmund Freud (1856–1939) repeatedly came up against the fact that he could not successfully treat fears, neuroses or obsessions using the means available to medicine. He therefore set out to find new forms of therapy in this field.

Freud had already studied brain anatomy and in Paris he investigated the symptoms of hysteria under the guidance of the neurologist Jean Martin Charcot (1825–93). Freud also learned the technique of hypnosis in France. With the help of suggestion and hypnosis, the doctor hoped to bring repressed traumatic experiences "to the surface," since he believed these traumas to be at the root of many illnesses lacking an organic cause. The patient was then to "work through" them. This was the first step in Freudian psychoanalysis, which took the subconscious into account when diagnosing and applying therapy. Later, Freud would distance himself from hypnotic-suggestive methods and turn more towards others such as free association and the interpretation of dreams. For Freud, dreams were mirrors in which he could observe the subconscious. Deciphering them offered him the possibility of unearthing the buried, repressed or suppressed life experiences that he believed were the cause of the mental suffering of his patients.

Freud did not stop there, however, since many questions remained. How does a neurosis arise? What is generally decisive in the mental development of a human being? In his research he encountered an aspect that had previously been mostly ignored, sexuality. This he saw as a dominating feature and accorded it a central place in the system of human life experience. This approach broke taboos and made many people uneasy, although it had the result of providing important explanations for the reasons behind a large number of mental disturbances.

Freud was of the opinion that sexuality did not start at puberty but in the years of early childhood, and that the way it was experienced was a decisive factor for the psyche. During his self-analysis, begun in 1897, he recognized a reason for this: the wish of the male child for union with his beloved mother and the wish to eliminate the hated father, seen as a rival. Freud called this the Oedipus complex, after the Greek myth of Oedipus, who, as the oracle had foretold, unknowingly killed his father and married his mother.

In his practice, Freud tried to uncover such subconscious childlike patterns of behavior and to work through them in retrospect. His approach is still a branch of psychology known today as "Freudianism." Criticism of this system is usually directed at Freud's far-fetched concept of sexuality. But his paramount lasting contribution was to demonstrate the importance of the subconscious.

Sigmund Freud believed that sexuality played a dominant part in human life.

Radioactivity: the beginning of a glowing era

Marie Curie (1867-1934), Pierre Curie (1859-1906)

Radioactivity refers to the spontaneous processes of transformation within atomic nuclei whereby energy-laden rays and particles are emitted into the surroundings, a property of certain elements. When Marie Curie used the term for the first time, even she had only a vague idea of what the phenomenon actually involved.

1898

IN THE YEAR 1898

> The article "*J'accuse*" appears on the title page of the newspaper *L'Aurore*. In it the author Émile Zola accuses and deplores the unjustified condemnation and banishment of the Jewish officer Alfred Dreyfus. A dispute erupts that throws France into a serious political crisis. Zola has to flee to England.

> The Russian Social-Democratic Workers' Party of Russia is established in Minsk. From it Lenin's Bolsheviks emerge in 1903.

> The German Reichstag passes the first fleet bill, thus starting the arms race with Britain.

> The Austrian empress Elisabeth, nicknamed "Sissi," is murdered at Lake Geneva.

In 1891, the young Pole Marya Sklowska (as she then was) arrived in Paris to study physics at the Sorbonne. She was particularly interested in the recent discoveries in the field of radiology made by Wilhelm Conrad Röntgen and Antoine Becquerel. In 1895 Röntgen discovered an unknown type of radiation using a gas discharge tube. Röntgen sealed off the light emitted by the apparatus with black paper but in spite of this the radiation made crystals fluoresce and blackened photographic paper when the apparatus was turned on. A year later Becquerel discovered that such radiation was also emitted by natural uranium salts.

Marie Curie repeated Becquerel's experiments with pitchblende, an ore containing uranium that occurs in small amounts in the soil. In the course of these experiments she discovered that the ore emitted rays even more intense than pure uranium, so she concluded that it must contain other more energy-intensive elements. Together with her husband, the physics professor Pierre Curie, she discovered radium and polonium, elements that also emitted radiation. The Curies thus demonstrated that radioactivity was a property that was shared by various elements in nature. The radiation was a property that was not caused by the chemical or physical condition of the initial substance but by processes occurring within it. The door to the study of nuclear physics had just opened.

In the following years, other scientists discovered further radioactive substances. It was also soon realized that radioactivity was a much more intense source of energy than had previously been thought. While the British scientist Ernest Rutherford discovered the theoretical principles of the structure of the atomic nucleus, the Curies continued to concentrate on radium.

The element they had discovered played an important role in cancer therapy. Radioactive rays from radium damaged the living cells in cancer tumors much more than the healthy ones. Carefully aimed radiation could therefore destroy cancer cells without damaging the surrounding tissue too seriously. Today less aggressive substances such as cobalt isotopes are used.

In 1903 Pierre and Marie Curie and Becquerel were jointly awarded the Nobel Prize for Physics for their discovery of radioactivity. Marie Curie was the first woman ever to receive such an honor. In 1911, after her husband's death, Marie Curie received a second Nobel Prize, this time for chemistry, for her research into radium. In 1934 Marie Curie died from leukemia that had been caused by excessive exposure to radiation. Her daughter Irène and her husband Frédéric Joliot continued Marie Curie's work. In 1935 they received the Nobel Prize for Chemistry for artificially producing radioactive elements through radiation. The constant search for new radioactive substances eventually led to the discovery of nuclear fission and the consequent development of atomic energy and nuclear weapons.

Marie Curie's daughter Irène continued her mother's work and, like her, was awarded a Nobel Prize.

Viruses: changeable pathogens

Martinus Willem Beijerinck (1851-1905)

At the end of the 19th century there were still some micro-organisms that had remained unidentified, and there were still several incurable diseases, ranging from influenza to rabies, that claimed many victims each year. Then scientists discovered viruses.

The French chemist Louis Pasteur (1822–95) had already identified the pathogen of anthrax and chicken cholera, but in spite of all his efforts he did not succeed in discovering the cause of rabies. Pasteur rightly suspected that whatever it was had to be smaller than the bacteria already identified – in fact too small to be perceived by the technical means then available.

The Russian botanist Dimitri Iosifovich Ivanowsky (1864–1929) was able to confirm this theory in 1892. He was studying tobacco mosaic disease. Diseased tobacco plants displayed a mosaic-like change in the leaves, and their sap infected healthy plants. Ivanowsky ran this sap through a filter that prevented all bacteria from getting through. Nevertheless the sap remained infectious after it had been filtered, from which he concluded that bacteria could not be the cause of the tobacco mosaic disease.

In 1898 the Dutch botanist Martinus Willem Beijerinck independently made the same discovery. His research marked the beginning of virology. He gave the tiny pathogens the name "filterable virus" (from the Latin *virus* = poison). In 1898 the German bacteriologist Friedrich August Löffler (1852–1905) discovered the first viral disease among animals, foot-and-mouth disease. Subsequently other viral infections were found including yellow fever, infantile paralysis, measles, mumps, chickenpox, and influenza.

Soon virologists were able to describe viruses more precisely. They were a transitional form between living and inanimate material. Unlike bacteria they had no metabolism of their own and were parasites living off a host cell. In 1935 American biochemists crystallized the tobacco mosaic virus and obtained important insights into its core. In the center of a virus is nucleic acid (DNA or RNA), surrounded by protein. After the pathogen has "eaten" a hole in the cell wall under attack, the nucleic acid penetrates inside the cell and infects it with its own genes. The host cell then transmits the genes of the virus when it divides, and thus the disease breaks out.

The search for suitable vaccines against viral infections subsequently proved quite difficult. As in the prevention of bacterial infections, vaccination was based on the injection of weakened pathogens. But viruses are very aggressive and it was very difficult to find a "harmless" pathogen that only caused mild symptoms yet still stimulated the production of antibodies.

It was only when cells began to be bred in test tubes that a decisive breakthrough in the search for a vaccine became possible. The American microbiologist John Franklin Enders (1897–1985) succeeded in breeding the poliomyelitis virus in the laboratory. Then in 1957 the American microbiologist Albert Bruce Sabin discovered a weak type of virus for each of the three variants of poliomyelitis and as a result produced a suitable vaccine. In the 1960s and 1970s virologists discovered many more vaccines through the ability to breed viruses on living cells.

The most stringent safety precautions are necessary when carrying out research on viruses, as shown here in a Bayer laboratory where the HIV virus is being studied.

The airship: aviation takes off

Graf Ferdinand von Zeppelin (1838-1917)

In the early 20th century on the shores of Lake Constance an airship took off, opening up new perspectives for civilian air transport. Today there are only a few advertising airships to recall this invention that was so revolutionary in its time.

△ Today airships usually conjure up the image of a floating advertisement.

Since the time of Greek antiquity, people have endeavored to realize their dream of flying using every kind of method. Some have tried it with self-built wings while others have used the lighter-than-air property of certain gases to overcome gravity. The brothers Étienne-Jacques Montgolfier (1745–99) and Michel-Joseph Montgolfier (1740–1810) developed the first hot-air balloons. But the great disadvantage of these balloons lay in the fact that they were hard to steer even in fine weather and they were dependent on favorable winds. A scheduled air transport service using hot-air balloons was out of the question.

At the end of the 19th century, engineers in the USA and Europe tackled the problem from the aerodynamic point of view. Otto Lilienthal (1848–96) favored the glider and was unsuccessful. However in the early 20th century, the brothers Wilbur Wright (1867–1912) and Orville Wright (1871–1948) succeeded in flying a powered aircraft for several minutes. Count Ferdinand von Zeppelin (1838–1917) chose a different route. He was inspired by the earlier experiments with balloon flight and set out to improve this technically. Before Zeppelin, scientists had already attempted to make airships in France, with a non-rigid form kept in shape by the pressure of the lifting gases, hydrogen or helium. But these were inherently unstable, and with a speed of 6 mph they were not particularly fast. Zeppelin created a stronger airship with a rigid frame that proved to be faster and controllable. In 1898 he established a joint stock company for developing airship flight. Together with the engineer Theodor Kober (1865–1930), he developed a rigid airship with a light aluminum framework that supported the balloon envelope and was fitted with a gondola for passengers and staff. With a length of 420 ft and a diameter of 39 ft, the size of this first airship was remarkable. With propellers driven by two internal combustion engines, the "Zeppelin" made its maiden flight over Lake Constance on January 2, 1900, reaching a speed of 20 mph.

This airship immediately attracted attention. The military were interested in the Zeppelin for reconnaissance, and several European countries offered prizes for long distance flights and speed records. Zeppelin's own company and the later Luftschiffbau Zeppelin GmbH received sufficient financial support to launch commercial air operations carrying passengers in 1910. The future destiny of the Zeppelin was commercial rather than military because its large envelope of inflammable gas was an easy target for enemy airplanes in World War I.

After the end of the war the successors of the Zeppelin made regular flights across the Atlantic. Great Britain and the United States also built fleets of airships. But when the *Hindenburg* burst into flames on landing near New York in 1937 with the death of 36 passengers, the operators of the Zeppelin fleets discontinued their flights. Today, airships are used almost exclusively for the presentation of advertising messages in the sky or for transportation over rough terrain. Count Zeppelin's merit however remains indisputable. He courageously put his vision of regular passenger air transport into action and thus opened the way for commercial aviation.

The catastrophe of the *Hindenburg* in 1937 put an end to the great era of airships.

The Palace of Minos: not a myth but reality

Sir Arthur Evans (1851-1941)

Apart from the excavations in Pompeii, no other building in the ancient world reflects the life of its inhabitants so vividly as the vast, magnificently equipped Minoan palace of Knossos in Crete. But the most immediate evidence of Minoan culture, written on clay tablets, has so far revealed only a small part of its secrets.

1900

IN THE YEAR 1900

> In London the Labour Representation Committee is established. The Labour party follows it in 1906.

> Great Britain occupies the Boer states of Transvaal and Orange Free State, and declares that the Boer War is ended. However the Boers continue to conduct a guerrilla war.

> Paris begin construction of the first Metro route.

In the 3rd and 2nd millennium BC the bronze age "Aegean" culture prevailed on the Aegean islands, the Greek mainland, and the west coast of Asia Minor. Only the island of Crete formed an autonomous area, where the Minoan culture flourished. The latter takes its name from the mysterious King Minos, who according to mythology was a son of Zeus and of Europa, and reigned from his palace in Knossos, Crete.

According to myth, Minos once refused to sacrifice a bull to Poseidon. Offended, the god caused the woman Minos loved to fall in love with the bull, and she bore him the Minotaur, a creature that was half-human and half-bull. Minos locked the creature up in a labyrinth. When the Athenians murdered his son Androgeos, Minos declared a destructive war against them and demanded seven boys and seven virgins as tribute, who would be sacrificed to the Minotaur every nine years. Theseus then tracked down the Minotaur in its labyrinth and killed it.

Was this story merely a legend? The British archaeologist Arthur Evans strongly believed in the truth of Homer's tale, as did his colleague Heinrich Schliemann (1822–90). A visit to Athens with him had awakened his interest in early Greek history. In 1894 Evans first visited Crete in search of artifacts with Minoan characters. The myth fascinated the prosperous archeologist so much that he bought the land at Mount Kephala, including Knossos. He had a suspicion that the remains of the royal palace were here. In 1899 he obtained permission to dig and immediately began excavating.

Luck was on Evans's side. In 1900 he discovered the first cache of writing tablets, the objects that he coveted the most. In the course of his excavations the Palace of Knossos proved to be a very extensive, large scale complex, built completely of clay bricks. The archaeologists found throne rooms, inner courtyards, and staircases flanked by large red columns.

The most astonishing discoveries made by Evans and his colleagues in Knossos were the numerous frescoes, including the famous "bull leaper" or the so-called "Parisian." The archaeologist himself considered the many thousand writing tablets to be the most important finds. These included pictograms and the so-called "Linear A" and "Linear B" scripts. In 1953, the architect Michael Ventris succeeded in deciphering "Linear B" at least to some extent, identifying the language as Greek. "Linear A" has still not been decoded.

Unlike Schliemann, who had to endure hostility, criticism, and mockery throughout his long life, Evans was recognized as a serious archaeologist all his life, and was knighted in 1911. He remained on Crete until it was invaded by the Germans during World War II.

The extent of the site only became apparent when the Palace of Knossos was excavated.

Blood groups: A, B, and O, a simple classification

Karl Landsteiner (1868-1943)

IN THE YEAR 1900

> In Austria women are allowed to become doctors and pharmacists.

> Sigmund Freud publishes *Die Traumdeutung* (*The Interpretation of Dreams*), the standard work of psychoanalysis.

> The World's Fair opens in Paris.

> The civil code is imposed in the German empire.

Since the mid-17th century physicians tried to compensate for the loss of "red juice" or blood resulting from a hemorrhage or severe bleeding by a blood transfusion. In spite of occasional successes, there were often serious complications that led to the patient's death.

In 1900 the Austrian physician Karl Landsteiner discovered the solution to the problem. Landsteiner took blood from himself and his colleagues, and separated it into plasma and red blood corpuscles. He then mixed the plasma samples with unrelated red blood corpuscles. He observed that in some cases the plasma formed visible clumps with the red blood corpuscles, while in others it did not. Landsteiner concluded that the agglutination was the result of the following process: blood corpuscles sometimes agglutinate into clumps when added to the serum of unrelated blood.

This conclusion led Landsteiner to the discovery of the existence of different blood groups. He divided human blood into four groups, A, B, AB and O, thus creating the blood group system that is still used today. The blood group of a person is determined by the biochemical characteristics of the surface of the red blood corpuscles and its antigens, a substance that causes the formation of antibodies.

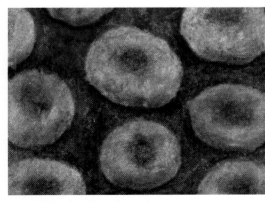

△ Red blood cells enlarged.

There are other divisions besides those of the ABO blood group system. The best known is the Rhesus blood group system. It distinguishes several antigens, known as Rhesus factors, that are present in red blood corpuscles. The discovery of this system was made by Landsteiner and his colleague Alexander Wiener. In 1940 they injected the red blood corpuscles of a rhesus monkey into a rabbit, as a result of which the rabbit developed antibodies against the monkey's blood. In further experiments the two scientists discovered that this rabbit serum, pre-treated with the blood of a rhesus monkey, could also lead to the agglutination of human red blood corpuscles. This agglutination is known as the rhesus factor and people whose blood have this characteristic are described as rhesus positive. Like all the characteristics of a blood group, this factor is inherited.

Landsteiner's research fundamentally changed medicine. The discovery of blood groups made safe blood transfusions possible since the blood type of the blood given could be matched to that of the recipient, instead of the indiscriminate transfusion where success was rare and a matter of chance. In addition, it has played an important part in forensic medicine by making it possible to establish paternity or to convict criminals on the evidence of blood stains.

Once blood groups were discovered, doctors in many surgical wards took the trouble to test whether the blood of the donor matched that of the patient, but remarkably it took time for the technique to be accepted and was widely thought to be a waste of time. It was only after World War I that the importance of matching blood groups was generally recognized. Landsteiner was awarded the Nobel Prize for Physiology in 1930.

Karl Landsteiner discovered the existence of blood groups and classed human blood into four groups, A, B, AB and O.

A

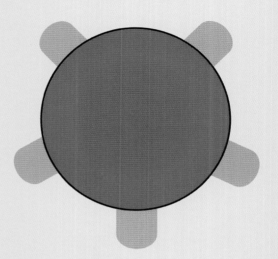

B

AB

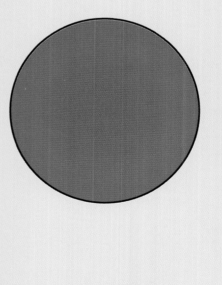

0

The first powered flight: to whom is the honor?

Gustav Weisskopf (1874-1927), Wilbur (1867-1912) and Orville Wright (1871-1948)

Who flew the first powered flight? While for a long time the Wright brothers were thought to be the pioneers of powered flight, research in the 1960s brought to light evidence of a new challenger: Gustav Weisskopf.

Gustav Weisskopf was a colleague of the gliding pioneer Otto Lilienthal (1848–96). Together with Lilienthal, whose experiments based on the flight of birds provided the first reliable information about flying, Weisskopf undertook several experimental flights in Berlin towards the end of the 19th century. In 1895, he emigrated from Germany to the USA, where he built gliders and experimented with various ways of powering them. In 1899, however, he crashed into a house while flying a steam-powered airplane. His first success came with another model, the "Number 21." This had a closed fuselage and folding wings like the birds it was modeled on. The remarkable feature of this plane was its built-in, home-made gasoline engine. On August 14, 1901, in Bridgeport, Connecticut, USA, Weisskopf rose 50 ft into the air with this machine and flew a distance of 900 yards. It was the first successful powered flight.

In 1902, the next model, "Number 22," achieved a distance of 7 miles before the flight ended with a crash landing in the ocean. Weisskopf managed to save himself but "Number 22" drifted away and sank. Financially and physically somewhat battered, Weisskopf continued to work on new flying machines. As he had absolutely no head for business, the inventions of this fanatical pilot never brought him any financial gain. Weisskopf did not understand how to make the public aware of his achievements and his exploits were therefore soon forgotten.

From an early age, Orville and Wilbur Wright had also been interested in flying and they too had undertaken many flight experiments.

Whereas Gustav Weisskopf made monoplanes, the Wright brothers flew biplanes. Until the 1930s, most airplanes were constructed with two, three or even four wings above each other, on the assumption that more wings would result in greater lift and stability. The monoplane did not become the dominant type until the design was changed so that a wing could support its own weight and the stresses occurring in flight without external struts.

Whenever the Wright brothers encountered a technical problem, they turned to other flying pioneers and offered them money for information. Whether or not Gustav Weisskopf sold details of his knowledge to the two smart brothers is not known, but it is possible that he contributed in this way to the event that went down in history as the first powered flight. In 1903, Orville Wright rose into the air from the dunes of Kitty Hawk, North Carolina, USA in a powered airplane. As they held public flying exhibitions in France and also worked closely with the American War Department during World War I, the Wright brothers achieved an important place in the history of flying.

In 1942, Orville Wright asked for written certification that he and his brother had been the pioneers of powered flight. In 1964, a commission set up by the American aviation authorities to examine the facts of the case discovered hitherto unknown papers belonging to Weisskopf that documented the first flights taken by him.

Neither Gustav Weisskopf's plane nor that of the Wright brothers had been designed to carry a large number of passengers.

Transport: People become mobile

Illustration of Moses crossing the Red Sea, dating from the 12th century.

A basic need?

Even when the concept of transport and travel were far from easy, human beings have always been driven by a desire to carry people or freight easily and comfortably. One of the earliest solutions was the taming and breeding of pack animals that did the walking and carrying for their masters. Beyond this, the first real progress in transport was the result of two technical inventions. The invention of the wheel in about 3000 BC considerably reduced friction and thus spared man and animal much effort, while the invention of the yoke and harness enabled animals to pull carts. The other requirement of even a simple cart was a relatively flat path or road, which is why technical innovations in transport were always accompanied by improvements in the road network. After the fall of the Roman Empire its excellent road network fell into disrepair. This was a major reason for the slowness in the transport of people and goods until the 19th century. Road building was also prompted by military needs, in order to move troops as quickly as possible.

Progress

The four-wheeled cart with a swiveling front axle was invented in the Middle Ages. This invention led to further improvements in the harnessing of draught animals, the use of horses instead of oxen, and stronger wheels that broke less often. But in the Middle Ages, if people wanted to transport people or goods realtively quickly, they traveled by water. In fact shipping by water is still the most inexpensive form of transport today.

The next important technical innovation was developed in the 15th century, the transition period between the Middle Ages and the modern era. It was the coach, which differed from the cart in that the undercarriage was separate from the body of the vehicle. The passenger part of the vehicle was now suspended by chains and later by straps. This meant that it no longer rested directly on the axle, making traveling much more comfortable. However, in the Middle Ages people considered traveling in a carriage a dishonorable and shameful activity, something reserved for the old and the sick, and for women.

But views gradually changed. Women may have been the first to realize and appreciate the advantages of this new means of transport but they were soon joined by the men. In the 16th and 17th centuries magnificent coaches were seen as a status symbol of the aristocracy. In the 17th century carriages were generally preferred to saddle horses and they were no longer only restricted to the ruling class. Those who could afford it soon discovered the advantages of traveling by coach, which later became more comfortable with the addition of springs. However, the discomfort of a long coach journey should not be underestimated. Reports at the time were full of the "torture" that travelers had to endure because of bad road conditions. Coaches were also extremely slow, and experienced walkers could often walk further in a day than a coach.

The railroad revolution

It was industrialization in the 19th century that improved the situation in both these respects. In 1830 the first public railroad connection between Liverpool and Manchester was inaugurated. Five years earlier a public railroad line had been built to transport freight between the English towns of Stockton and Darlington. In the coal mining industry steam locomotives had already been used since the beginning of the 19th century to transport coal within a coal mine.

In spite of certain reservations towards this new technology based on health reasons—it was thought that traveling at such an "unnatural" speed was bound to harm the body—people were soon converted to this new concept of travel. They had never traveled so fast or so comfortably from one place to another. Even a speed of 9 mph was a marked improvement, since in 1800 mail coaches only averaged 2½ mph. As a result, railroads were the undisputed winner. In 1843 the German poet Heinrich Heine was so excited about a train journey he made in France that he compared the invention of

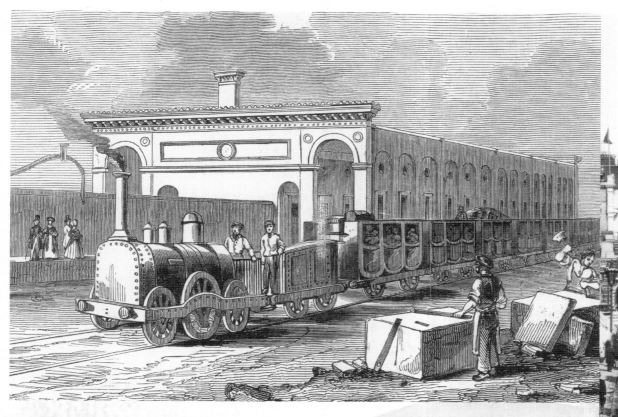

The transport revolution started in England at the beginning of the 19th century. This is the railroad station in Cambridge.

the railroad with that of gunpowder and printing. As far as public transport was concerned, the railroads of the 19th century were vastly superior to the mail coaches of the 18th century. A real transport revolution had occurred, bringing places closer together that had previously appeared impossibly far from each other. It is therefore not surprising that railroads had such an impact on people's everyday life.

Industrialization

Technically railroads were based on two things: the invention of the steam engine that marked the beginning of industrialization, and the invention of rails. The latter had already been used in coal mines in the 16th century, but major progress was only made towards the end of the 18th century with the introduction of iron rails. This became possible with improvements in iron smelting. In 1801 England already had a public railroad network with horse-drawn trains. The introduction of the steam engine then enabled the means of traction to become mechanized. The efficiency of locomotives greatly increased in the 19th century with steam-driven trains that could reach a speed of 75 mph, and in 1907 a top speed of 96 mph was achieved.

But the decisive breakthrough of the railroads was not based only on their technical superiority. By the 19th century plenty of coal was available for stoking the engine, while fodder cereals for horses were becoming increasingly expensive as a result of the increase in population during the 18th and 19th centuries that pushed up prices. Consequently the running costs of railroads were always lower than horse-drawn vehicles.

Transport chaos already existed in large cities such as London at the end of the 19th century, long before the spread of the automobile.

The automobile conquers the world

For individual transport, people still relied on the horse and carriage. This changed in 1886 when Carl Benz (1844–1929) and Gottlieb Daimler (1834–1900) independently developed a working motor-driven vehicle. At few years earlier, engineers in America and Europe had been trying to develop an internal combustion engine running on gasoline. In 1876, after initial successes in France, Nikolaus August Otto (1832–1891) succeeded in making the first working four-stroke internal combustion engine. Benz and Daimler made use of this invention and in this way intiated the triumphant success story of the automobile.

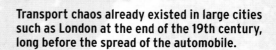

The invention and development of the automobile marks the beginning of individual transport.

277

Alpha, beta, and gamma rays: positive, negative, and neutral

Ernest Rutherford (1871-1937)

In discovering radioactivity, Henri Becquerel also arrived at a sensational conclusion, that apparently inert matter such as uranium also emitted energy-intensive rays as it spontaneously disintegrated. But the origin and nature of this radiation were not understood for many years.

1902

IN THE YEAR 1902

> Arthur James Balfour becomes the new prime minister of Great Britain.

> A peace treaty formally ends the Boer War between Great Britain and the Boer Republics, the Orange Free State and the Transvaal. Both countries become British colonies.

The discoveries made by Becquerel and by Marie and Pierre Curie gave a new impetus and direction to the research of one scientist in particular, the New Zealand-born physicist Ernest Rutherford. Originally he had been mainly interested in electromagnetic fields but now he turned his attention to radioactive radiation. Rutherford observed that it was not only different elements that emitted different radiation. He found that even the radiation produced by a single element was not homogenous and had a greatly varying power of penetration. Radioactive radiation, he concluded, must consist of at least two components: alpha particles, which can penetrate only a few hundredths of a millimeter of aluminum, and beta particles, whose penetration power is a hundred times stronger.

The French physicist Paul Ulrich Villard (1860–1934) discovered a third kind of radiation, gamma rays, whose power of penetration was even greater than that of beta rays. In addition, Rutherford also noted a strong deflection in the path of the beta rays in the direction of positively charged poles, while the less powerful alpha rays were deflected in the direction of negatively charged poles. Gamma rays, on the other hand, did not deflect in either direction. Based on these results, he concluded that beta rays consisted of negatively charged particles (electrons) and alpha rays of positively charged particles (protons), while gamma rays were waves of energy with no electrical charge. Rutherford also deduced from their mass that alpha particles consisted of double positively charged helium ions, that is, helium atoms with a nucleus consisting of two protons.

He corroborated this assumption with spectroscopic observations.

But if elements produce helium ions when they disintegrate (alpha decay), then radioactivity must bring about the transformation of a chemical element into something else. When the atomic nucleus with a helium ion loses two protons, an element is created that is two numbers lower in the periodic table. By contrast, in the case of beta decay an electron is produced that increases the element's atomic number by one. Because radioactive transmutation produces an element that is usually also radioactive, it decays further, resulting in a series of disintegrations. Gamma radiation, on the other hand, produces no change; it is an extremely short-wave, energy-intensive electromagnetic radiation. It is produced by the atomic nucleus during alpha or beta disintegration.

The discovery of the various types of radioactive radiation was extremely important both in relation to the use of atomic energy and protection against radiation. Among other things, radioactive decay has made it possible to determine geological eras. In 1902 Ernest Rutherford published his findings on radiation created by the decay of chemical elements in an article entitled *The Cause and Nature of Radioactivity*. His discovery was of major importance in the field of nuclear energy and radiation protection.

The discovery of the existence of various kinds of radioactive radiation was very important in the use of nuclear energy and protection against radiation.

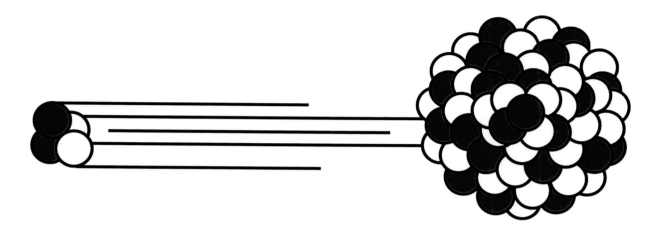

α

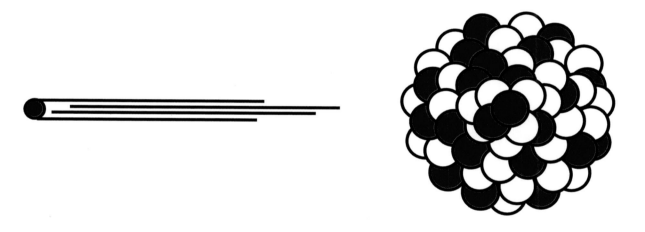

β

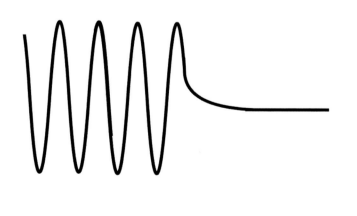

γ

Hormones: the mystery of the endogenous messengers

Ernst Henry Starling (1866-1927), William Maddock Bayliss (1866-1924)

1902

IN THE YEAR 1902

> The Aswan Dam is officially opened in Egypt.

> An eruption of the volcano Mount Pelée in Martinique in the French Antilles claims 30,000 lives.

> In Los Angeles the first permanent movie theater is opened.

How does the human body regulate its various functions, such as digestion, for instance? It does so by producing its own regulating substances, a fact that was discovered by two physiologists Ernst Henry Starling and William Maddock Bayliss in 1902.

In the course of experiments on a live animal the two scientists discovered that body functions were regulated by other factors besides nerve impulses. After severing all the nerves leading to the pancreas, a gland of the digestive system, they found that the organ still functioned and continued to produce digestive substances when the acidic content of the stomach reached the intestines. As soon as the mucous membrane of the small intestine came into contact with the gastric acids, it produced a secretion that stimulated the pancreas to produce these digestion-promoting substances. This substance, secreted by the mucous membrane of the duodenum, was named "secretin" by the two scientists. In 1904 Starling proposed calling all the substances that activated the organs "hormones."

Soon they made important scientific findings about these newly discovered substances. They were produced in various parts of the body. The hormones produced in the endocrine glands go straight to their site of activity through the blood. In contrast, the nerve cells in the diencephalon convert electric impulses into chemical (hormone) signals, neuro-hormones, while tissue hormones are produced by individual cell tissue. All hormones perform the same task. As they sit in certain cell points, called receptors, they carry information and activate the cells to a genetically programmed metabolic process, for example the formation of a new hormone or enzyme. Many hormones work independently while others interact with each other. The center of the hormonal system is the hypothalamus in the brain and the pituitary gland.

The search for further hormone-producing glands proceeded rapidly. The substance discovered in 1901 in the suprarenal glands by the chemist Jokichi Takamine (1854–1922) was identified as adrenalin (formerly epinephrine). This stimulates the glucose metabolism during physical activity or stress in order to provide the body with instant energy.

In 1921 a young physician Frederick Grant Banting (1891–1941) and his assistant Charles Herbert Best (1899–1978) made a pioneering discovery, the treatment of diabetes. The pancreas of diabetics produces insufficient insulin, a metabolic hormone that is responsible for processing the sugar (glucose) in the body. Banting and Best succeeded in isolating the insulin in the pancreas of live animals and injected it into diabetic patients. In this way they regulated the hormone deficiency of diabetics.

In 1929 the chemist Adolf Friedrich Johannes Butenandt (1903–95) isolated the sex hormone in the ovaries and testicles. Tadeus Reichstein (1897–1996) and Kendall together discovered a whole group of hormones, the corticosteroids produced by the suprarenal glands. They succeeded in isolating four of the six active hormones and in producing a synthetic version of one of them, corticosteron. This led to the development of cortisone, which is used today as an effective anti-inflammatory treatment.

The centre of the hormonal system is the hypothalamus, which is situated in the brain and the pituitary gland. Hormones convey information throughout the body.

2

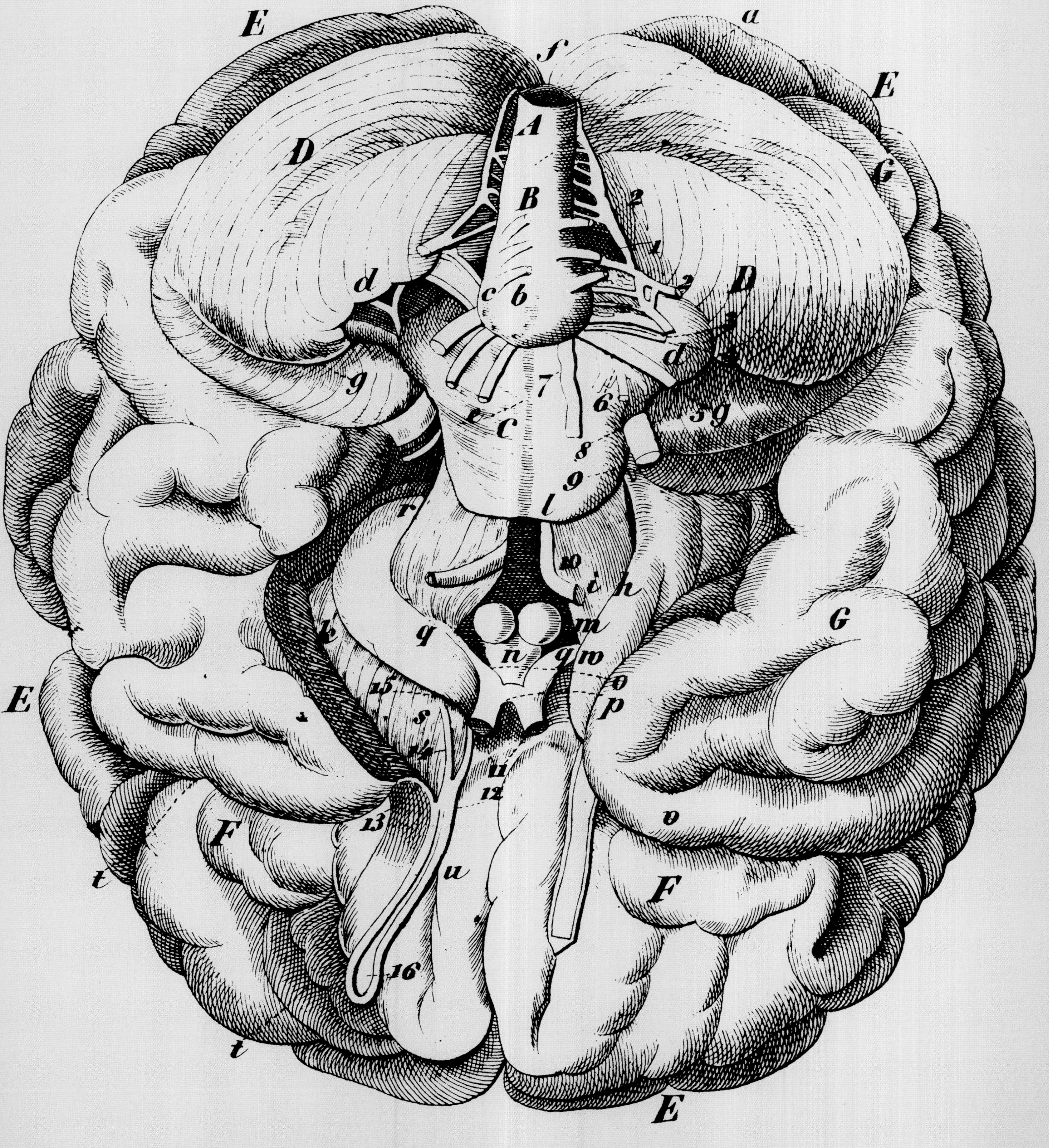

E
a
f
E
A
D
G
B
2
1
2
d
c
b
D
d
g
7
6
3g
C
8
9
l
r
10
i
h
k
q
m
G
n
g
w
E
15
o
p
s
14
11
12
13
F
v
t
u
F
16
t
E

Chaos theory: the power to create something out of nothing

Henri Poincaré (1854-1912)

Greek mythology perceived "Chaos" as the original condition of the world, the emptiness that preceded the development of the universe. The Christian idea of the divine "creation from nothing" displaced this interpretation. But in 1903 Henri Poincaré was the first theoretical thinker to discover the inventive demon in chaos once more: the notion of "non-linearity" and its spontaneous power of producing order.

IN THE YEAR 1903

> The USA passes a law forbidding the immigration of criminals, prostitutes and other undesirables.

> The exiled Russian Workers' party splits between the moderate Mensheviks ("for the minority") and the radical Bolsheviks ("for the majority").

> The American travel and adventure writer Jack London publishes his novel *Call of the Wild*.

> In the elections for the German parliament, the Catholic Center Party and the Social Democrats emerge as the strongest parties.

The concept of chaos theory only originated in the 1970s. It stands for the discovery of so-called non-linear dynamics in the fields of mathematics, physics, and chemistry. Therefore, the principle of chaos theory itself derives from the principle that even an apparently completely stable system, such as the solar system, is always undergoing a state of "rest" from disorder, and this may plunge into chaos without any outside impulse. Conversely, chaos has powers that create order.

Since the 16th century science was already engaged in imposing order on the world by expressing it in numbers, laws, and forms. With the development of "mechanical philosophy" by Isaac Newton (1642–1727), scientists believed that this objective had been achieved and that order had been brought to time and space. The mathematician Pierre Simon de Laplace (1749–1827) formulated a sentence that expressed this belief clearly: "If one could exactly measure the position and movement of all points in the universe, the rest of eternity could be calculated."

In the late 19th century, however, the mathematician Henri Poincaré came up against the limiting factors of such theories while studying planetary orbits. It was admittedly possible to calculate the tracks of two bodies, for example the sun and the earth, using Newton's equations for the attraction between planets. But if a third body was added to the calculation, the equation could no longer be solved mathematically. Some orbits during even the smallest disturbance "escape" from the solar system and put the planetary system astronomically out of balance. Poincaré had discovered that the smallest "cause" could trigger processes of great complexity. He also already recognized the hidden power of such processes, that spontaneously create new structures on other planes.

In particular the physicist and chemist Ilya Prigogine, born in Russia in 1917, demonstrated the proof of these processes of spontaneous formation of order in nature. According to the classic laws of thermodynamics, time only goes in one direction, that of increasing loss of energy and with it of order. Prigogine however showed that the course of time is reversible: as a result of insignificant, coincidental changes, systems are caught up in turbulences where the spontaneous creation of order can take place at certain points of intersection or "bifurcations." According to Prigogine, human life originated in the course of the history of such bifurcation points.

Today, chaos theoreticians are trying to understand creation through the pattern of the spontaneous formation of order from disorder, and thus the entire cultural-historical development of the human being.

Fraktals demonstrate the spontaneous creation of order from disorder.

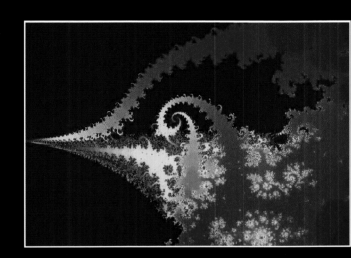

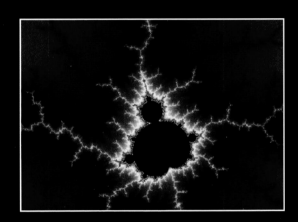

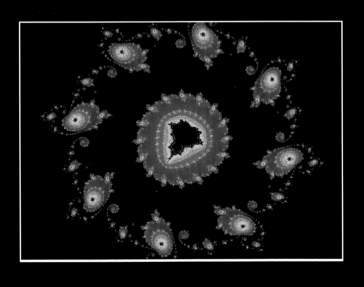

Radar:
the end of blind navigation

Christian Hülsmeyer (1881-1957)

Christian Hülsmeyer's radar apparatus could locate ships or planes accurately through the densest fog and determine how quickly and in what direction they were moving. But as was the case with so many exceptional inventions, radar had first to convince the followers of tradition – in this case those who would rather trust the foghorn – of its advantages.

1904

IN THE YEAR 1904

> The Russian physiologist Ivan Petrovich Pavlov receives the Nobel Prize for Medicine for his research into the conditioning of reflexes.

> In the German colony of Southwest Africa the Herero rebel against the settlers. German troops brutally suppress the uprising and in the process the Herero tribe is almost wiped out.

> The Irish nationalist leader John Edward Redmond demands independence for his country from Great Britain.

> The Russian-Japanese war erupts over Manchuria and Korea.

On May 18, 1904, the engineer and high-frequency technician Christian Hülsmeyer presented his "telemobiloscope" to an audience in Cologne. This was an apparatus for use by ships that could locate other shipping even in thick fog at distances of up to 2 miles.

In 1886, the physicist Heinrich Rudolf Hertz had proved that electromagnetic waves are reflected back from obstacles. It was on this principle that Hülsmeyer's apparatus was based; it transmitted electromagnetic waves in the form of short pulses of radio waves from a parabolic antenna, that is, an antenna with a curved surface. This sent the waves out into space, a metal reflector intensifying them further. When the waves met an obstacle, the object reflected the impulses. These reflections varied in power depending on the material of the obstacle. In the pauses between the impulses, the antenna received the electronic reflections like an echo, and these were then converted into an acoustic signal. By calculating the lapse of time between the transmission of the impulses and the return of the reflection, Hülsmeyer could determine the distance of the obstacle. The measurements were repeated rapidly in succession to give an idea of how the position of the object changed and how fast it was moving. Using the telemobiloscope, it was now possible to locate objects with great accuracy completely independently of visibility. Particularly at sea it was a great advantage to be able to recognize approaching ships from a distance. The audience at Hülsmeyer's premiere followed his introduction with great interest. However, he was unable to find a patron or ship owner, let alone the German navy, to invest in his device; experts were dubious about its reliability, or they did not think it was necessary.

In the 1920s, radio engineers carried out further experiments with the telemobiloscope. They tried out various frequencies, antennae, impulses, and receivers in order to convert the acoustic signal of a location into a visual one. At the beginning of the 1930s, Robert Watson-Watt (1892–1973) made a decisive step in this direction; he connected a cathode-ray tube to the receiver of the telemobiloscope. The engineer in charge of the machine could now see where and at what distance the located object was to be found. This construction was named "radar," an acronym for "RAdio Detection And Ranging."

During World War II the apparatus was designed specifically for military use. Great Britain for instance built a whole chain of radar stations on the south and east coasts and used them in defense against air attack. Later in the war microwave radar was used by aircraft themselves. Today radar is used mostly in military and civilian shipping and aviation. The most modern radar uses an interrogatory signal. Instead of a passive reflection, an answering machine on board the located object sends back coded information. With the massive increase in air traffic, radar is absolutely essential for safe air traffic control.

Today the safety of shipping movements and navigation depends heavily on radar.

Genetics: how heredity works

William Bateson (1861-1926)

> Robert Koch is awarded the Nobel prize for medicine.

> The Russian army uses force to put an end to a protest demonstration by 30,000 workers.

> The transport workers' strike in Chicago turns violent when strike-breakers from the southern states try to end it.

> US president Theodore Roosevelt reaffirms that Latin America is an American sphere of interest.

Theories about how the characteristics and features of parents are passed on to children already existed in ancient Greece. But it was Mendel's Laws and the research based on them that in the early years of the 20th century laid the foundation for genetics, the systematic study of heredity.

The experimental work of the botanist Gregor Johann Mendel (1822–84) on heredity in sweet peas laid the foundation for the laws of heredity. Mendel carried out cross-breeding experiments with sweet peas in the gardens of the Augustinian monastery of St Thomas in Brunn and noticed that the results conformed to certain rules. He came to the conclusion that the properties he was studying (such as color or habit) were inherited as separate units, independently of each other. These units came in pairs and were called "elements" by Mendel. Later scientists referred to them as "genes."

Mendel's pioneering work remained unnoticed for 34 years. It was only in 1900 that a group of researchers that included the botanist Hugo de Vries (1848–1935) discovered Mendel's article "Experiments with Plant Hybrids" and decided to continue Mendel's research. De Vries confirmed the laws established by the Augustinian monk through cross-breeding experiments of his own, and he also discovered further conformities to natural laws. In 1901 he noticed a new characteristic in an evening primrose that was probably the result of a sudden change in a gene. Dr de Vries called this phenomenon "mutation."

In 1902 the scientist Walter Stanborough Sutton (1877–1916) came to the conclusion that Mendel's heredity factors were located in the chromosomes. Chromosomes are microscopically small structures of the cell nucleus that are made up of deoxyribonucleic acids (DNA) and proteins, and which represent the heredity substance of the higher organisms.

However, the true founder of genetics was the biologist William Bateson (1861–1926). In 1900 he too discovered Mendel's work, which confirmed his own observations. As an enthusiastic advocate of Mendel's theory, Bateson became the pioneer of genetics in the 20th century. In 1905 he established that chromosomes are the carriers of inherited characteristics, and discovered the existence of genes. Together with the geneticist Reginald Crudell Punnett (1875–1967), he proved that genes could influence each other mutually.

Another important step forward in genetics was the discovery made in 1909 by the biologist Wilhelm Johannsen (1857–1929), who defined the "genotype" as the carrier of identical hereditary characteristics, as opposed to the "phenotype," which carried its external characteristics.

Genetics reached a high point after World War II, when the chemical composition of the gene became the subject of new research. Since then modern genetics has made enormous strides. As well as studying the connections in heredity between various organisms, geneticists are also intervening in genetic make-up through genetic engineering. The cloned sheep "Dolly" of 1996 was the striking result of genetic engineering.

It was genetics that explained how certain characteristics were carried on to the next generation.

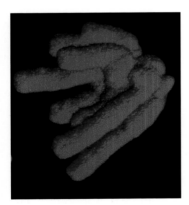

△ Chromosomes are the carriers of genes.

Vitamins: vital elements of nutrition

Christiaan Eijkman (1858-1930), Frederick Gowland Hopkins (1861-1947)

During the time of the great sea voyages of discovery, sailors often spent months at a time at sea. Fresh fruit and vegetables were rarely on the menu. Many mariners suffered from weight loss, muscular atrophy and bleeding – they had scurvy, the disease dreaded by sailors.

1906

IN THE YEAR 1906

> In London, the *Labour Representation Committee* becomes the *Labour Party.*

> In Moscow, Tsar Nichols II opens the Duma, the first Russian parliament. It has little power.

> In Austria, the direct, general, equal, and secret right to vote is introduced for all male citizens.

> The construction of the British armored warship *Dreadnought* is finished. It is the largest in the world and causes a new upsurge in the arms race between Germany and Great Britain.

△ **Vitamin-rich vegetables.**

What was the cause of this sickness? The Scottish doctor James Lind (1716–1794) looked for the answer in nutrition. In 1747 he distributed various foods amongst sailors suffering from scurvy. Lind discovered that citrus fruits relieved the symptoms radically.

In 1886, medical research turned its attention to a further indeterminable sickness that began with symptoms of weakness and pain. Beriberi (from the Singhalese *beri* = weakness) occurred in countries where the inhabitants ate a lot of polished rice, that is, rice with the inner husk also removed. The Dutch doctor Christiaan Eijkman (1858–1930) was a serious proponent of the theory that all sicknesses arose from germs. In 1886 he traveled to Java in order to research the causes of beriberi, taking with him some chickens to use in his experiments. However, he was unable to prove that the sickness was caused by a bacterial infection. In 1896, the animals that had been fed with polished rice showed symptoms similar to beriberi. When they were fed with normal feed they recovered. At first Eijkman believed that there was a poison in the rice that remained unneutralized in the grain when the husk was removed, and that this caused the beriberi. But this proved not to be the case. The proof that substances contained in food have an important influence on the health of humans and animals was found by another scientist.

Until then, scientists studying nutrition had focused their attention mainly on the proteins whose molecules were composed of various amino acids essential to life. In 1900, the English biologist Frederick Gowland Hopkins (1861–1947) discovered a new amino acid, tryptophan. He noticed that the protein "zein" lacked tryptophan. If laboratory animals were given this "incomplete" protein as their only source of protein, they died. This was not the case with any other nutritional protein. However, if Hopkins added zein to the amino acid, the life expectancy of the animals was increased. Therefore, amino acids were important substances that the body can only manufacture in part by itself. Some cannot be synthesized in the body, however, and must be obtained from the diet. In 1906 he put forward the theory that food must contain elements that promote good health.

Unlike nutrients, vitamins do not supply energy. In 1912, the biochemist Casimir Funk suggested the name "vitamin" (Latin *vita* = life) for these substances in the erroneous belief that they were all amines (nitrogen compounds). In 1913, on the initiative of the biochemist Elmer Vernon McCollum, the naming of the different vitamins by letters was accepted. After the discovery of vitamins A, B, C and D, the vitamins E and K followed. It was soon found that food containing the vitamin B had so many different components that the biologists enlarged the terminology to include vitamin B1, vitamin B2 and so on.

Vitamins are organic compounds that are soluble either in water or in fat. Their concentration in the body has an influence on growth, a well-functioning immune system, and on the metabolism.

Crystal photograph of vitamin C. Vitamins ensure the proper operation of the immune system.

The model of the atom: matter takes shape

Ernest Rutherford (1871-1937)

The phenomenon of radioactivity and in particular the discovery of the three types of radiation (alpha, beta and gamma rays) proved conclusively that the atomic nucleus could not be a stable mass. But what does an atomic nucleus look like?

For a long time atoms were believed to be spherical and elastic, with a structure filled with matter that obeyed the laws of classical mechanics. If correct, this theory would have meant that alpha particles colliding with atoms should bounce off them and be strongly deflected.

Ernest Rutherford put this to the test and bombarded a thin sheet of gold foil with alpha rays. A large proportion of these rays penetrated the material and was only slightly deflected. On the basis of this test, Rutherford concluded that an atom consisted mainly of empty space.

In 1904 the physicist Joseph John Thomson developed the theory that atoms consisted of a spherical charged structure that in turned contained moving electrons. Positive and negative charges were distributed evenly in the atom. But Ernest Rutherford discovered during his research that a very small number of particles were very strongly deflected. He believed that this was caused by positively charged centers inside the atom.

After carrying out a mathematical analysis of his research, Rutherford concluded that an atom was made up of a positively charged atomic nucleus and a negatively charged shell. The mass was concentrated in the nucleus while the electrons rotated continuously around it, like the planets around the sun. He concluded that the nucleus was minute and that the distance to the shell was very large in comparison. Roughly speaking, the nucleus was about 10,000 times smaller in diameter than the atom of which it was the centre.

The fundamental principle of Rutherford's model of the atom, produced in 1911, is still valid today. In modern nuclear physics it is assumed that the nucleus contains positively charged protons as well as uncharged neutrons that are about the same weight and are held together by strong nuclear forces.

Rutherford had already predicted the existence of these neutrons, although technology at the time only allowed him to prove the existence of charged particles. The number of electrons in the atom that rotate round the nucleus corresponds to that of the protons of the nucleus and is the same as the atomic number of the element in the periodic table.

According to the laws of electrodynamics an accelerated, active charge, such as the electrons on the atomic shell, should produce energy in the form of light, thereby losing some kinetic energy before finally sinking towards the nucleus. But at the time scientists were unable to explain why this was not the case. The interaction between the nuclear particles could be expressed in mathematical formulae but it could not be portrayed. In spite of unanswered questions and further new discoveries, Rutherford's model of the atom formed the theoretical basis and the starting point of modern nuclear physics.

The atom. The mass is concentrated in the core while the electrons on the outer shell circle round it continuously.

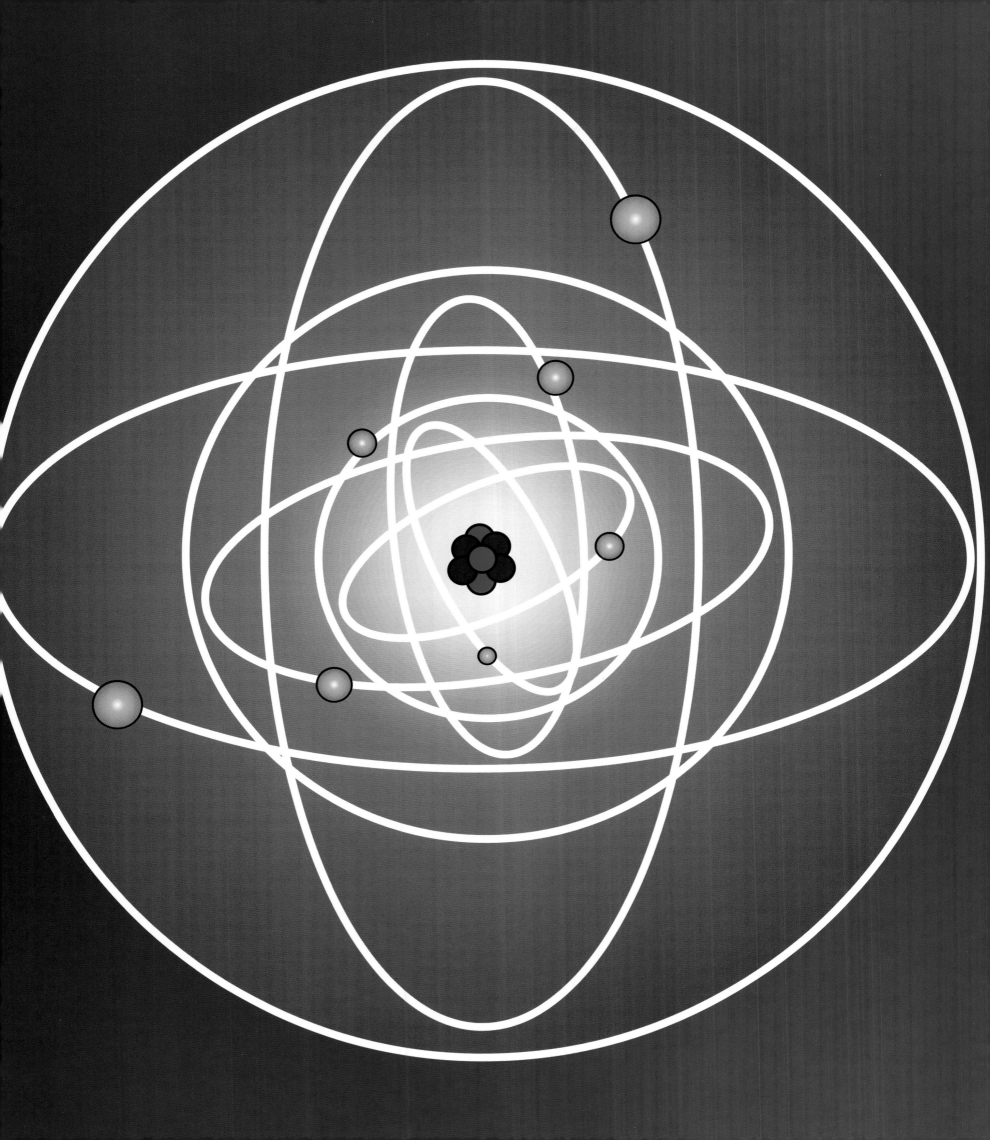

Continental drift: the primeval continent becomes today's earth

Alfred Wegener (1880-1930)

△ The polar scientist Alfred Wegener was ridiculed at first.

How did the appearance of the earth originate? This question has occupied geologists since the 18th century. The supporters of the various theories argued vigorously, all participants believing themselves to be correct. But when the meteorologist and polar scientist Alfred Wegener formulated his theory of continental drift in 1912, his colleagues only mocked him.

At the end of the 18th century science turned to some new geological questions, such as how the earth's crust had originated and what forces influenced it. Between 1790 and 1820 two protagonists dominated the debate about the formation of the continents and the seas separating them: the geologist James Hutton (1726–97), and Abraham Gottlob Werner (1749–1817). They held directly opposing views. Hutton and his supporters, the "Plutonists" or "Vulcanists," believed that the creative power of the earth came from a "central fire" within the interior of the earth, while Werner and the "Neptunists" were convinced that all rock had crystallized from the water.

Even before the development of these theories, scientists had noticed the strange correspondence of the various coastlines of the continents. How had this originated? A tenable explanation was first formulated by the astronomer, meteorologist, and polar researcher Alfred Wegener (1880–1930). He was a professor of meteorology and geophysics in Graz, but his actual interest was polar research. In about 1910, Wegener came on the idea that the five continents that today are separated by the oceans could once, before the Permian era about 225 million years ago, have been components of a gigantic, interrelated continent in the prehistoric Panthalassa, "whole ocean." After the breakup of this Pangaea ("whole earth"), the soils moved apart over millions of years in a slow yet constant current on the deeper strata. The arrangement of the folds, compressed sections, and overlapping parts expressed itself in earthquakes or seaquakes that occurred again and again. As further evidence for this thesis, apart from the agreement of the coastlines, Wegener named the continuation of mountain ranges and the correspondence of fossil fauna and flora on both sides of the Atlantic. He also observed comparable sequences of geological strata on both sides of these oceans.

Wegener brought his results to the public for the first time in 1912, but attracted only scorn and mockery. Nevertheless, he remained convinced of his theory. In 1915 he published his book *The Origin of Continents and Oceans*. As a result, geology had to reconsider numerous geophysical, geological and paleo-climatological questions. The former theories of land bridges sunk deep in the sea became unnecessary.

Research after World War II confirmed many aspects of Wegener's theory. Uncertainty only prevailed – as they had with Wegener himself – over the forces that had caused this continental drift. He himself had cautiously suspected convection currents in the magnetic subsoil of the earth. Along extended fracture cracks, molten material pushes under the oceans from the mantle and solidifies in humps on the surface. The earth's crust slides off this inclined plane, and presses the continental plates before it. Wegener's revolutionary hypothesis is taught today as "plate tectonics," and has now become a matter of general knowledge.

Today scientists believe that earthquakes are linked to continental drift.

The assembly line: cars are produced as piece-work

Henry Ford (1863-1947)

"Mass production for mass consumption!" was the motto of the American industrialist Henry Ford. In this way he wanted to make the expensive automobile available to all. By introducing the assembly line he achieved his goal, and paved the way for modern industrial production.

Automobiles were being produced almost individually by hand when Ford started work in car production. His goal was to "democratize the automobile" by speeding up production and lowering the price. To achieve this he built upon the experience of others who had thought along these lines. The American engineer Frederick W. Taylor (1856–1915) had looked for ways of making more economical use of human labor. He had broken down the assembly sequence into single steps and rearranged them using greater efficiency as his criterion. Time and motion studies of the workers provided information as to how the product could be assembled better and quicker. Taylor hoped that this rationalization of the work process would also result in more fairness in paying wages, since those who worked harder would be paid more. Ford also found inspiration in the Chicago slaughterhouses, where transport belts had been in use since 1870 so that each step of the work process could be completed individually.

Henry Ford put Taylor's theories into almost perfect practice and also adopted the moving-belt conveyor. In 1913, he introduced the production of automobiles on assembly lines. Each piece of work was transported mechanically to the next worker and so would always be in the right place at the right time. With this revolutionary innovation in the assembly process, the son of humble Irish immigrants had fulfilled his dream: lower production costs meant a lower price for the finished product and therefore many more people could afford a car. At the same time, good wages boosted consumption – and his profits. Every worker needed money; the more he worked the more he earned, and therefore the more he would spend (on a car for instance). Ford saw the piece-rate pay system as the single motivational force for a worker. He usually hired unskilled workers who were trained quickly. He regarded short work hours and a wage based on piece rates as necessary conditions for the "consumption for all." This philosophy has been called "Fordism" ever since.

About 15 million Model T Fords had rolled off the assembly line times by 1927. In order to satisfy such mass demand, the automobile had been completely standardized as a product. There were only slight variations in the bodywork and the only color offered was black.

Sadly, the introduction of the assembly line had its downside. Henry Ford did realize that making the same movements over and over again subjected his workers to a fatiguing routine. However, he believed that he was fulfilling their needs by paying good wages for work without intellectual stress. By the 1930s it was obvious that Fordism could not live up to expectations. People realized that it was not just the incentive of good wages but also the working atmosphere that determined the productivity of the employees. Therefore, industrial production partly returned to more complex assembly sequences carried out by several workers working together. Although the assembly line survives, most operations are now usually carried out by robots.

The assembly line was designed to ensure that each component reached the right place at the right time.

1913

IN THE YEAR 1913

> New York celebrates the official opening of Grand Central Station, the biggest railway station in the world.

> The German Parliament decides to increase the strength of the army.

> George Bernard Shaw's *Pygmalion* opens at the Burgtheater in Vienna, Austria.

> Woodrow Wilson is sworn in as the new President of the United States.

△ It was hoped that the rationalization of the work process through the division of production into separate stages would lead to fairer pay for the workers.

The echo-sounder: the depths reveal their secrets

Paul Langevin (1872-1946)

1915

IN THE YEAR 1915

> After a German U-boat sinks the passenger steamer *Lusitania* with 120 US citizens on board, the USA considers intervention in World War I.

> German airships begin attacking the east coast of Great Britain.

> German troops conquer Poland.

The sinking of the ocean giant *Titanic* after colliding with an iceberg was proof of a serious shortcoming in navigation. Obstacles below the surface of the sea were often discovered too late or not at all, with catastrophic results. The physicist Paul Langevin eventually invented an apparatus that sent out waves of sound into the depths of the sea. If the waves were reflected, an obstacle had been located and action to avoid it could be taken.

In 1912, the terrible news of the sinking of the supposedly unsinkable ocean liner *Titanic* shook the world. The accident tragically proved that the navigation equipment of the day was not sufficient to warn against the dangers lurking in the deep.

A year after the tragic accident, the physicist Alexander Behm (1880–1952) began his first experiments in locating obstacles under water. He developed a machine that combined a transmitter and a receiver, a forerunner of the echo-sounder.

In Behm's apparatus, a plumbing charge was detonated on one side of the ship. This sent an acoustic signal that returned as an echo when it was reflected off the floor of the ocean or an obstacle. An apparatus on the other side of the ship received the sound and, by calculating the time difference between the sending of the acoustic impulse and its return, it could determine the distance of an obstacle or the depth of the water.

In 1915, the French physicist Paul Langevin (1872–1946) modified the construction. He used ultrasonic waves to sound the ocean floor and to give early warning of icebergs. Langevin attached a series of microphones to the bow of a ship. His "hydrophones," as they were known, transmitted acoustic signals with a frequency of over 20 kilohertz that the human ear cannot hear. As soon as these sound waves bounced off an object, their signal was reflected. A special apparatus on board the ship received the impulse and calculated the distance between the ship and the object.

Regrettably, the first applications of the echo-sounder ran counter to its original purpose of saving lives. In World War I it was used, at least indirectly, as a weapon. The British Royal Navy used a slightly modified version of an echo-sounder called an ASDIC (Anti-Submarine Detection and Investigation Committee) that created an active sound signal. The sound waves of the machine sounded to the human ear like a soft "ping." If the sound was reflected, the sailor operating the equipment could calculate the size, direction, speed and depth of an enemy submarine, which could then be attacked and destroyed.

Today, echo sounders are found on ships of all sizes, enabling shallow water and underwater obstacles to be detected. They are also used for locating shoals of fish and in geological surveys. Very finely tuned measuring echo-sounders survey the ocean floor by sending out thousands of soundings each hour, and in this way the underwater landscape of hills and valleys can be accurately mapped.

If the Titanic had been equipped with an echo-sounder she would probably not have struck the iceberg in 1912.

The theory of relativity: new theories of space and time

Albert Einstein (1879-1955)

> For the first time in a war, poison gas is used in action. German troops use chlorine gas against French soldiers in the battle of Ypres.

> The German colonial army in Southwest Africa surrenders to the British Union of South Africa under General Louis Botha.

> Portugal comes under a military government following an officers' coup.

> The German government rations bread and flour. Two days a week no meat can be sold.

The theory of relativity is the greatest and most significant intellectual achievement of the 20th century. It radically altered the perception of space and time. As a result of his theory, Albert Einstein was recognized as one of the greatest physicists in the world. The popular summary of his theory, "Everything is relative," was always rejected by Einstein himself. He much preferred "The good Lord does not throw the dice!"

In 1887 two United States physicists Albert Abraham Michelson (1852–1931) and Edward Williams Morley (1838–1923) carried out an experiment in which they observed that the speed of the light remained constant. But how was this phenomenon to be interpreted? In 1905 Albert Einstein, who was then working as an examiner at the patent office in Bern, Switzerland, proposed a solution that revolutionized human understanding of space and time: the special theory of relativity.

Einstein started from the assumption that the speed of light, approximately 186,000 miles per second, was the absolute limit. Nothing could be faster, neither matter, nor radiation, nor information. In addition, the speed of light always remains constant, independently of how fast the source of light or the observer moves, a theory based on the so-called "Lorentz transformation." It replaced absolute time with time that was dependent on moving conditions. For instance, the time indicated by a moving clock would always appears slower to an observer who was not moving with it than to an observer who was moving with it at the same speed. The same would be true of the spatial measurements of a body, which would appear shorter to a stationary observer when it approaches at the speed of the light. Space and time lose their absolute meaning.

But Einstein also discovered that the speed of light in a vacuum always remained constant, independently of how fast the source of light or the observer moved. In 1907 Einstein put forward his theory of the universal equivalence of mass and energy, which he expressed in the famous formula $E = mc^2$ (Energy = mass times the square of the speed of the light). The application of this formula is found, for instance, in the nuclear fission of a hydrogen bomb.

In his general theory of relativity of 1915, Einstein established the relation between gravitation and the space-time continuum. Starting from the premise that the curvature of space was created by the existence of mass, Einstein concluded that a beam of light passing close to the sun must be deflected towards the sun. Previously scientists had believed that a beam of light described an absolutely straight course under all conditions. Einstein's theory was confirmed in 1919 by the findings of an expedition of the British Royal Society to the Gulf of Guinea to observe a solar eclipse. The results of their measurements proved that Einstein's theory was indeed correct.

Other parts of Einstein's theory, such as the relativistic dilation of time whereby clocks move more slowly when they move, could only be proved after his death. Many of Einstein's propositions are still waiting to be confirmed experimentally. Nevertheless research into the structure of the universe or the science of cosmology would be unthinkable today without Einstein's general theory of relativity.

Albert Einstein. Parts of his theory of relativity could only be proved after his death.

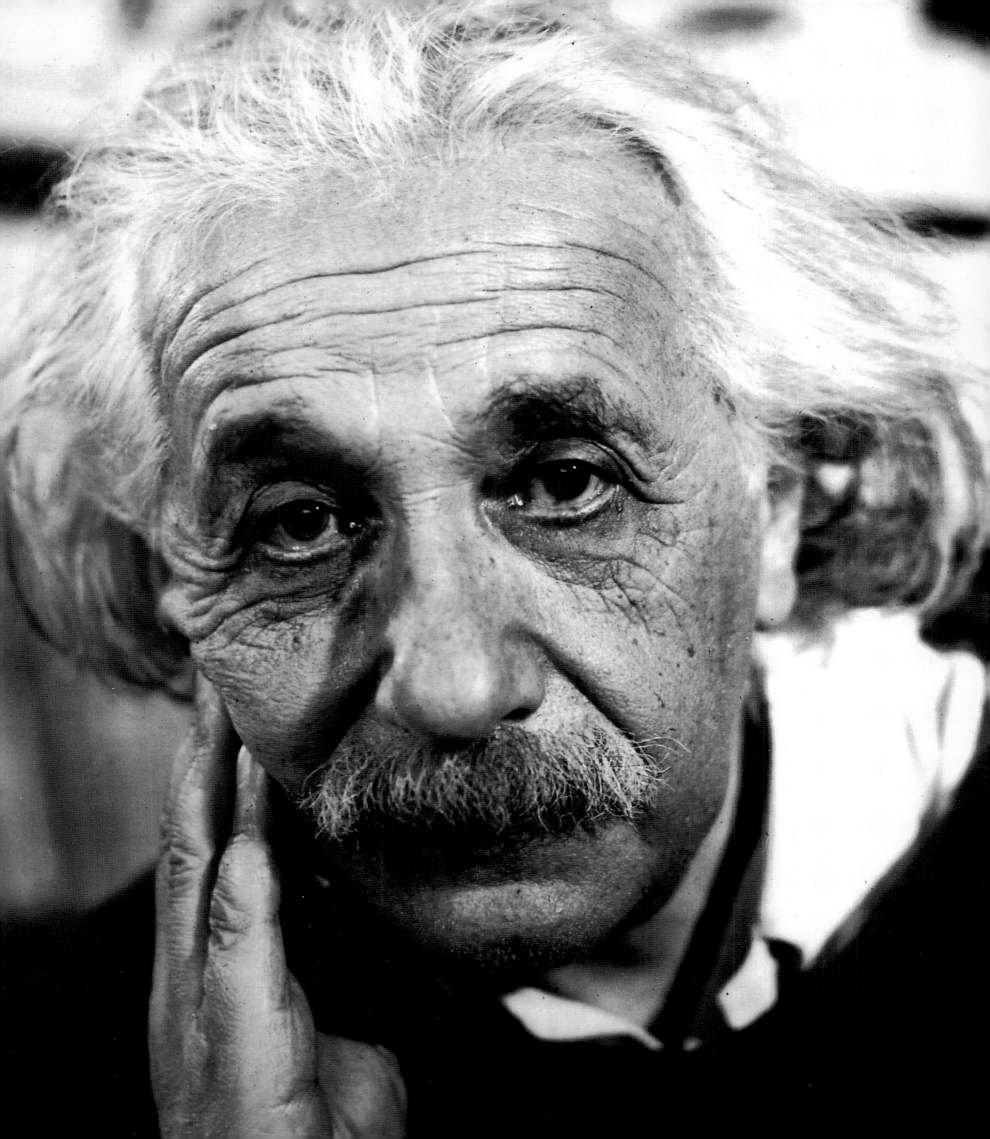

Communication bee-style

Karl von Frisch (1886-1982)

A bee discovers a field of flowering clover. No other bee is around. But in no time at all hundreds of bees have swarmed towards the field of clover. The first bee must have communicated with the others in some way. But how did it do this? This riddle was solved by the Austrian biologist Karl von Frisch.

1919

IN THE YEAR 1919

> In Berlin soldiers of the Volunteer Corps suppress the January revolt of the Communist Party of Germany and murder the leaders of the Spartacus League, Rosa Luxemburg and Karl Liebknecht.

> Friedrich Ebert (SPD) is elected first President of the Weimar Republic.

> In Paris, the allied victors establish the League of Nations to preserve peace. The USA decides not to join as the League is not in accordance with its ideas.

> The Peace Treaty of Versailles ending World War I is signed.

> The US Congress passes the Eighteenth Amendment to the Constitution: Prohibition forbids the manufacture, transport and sale of alcohol.

△ Bees are able to convey information about the whereabouts of food to the rest of the hive.

A swarm of bees consists of from 10,000 to 60,000 sterile female worker bees and a queen. In summer, thousands of male drones flock to the swarm. Their only aim is to fertilize the queen. Only six to ten drones succeed in achieving this. After the nuptial flight the worker bees drive the drones out of the beehive in a dramatic battle. Assuming the queen's thousands of eggs have been fertilized, the worker bees remain in the beehive for three weeks to build the honeycomb and take care of the brood. Only then do they swarm out to gather the valuable nectar and pollen.

In 1919 the biologist Karl von Frisch carried out a scientific study of the life of honeybees. Frisch discovered that the bees' sense of smell is very similar to that of humans. He also found that they were able to differentiate between all the colors except red. In order to orientate themselves outside the beehive, the bees used the polarized light of the sun as a kind of compass. This enabled them to find their way even when the sky was overcast, from their memories of polarized light patterns when the sun was shining. Frisch was also the first to observe that the worker bees communicated between themselves and exchanged information, such as where to find a field full of flowers or a "rich" forest. Their "language" was the dance.

Worker bees returning to the beehive after a successful expedition to collect nectar would tell their companions where to find this source of food by dancing. Frisch noted that there were two basic forms of dance, each with its own particular meaning. If the returning worker bees were doing the "circling dance" it meant that the source of food was within a radius of about 100 yards. The other worker bees swarming out would then be guided mainly by the specific fragrance of the type of flower whose pollen the dancing bees had carried inside the beehive on their fine hairs. If the food was situated more than 100 yards away the bees would dance the "wagging dance" on the honeycomb, by which they conveyed an accurate description of the route to follow.

The wagging dance describes a compressed figure of eight. The direction of the dance gives the other bees information on the angle between the connecting lines of the "beehive-sun" and of the "beehive-plants." The frequency of the wagging movements made by the bees with the rear part of their bodies shows how far the flowers are from the beehive: the further away the flowers are, the slower the rhythm of their dancing and the more elongated the figure of eight becomes in each dance figure. This enables the other bees to work out a precise flight schedule.

In 1973 Karl von Frisch was awarded the Nobel Prize for Physiology and Medicine together with Konrad Lorenz (1903–89) and Nikolaas Tinbergen (1907–88) for their achievements in the field of behavioral research on animals. Their work overturned the general belief that only the more highly developed living creatures were capable of communication.

Without their "wagging dance," decoded by Karl von Frisch, the complex society of a bee colony would be unable to function.

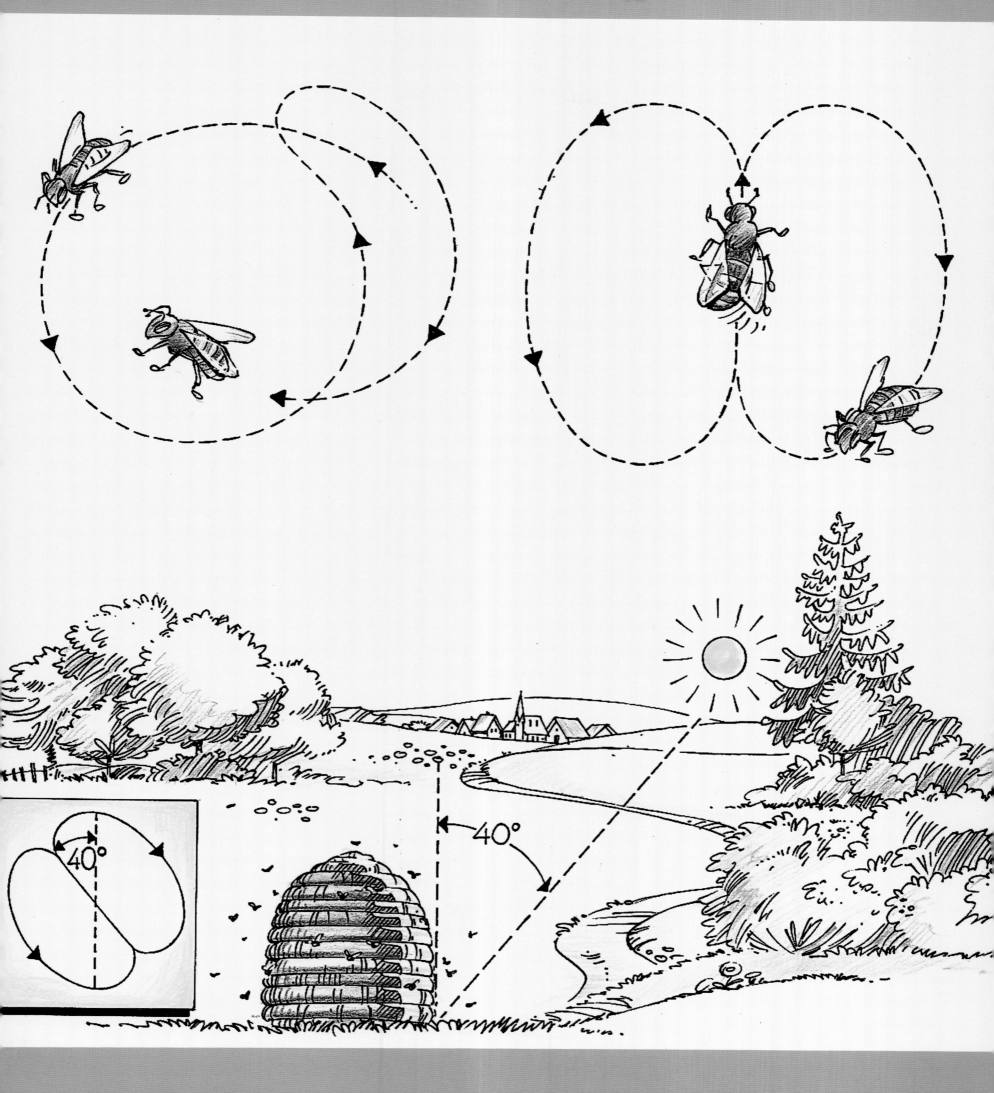

Aviation: Conquering the sky

A dream as old as mankind

To be able to fly like a bird—people have wanted to do this for thousands of years. Greek mythology tells for instance of Daedalus, who, with his son Icarus, tried to flee from the island of Crete by flying. But it was not until about 200 years ago that it looked as if this dream might one day become reality. In the early days of aviation, the inventors thought mainly of simple flying techniques based on what they could see around them. The focus of attention was always on imitating the flight of a bird. In daredevil feats, the experimenting adventurers recklessly threw themselves from hills and cliffs with wings made of feathers, fabric, and primitive struts, only to be brought rapidly down to earth with a thud.

Airships made it possible to transport large numbers of passengers in the air for the first time in history.

One of the first to reflect in a scientific way on the manner of moving through the air was the Italian painter and natural scientist Leonardo da Vinci. In 1500 he even drew sketches of helicopters and parachutes. His experiments with gliding and flapping wings, however, were all destined to fail. The human body is too heavy for it to be able to rise into the air by itself and keep itself there by flapping some form of wing.

Technology makes it possible

Several centuries later, inventors finally realized that without mechanical propulsion, man's flights would be limited to gliding. In the 18th century the predecessors of modern hang-gliders sailed more or less successfully through the air. Their pilots launched themselves courageously from mountains and towers with home-made wings. However, all too often, a crash landing was the conclusion of a short glide through the air.

At the beginning of the 18th century the idea began to crystallize that a flying machine must be lighter than air in order to lift itself from the ground. A direct predecessor of the hot-air balloon was floated into the air by a Brazilian priest before the eyes of the Portuguese King and his court in the audience chamber on August 8, 1709. The construction was in the form of a trough carried by a bladder made of canvas that was filled with air that the priest heated with candles. Seven decades later, in 1783, the French brothers Montgolfier succeeded in sending a technically superior variation of the hot-air balloon into the sky.

In the same century, ballooning became a sport for the rich all over Europe. Whether filled with hot air, or later with hydrogen, balloons dominated the skies for many years. However, none of these balloons could be steered. They flew where the wind carried them. For decades, the builders did not realize that the balloon was effectively part of the wind and had to travel with it at the same speed.

In the 19th century constructors concentrated their energies on the further development of hang-gliders and balloons. In 1804, for the first time, the British inventor Sir George Cayley designed rigid gliding wings for a human flyer. This was the first time a successful flight of any significant duration had been achieved using a construction that was heavier than air. This innovation stood as a signpost for almost a hundred years.

The airship is born

In the course of further development of the balloon, pioneers soon recognized that cigar-shaped balloons were more aerodynamic than round ones. The first "flying cigar" was constructed by the Frenchman Henri Giffard in 1852. He went on a flight that lasted for 3½ hours and covered a distance of 17 miles. This first truly free-flying airship was 144 ft long and was powered by a steam engine.

Towards the end of the 19th century the German engineer Ferdinand Graf von Zeppelin constructed the first steerable rigid airship. In 1900, the airship *Graf Zeppelin* rose into the air on her maiden flight. The development of a powered airship that

In 1909 Louis Blériot was the first to cross the English Channel in a powered aircraft.

Modern airliners with jet engines make flying a fast and pleasant means of travel, affordable for most people.

could be steered was successful, and in 1909, Zeppelin offered the first scheduled flights to the public.

Pioneering work with gliders

The spectacular gliding experiments of the German inventor Otto Lilienthal were significant in the final years of the 19th century. In 1891, he was able to cover a distance of 380 yards with his kite-like flying gliders. But attempts at powered flight made by other pioneers at the same time as the balloon experiments in the 19th century were all doomed to failure.

The airplane fanatic Gustav Weisskopf took up where Lilienthal left off. He started to work on powered flying machines, and in 1901 he made the breakthrough, taking off in his home-made aircraft to make the first manned powered flight in history. For a long time this great pioneering feat was forgotten as he did not make it public in any way.

However, with this achievement he preceded the Wright brothers in the United States, who had also been intensely occupied for years with the mysteries of powered flight. In 1903 the brothers made their first powered flight and by 1908 the US War Department was using the inven-

tion and thinking about industrializing the construction of airplanes. The aircraft constructor Louis Blériot flew over the English Channel from France to England in his motor airplane in 1909. The flight took just 27 minutes.

Planes in operation

In World War I, aircraft were called into use for the air force. In Germany too the Zeppelins were no longer transporting passengers to cities, but were carrying bombs to Britain. However, directly after the war, passenger flights using converted military planes started to become routine. On August 25, 1919, the first four passengers in European skies flew from London to Paris.

In the same year, the German aircraft constructor Professor Hugo Junkers was the first to conceive the idea of large passenger aircraft for scheduled flights. During the 1920s, the network of flight routes was extended and countless airline companies were founded. However, in those days flying was not only a very expensive undertaking, but also an extremely risky one; many machines had to make emergency landings due to technical difficulties and some even crashed. At the same time as these developments in commercial flight

were taking place, large numbers of adventurers and pioneers were attempting to cross the Atlantic or set up other long-distance records. An exceptional feat was achieved by Charles Lindbergh in 1927 when he made the transatlantic flight from New York to Paris, flying solo and without stopping.

Since that time, flight safety and speed have increased dramatically. In the early 1940s the first jet propulsion engines were developed. In 1947, the American pilot Charles Yeager was the first to break the sound barrier in horizontal flight at 763 mph, in a rocket-powered aircraft. Since 1976, British Airways and Air France have operated the supersonic jet Concorde on transatlantic flights. At over 1,600 mph, the Concorde is faster than any other commercial aircraft.

Weather forecasting: a sunny outlook for meteorologists

Vilhelm Bjerknes (1862-1951)

It was the French emperor Napoleon III who encouraged the development of accurate weather forecasting. Many of the French navy's ships involved in the Crimean war were lost during a violent hurricane storm in the Black Sea on November 14, 1854. Shocked by this event, he asked for the meteorological conditions behind this terrible storm to be examined.

As a result the French astronomer Urbain Leverrier (1811–73) gathered together meteorological observations from the whole of Europe. By analyzing these he discovered that the storm was heralded by a low pressure whirlwind and left measurable traces across hundreds of miles while it developed. Until then the representation of a spatial sequence of weather phenomena had only been formulated as a theory by a few avant-garde scientists. The most famous of them was the German physicist Heinrich Wilhelm Brandes (1777–1834), who in his book *Contributions to Meteorology* mentioned "causes that spread across Europe as it were from place to place." By 1875 almost every industrialized country had set up meteorological services, thus laying the foundation for systematic data collection. The empirical phase of modern meteorology could now begin.

The important leap from observation to analysis was made by the Norwegian geophysicist Vilhelm Bjerknes 50 years after the events in the Black Sea. In 1904 he published his theory that forecasting the weather could only be possible by the application of mathematical physics, based on observed data. Known as numerical weather prediction, Bjerknes based his approach on the laws of physics, taking into account data on the air's motion, density, pressure, temperature, and humidity. In 1921, after years of intensive research and analysis, he put forward his "polar front theory." In it he described the natural laws that play a decisive part in the development and progress of low-pressure areas. Bjernkes's theory laid the foundation for weather prediction in temperate latitudes.

But even Bjernkes could not yet forecast the weather. First, he did not have the ability to measure the data of the higher atmospheric strata, and secondly, the necessary calculations could not be carried out quickly enough to avoid being overtaken by the reality of the weather itself. It was the English scientist Lewis Fry Richardson (1881–1953) who made a major contribution to the analysis and evaluation of the numerous data measurements. He was the first to develop a mathematical model to calculate the coming weather. In his book *Weather Forecasting through Numerical Processes*, published in 1922, he described his vision of a calculating center with 64,000 employees linked to each other, who would process meteorological data on a continuous basis. Richardson's never-realized scheme of a "human computer" might well have provided the answer, because relatively reliable weather forecasts only became possible with the introduction of computer technology in the 1950s.

But even modern meteorologists are far from being 100 percent accurate. This is because even with modern satellite technology it is literally impossible to observe all the weather phenomena everywhere in the world. Even minor local changes can confuse macro weather situations. So, even at the beginning of the 21st century, the level of accuracy for three-day weather forecasts is only 70 percent.

Weather forecasting became more reliable when computers could analyze and evaluate large amounts of data.

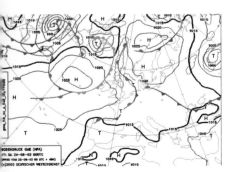

△ **Absolutely accurate weather forecasting is impossible even with modern technology.**

Neurotransmitters: how the nervous system works

Otto Loewi (1873-1961)

1921

IN THE YEAR 1921

> Ireland is divided into the British province of Ulster (Northern Ireland) and the independent state of Ireland.

> In Shanghai the Chinese Communist party comes into being. Mao Zedong is a co-founder.

> The German government agrees to the Allies' demands for reparations and undertakes to pay 132 billion gold marks over 66 years.

> Albert Einstein receives the Nobel Prize for Physics in recognition of his work on the quantum theory.

Ideas of how the nervous system works have changed over the centuries. In antiquity, people presumed that it depended on a "spirit" in the body, while later it was believed that electric currents flowed along the nerve fibers. But it was the physiologist Otto Loewi in 1921 who discovered the existence of biochemical substances transmitting electric impulses to the nerve ends.

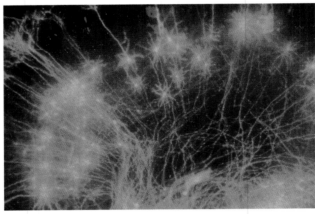

△ **Fluorescent image of nerve cells.**

The ancient belief that a special "spirit" flowed through the nerves had already been rejected by the Italian physician Luigi Galvani (1737–98) in 1791. Galvani joined the muscles of a severed frog's leg to two metal conductors. The resulting jerking of the muscle was interpreted by Galvani as a discharge of the nerves' own electricity. Indeed, small electric voltages could be observed passing along the nerves.

In the brain alone there are more than one hundred billion nerve cells (neurons) that are connected by a complex network of nerve fibers. The activity of the nervous system is based partly on electrical signals in the individual nerve cells and partly on chemical signals that run between them. The contact points between the nerve cells are called the synapses. A normal nerve cell can develop about 1,000 such synapses. The question is, how does an electric impulse jump across the gap between two synapses or nerve endings?

The body needs certain "messenger substances" to connect the cells.

This was proved by the German physiologist Otto Loewi in 1921 when he demonstrated that a stimulated nerve releases a chemical substance called a neurotransmitter. This was shown by an experiment in which the heart rate of one frog was slowed down, the fluid perfusing it was taken from it and passed into a second frog's heart, which then slowed down too. This indicated that the liquid contained a neurotransmitter.

This neurotransmitter crosses the gap between the individual nerve cells by converting the electric impulse into a chemical signal. Neurotransmitters work on the key-lock principle, in other words a neurotransmitter molecule fits perfectly into its relevant receptor. The transmitter substance was identified as acetylcholine by the English physiologist Henry Hallet Dale (1875–1969), and two other such substances are dopamine and serotonin.

There are in fact over 40 such transmitter substances. As well as leading to a better understanding of the nervous system, the discovery of these neurotransmitters has also helped in the diagnosis and treatment of illnesses such as Alzheimer's and Parkinson's disease, which are the result of a disturbance in neurotransmission.

The activity of the nervous system is based on the one hand on electrical signals in the individual nerve cells and on the other on chemical signals that run between them.

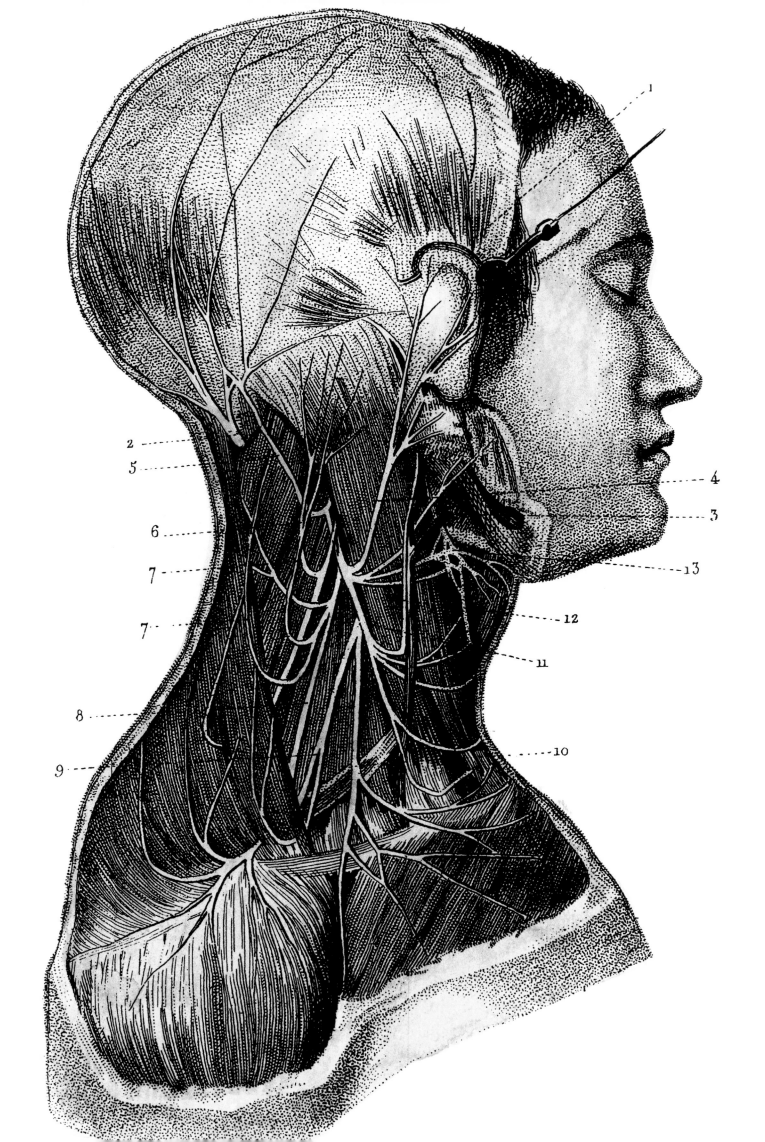

Television:
the whole world in a box

Wladimir Cosma Zworykin (1889-1982)

During the early 20th century the telephone and later radio made it possible to broadcast sounds to every corner of the world. This was the beginning of the universal spread of mass media. The next challenge for the scientists was the transmission of moving images, a problem that was even more demanding.

1924

IN THE YEAR 1924

> Vladimir Ilyich Lenin, the first government leader of the Soviet Union, dies in gorki.

> James Ramsay MacDonald is the first Prime Minister of a Labour-led government in Great Britain.

> The US Congress limits immigration from south-east Europe and Asia, and prohibits immigrants from Japan.

> Greece becomes a republic. King George II goes into exile in Romania.

The history of television started with the search for a technology that would enable the development of new devices that would be capable of transmitting at least ten pictures per second. This is the very minimum that is needed for persistence of vision to create an impression of movement, and it was extremely difficult to achieve. The first "photo-telegraphy" took place between Munich and Nuremberg in 1904 but it took 45 minutes to send just one picture.

The electronic transmission of moving pictures required that a scene should be scanned point by point several times per second. Then the luminosity that had been converted into electronic signals could be transmitted. At the other end, a receiver was required to convert the electronic signals back into optical signals with sufficient speed and to arrange them back again into a overall picture. In 1884 the German engineer Paul Gottlieb Nipkow built a mechanical apparatus that enabled pictures to be decomposed and reconstructed. The fundamental principle was a rotating disk, the Nipkow disk, with holes arranged in a spiral through which light could penetrate. The electronic reproduction of images was made possible by the Braun tube, developed by the physicist Karl Ferdinand Braun in 1897. Television sets and CRT computer monitors work on the same principle today. An electron beam inside the tube is guided by electromagnetic fields and produces a luminous point where it hits a fluorescent screen. In a modern television set the electron beam creates about 13 million points per second on the luminous layer of the screen, corresponding to 25 or 30 complete pictures per second.

In 1906 Max Dieckmann used the Braun tube for the first time as a photo-telegraph and succeeded in transmitting shadow photographs with a definition of 20 lines. The Hungarian scientist Dénes von Mihály improved the low performance of the apparatus by building a vacuum tube amplifier. In 1919 Mihály transmitted moving shadow-photographs over a distance of 3 miles (5 km).

The first television transmission tube was the iconoscope invented in 1924 by the Russian American physicist Vladimir Cosma Zworykin. It consisted of a signal plate on which the image was focused, scanned by an electron gun. At first the production of acceptable pictures was only possible in extremely good light conditions that could only be produced in a studio. Nevertheless, the iconoscope was a pioneering invention in the development of television because it operated completely electronically. The apparatus was presented for the first time in 1928 at the Berlin radio and television exhibition.

The first experimental television broadcasting by the British Broadcasting Corporation took place in 1929, using the Baird electro-mechanical system. This had a small screen that only measured a few square inches and a strongly flickering picture. The Radio Corporation of America demonstrated an all-electronic system in 1932.

The Scotsman John Logie Baird developed the television transmission technique invented by Zworykin.

Rockets: traveling to the stars

Robert Hutchins Goddard (1882-1945), Wernher von Braun (1912-77)

It sounds incredible: simple firework rockets were the forerunners of modern space rockets. The work of the scientists Robert Hutchins Goddard and Wernher von Braun in this area made a fundamental contribution to space travel and flights to distant planets so that in the 20th century many dreams were fulfilled. But unfortunately this also meant that modern military commanders had a new "wonder weapon" at their disposal.

A rocket consists of an impulse system and a thrust nozzle, which discharges an accelerated stream of gas. Thus the rocket experiences a recoil that drives it forwards. The control system guides the rocket in the direction required. Until the experiments of Oberth and later the American physicist Robert Hutchins Goddard, rockets normally used a solid fuel propellant. The solid fuel was inserted into the combustion chamber as a block or poured in directly. Goddard tackled the problems of fuel development while achieving the maximum impulse. By 1909 he had made plans for a liquid fuel rocket, using liquid oxygen and hydrogen to generate maximum recoil. These liquid materials had two advantages compared to solid fuel: the thrust was easier to control for steering, and the impulse was even throughout the flight. So, liquid fuel rockets could more easily maintain their trajectories and speed in space.

On March 16, 1926 he ignited his first liquid fuel rocket the "Moon Man," causing the doubters to fall silent. In less than 2.5 seconds, the rocket, barely 10 ft tall, flew a distance of 181 ft. In 1929 Goddard started building a rocket that was fitted with a camera and measuring instruments. Further experiments followed, culminating in the rocket of several stages each with their own motors that ignited one after the other. Once burnt out, the empty stages were simply abandoned so that the missile became lighter.

The second pioneer in the area of the rocket technology was the physicist Wernher von Braun, a student of Hermann Oberth. Since his youth von Braun had dreamed of space exploration. In the early 1930s years, he worked on the development of liquid-fuelled rockets. As early as December 1934, two of von Braun's rocket models, (A1 and A2, known as "Max" and "Moritz") were fired to a height of 7,200 ft. At the start of World War II, the Nazi regime recognized the military benefit of the technology and in 1939 it gave von Braun the task of building a large rocket. At the Peenemünde rocket research center in 1942, the engineer designed a rocket 46 ft tall, the A4 or V2, *Vergeltungswaffe 2* ("revenge weapon 2"). This liquid-fuelled rocket with its 25 tons of thrust put all previous attempts in the shade. Traveling at 5.4 times the speed of sound, it reached an altitude of 56 miles. Immediately Adolf Hitler ordered the world's first production of attack rockets. In the final years of the war, the German army fired thousands of V2 rockets filled with explosive on England, Holland and Belgium. This action caused hundreds of thousands of civilian deaths, but it did not change the course of the war as the Nazis had hoped.

After the German surrender, von Braun and many of his team moved to the United States. There from 1960 he constructed the most powerful rocket yet built, the Saturn V. When this rocket landed on the moon in 1969 the dream of mankind was finally fulfilled.

Originally used exclusively for military purposes, rockets have been used for space travel since the 1950s.

> On October 25, stocks on the New York Stock Exchange fall through the floor in the crash of "Black Friday." In the aftermath, a world economic crisis begins.

> Thomas Mann receives the Nobel Prize for Literature.

> In Hollywood the first Oscar Awards take place.

> In New York, the *Museum of Modern Art* (MoMA) opens its doors.

Penicillin: a wonderful fungus

Alexander Fleming (1881-1955)

The most famous antibiotic of modern times was named after a fungus, *Penicillium notatum*. Penicillin was discovered by Alexander Fleming, and the discovery made it possible to treat and cure serious diseases such as tuberculosis, typhus, and diphtheria.

At the end of the 19th century bacteriology had found ways of preventing infections. But once a patient had become ill, physicians were helpless. It was therefore vital to find a substance that could kill bacteria directly and effectively – an "antibiotic" (from the Greek *anti* = against, *biotikos* = related to life). Louis Pasteur (1822–95) had already discovered that certain molds had this property, but all attempts to produce a medicine from such molds had failed, mainly for financial reasons.

In the early 20th century the British bacteriologist Alexander Fleming (1881–1955) made an interesting discovery by chance, one that was to contribute significantly to the development of antibiotics. Fleming was growing bacteria in a gelatin culture medium, and he dyed the bacteria to make it easier to see. He was concentrating on a particular group of bacteria, staphylococci. On one occasion he failed to cool the medium. A little later he noticed that the bacteria had died in parts and that a greenish mold had developed. On closer examination he noted that a transparent zone had developed round the mold colonies, an area in which all the bacteria had died. His conclusion was that the mold was a bactericide, killing the microorganisms. Before he could continue his research Fleming had to identify and isolate this mold. He named the bactericidal substance "penicillin" after the mold.

Fleming found that penicillin did not attack the white blood cells in the human body and it was therefore suitable for treating infections. It was only later that he discovered how the substance worked. Penicillin was particularly effective at killing staphylococci and streptococci, the pathogens of anthrax and diphtheria. Their cell walls consist of interlinked sugar molecules. The penicillin blocks this interlinking, thus preventing the formation of new cell walls during the propagation of this microorganism.

Since the mold cultures grow very slowly, it was difficult to produce large amounts of this new bactericide and Fleming only used it occasionally to treat superficial wound infections. At first other scientists took little notice of this exciting discovery, but in 1938 a team of British scientists resumed Fleming's research. The pathologist Howard Florey (1898–1968) and the chemist Ernst Boris Chain (1906–79) eventually succeeded in isolating the bactericidal acids in the mold. With the support of the Rockefeller Foundation and the US Ministry of Agriculture, Florey and Chain paved the way for the industrial production of penicillin. Purified, concentrated penicillin was first produced in 1944. Initially the antibiotic was only available to the American army but it became available to the public on prescription in 1945. In the same year Fleming, Chain, and Florey were awarded Nobel Prizes for Physiology and Medicine.

Penicillin was the first effective antibiotic and every doctor's first choice of bactericide. It is true that microorganisms can build up resistance against a particular antibiotic in the course of time, but this happens less quickly in the case of penicillin.

With the discovery of penicillin it became possible to cure diseases such as tuberculosis and diphtheria.

EEG: the brain reveals its secrets

Hans Berger (1873-1941)

Psychiatry is the youngest branch of medicine, so as late as the end of the 19th century most mental illnesses could neither be explained nor effectively treated. The discovery of electroencephalography (*enzephalon* is ancient Greek for "brain") solved this problem. By tracking the brain waves, psychiatrists or neurologists can recognize functional disturbances of the brain and prescribe a suitable therapy.

In the 18th century during the Age of Enlightenment, new ways of thinking freed the mentally ill from the stigma that had been associated with their condition until then. Scientists and doctors no longer believed that the cause of aberrant behavior lay in sin or possession by devils, but in a sickness of the mind. The sufferers, who had been kept in lunatic asylums or madhouses in inhumance conditions, were now treated in hospitals for the mentally ill. A new and optimistic way of thinking was reflected in the forms of therapy and the manner of dealing with the sickness.

This new impulse had its origin in England and spread rapidly from there. The Quaker William Tuke (1732–1822) founded a private sanatorium in New York in 1794, and gave it the significant name of "The Retreat." William Griesinger (1817–68), one of the first German psychiatrists, lobbied successfully for the non-violent treatment of the mentally ill. Doctors now became interested in the patient's brain processes. As they could not look inside the head of a patient, they deduced as much information as they could from the patient's behavior. They could now differentiate between sicknesses such as dementia, paranoia, manic-depressive psychosis, and epilepsy, recognizing the external symptoms.

It was not until the 20th century that scientists could see what was happening inside the brain without having to perform an operation. In 1929 the German psychiatrist Hans Berger discovered that constant electrical currents were present on the human scalp. He believed that these would allow deductions to be made regarding to activity in the brain. In order to measure them, Berger constructed a fearful-looking machine, the electroencephalograph. He attached moistened silver plates to various points on the skin of the head with rubber bands or glue to serve as the conducting electrodes, and connected these to the registering apparatus with a cable. He electronically amplified the voltage difference in between two electrodes to operate a nib that recorded it on paper as a curve.

Berger interpreted the changes in voltage revealed by this curve, the electroencephalogram or EEG, as signs of brain activity. The EEG of a healthy baby shows up as a calm line without great fluctuations, whereas the brain waves of a young adult make small, regular zigzags that become flatter with increasing age. Disturbances in the function of the brain, such as are caused by a tumor, show up as large, irregular curves.

Today there is particular interest in making an EEG during sleep, which enables the deeper reaches of the brain to be studied. As a result, researchers have been able to discover the immense importance of sleep for the human organism.

As well as making life easier for the mentally ill of his time, Hans Berger opened up the human brain as a fascinating field for research.

The invention of the electroencephalogram provided the first insights into how the brain functions.

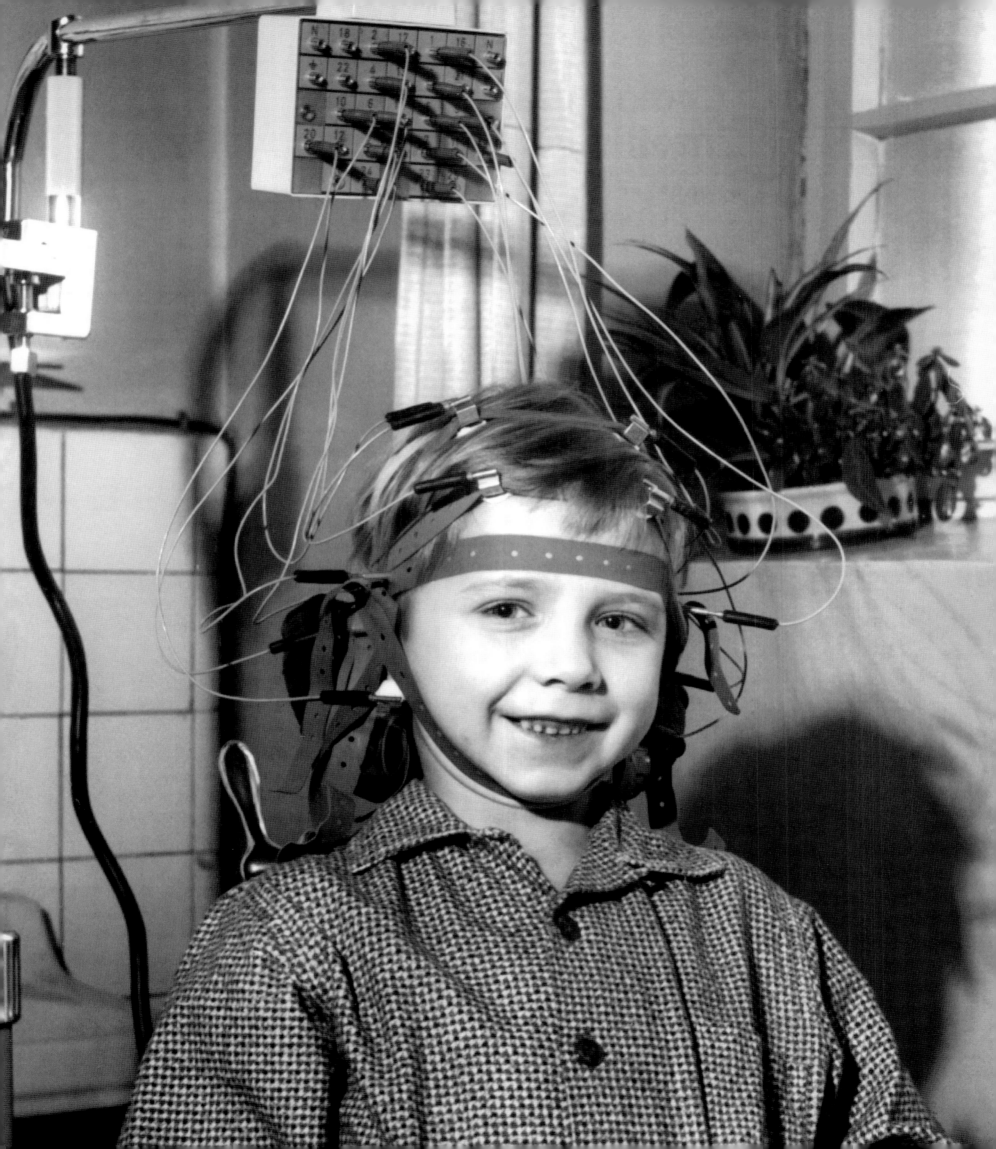

Computers: artificial intelligence becomes reality

Vannevar Bush (1890-1974)

> The German President Paul von Hindenburg dissolves Parliament after it rejects an emergency decree to deal with the financial crisis.

> American astronomers discover the ninth planet, which they name Pluto.

> In the Soviet Union, after the dispossession of the big farmers ("Kulaks"), a famine breaks out that claims millions of lives.

> Ho Chi Minh is the first Chairman of the newly founded Communist party in Vietnam, which is fighting for the end of French colonial power in Indochina.

Since the early 19th century there had been mechanical analog calculators that could calculate the tides, for instance. However, if the problems were too complex, the cogwheels, pinions, and levers were not flexible enough to solve them. In the 1920s therefore, technicians began to work on developing elements that could calculate electronically.

This was Vannevar Bush's main field of research at the Massachusetts Institute of Technology. Eraly on in his research Bush had developed electrical analog calculators capable of addition and subtraction. In 1927, components and wiring for multiplication and further electrical calculating elements were added. By 1930 Bush was ready to start up the electromechanical mainframe computer that was able to combine different operations and therefore to carry out complex calculations in fractions of a second. This was the first piece of computer "hardware." But a disadvantage of the analog computer was its limited precision. A digital computer, one that works with numbers on the principle of counting, was potentially much better suited to the task.

In 1833, the Englishman Charles Babbage (1792–1871) had used a simple form of program control in his Analytical Engine. His design for this device already included the components and basic structure of the modern computer (arithmetic and controlling units, internal memory, and input and output devices), but it was too costly to be produced. Much later, his countryman the mathematician Alan Turing (1912–54) was a pioneer in the development of the modern, stored-program digital computer.

During World War II, Turing was working on decoding the German signal codes. He helped to develop "Colossus" computer, so called because of its immense size; it was the first digital computer that worked with electronic vacuum tubes. With the help of these machines, the British succeeded in decoding the scrambled messages of the German Enigma cipher machine. As a person who liked unusual ideas, Turing was firmly convinced from the start that computers could copy human thought. In 1936 he developed the "Turing machine," a simple yet powerful conceptual computer that he called a "universal machine." It could, he announced, find the answer to any problem that could be solved mathematically or logically. The theoretical basis of his model was published in 1937 under the title *On Computable Numbers*. This theory was ground-breaking in the development of the modern computer. It led to the development of a mathematical universal language that was a prerequisite for the use of software – the programming of computers.

Independently of Bush and Turing, the German civil engineer Konrad Zuse (1910–95) also worked on an electrically programmable computer. In 1935, Zuse wanted to construct a "mechanical brain" to take over the tiresome, monotonous structural calculations that he had to deal with constantly. All the computers to date had used the decimal system, which was hard to transfer to electrical circuitry. Instead Zuse decided to use the binary system, devised by Leibnitz. The computer now worked solely with the numbers 0 and 1, which were translated into "power off" and "power on" respectively. All signals and instructions could be transmitted using the binary code and calculated using the Boolean algebra developed by George Boole (1815–64). Zuse had invented the method that has been used to program computers since 1948.

Having developed from analog to digital, computers have become much smaller with even greater performance.

Neutrons: at the heart of the matter

James Chadwick (1891-1974), Werner Heisenberg (1901-76)

The word atom is derived from the Greek *átomos* meaning "indivisible." In antiquity it was defined as the smallest indivisible particle that makes up the elementary components of the universe. The secrets of the atom were gradually unraveled during the 20th century, when the discovery of protons and neurons made it possible to get to the heart of the matter.

1932

IN THE YEAR 1932

> The Democrat Franklin D. Roosevelt wins the American presidential elections.

> The son of Charles Lindbergh, the American pioneer aviator, is kidnapped and murdered.

> With 37 percent, the National Socialist Party receives the majority of votes in the election for the German parliament, but cannot form a majority government.

> Aldous Huxley publishes his utopian novel *Brave New World*.

In the relatively young history of nuclear physics, which began towards the end of the 19th century, the year 1932 was undoubtedly a date of key importance. At that point scientists knew about the structure, which had been revealed in Rutherford's model of the atom produced in 1911, and the components of the atomic shell. But they were still in the dark so far as the atomic nucleus was concerned. The discovery of neutrons in 1932 completely changed the face of nuclear physics and marked the beginning of a new era.

Until then scientists only knew of two elementary particles: negatively charged electrons that rotated round the atomic nucleus, and positively charged protons. Rutherford had already discovered protons in hydrogen in 1914 after Niels Bohr had earlier successfully described the structure of the hydrogen atom. Hydrogen atoms are the smallest atoms because they only have one electron. If it is removed, a positively charged nucleus remains that is considerably smaller than the atom itself. In the course of his research Rutherford became convinced that he had discovered the smallest positively charged elementary particle, which he called the proton (from the Greek = "the first").

But what about the atoms of other elements that did not fit the formula, which stated that atomic nuclei had one proton? Physicists wrongly assumed that protons and electrons worked together. In 1920 Rutherford expressed the opinion that there must also be an electrically neutral particle besides the proton, but he was unable to prove the existence of such a "neutron." This was only achieved by his colleague James Chadwick (1891-1974), who discovered it during a series of experiments on radiation reactions in atoms.

Also in the same year the physicist Werner Heisenberg (1901–76) put forward his new theory of the atomic nucleus. He was the first to recognize that the atomic nucleus was made up of the neutron together with the proton, thus laying the foundation for subsequent research into nuclear physics. In particular, his proton-neutron model was able to provide precise information concerning the energy present in the atom. Further research also soon revealed under what circumstances these forces could be released. The nuclear fission that resulted from these discoveries marked the beginning of the successful development of nuclear physics.

In his study of theoretical physics, Heisenberg concentrated his research mainly on the development of a unitary theory of matter. Since 1932 many important findings had been made about the nature of the atom but what was missing was the idea that showed how the world could be reduced to a common denominator. Today this "world formula" has still to be discovered.

Research into neutrons with a particle accelerator is a technically complex operation. The smaller the particles, the greater the energy that is needed.

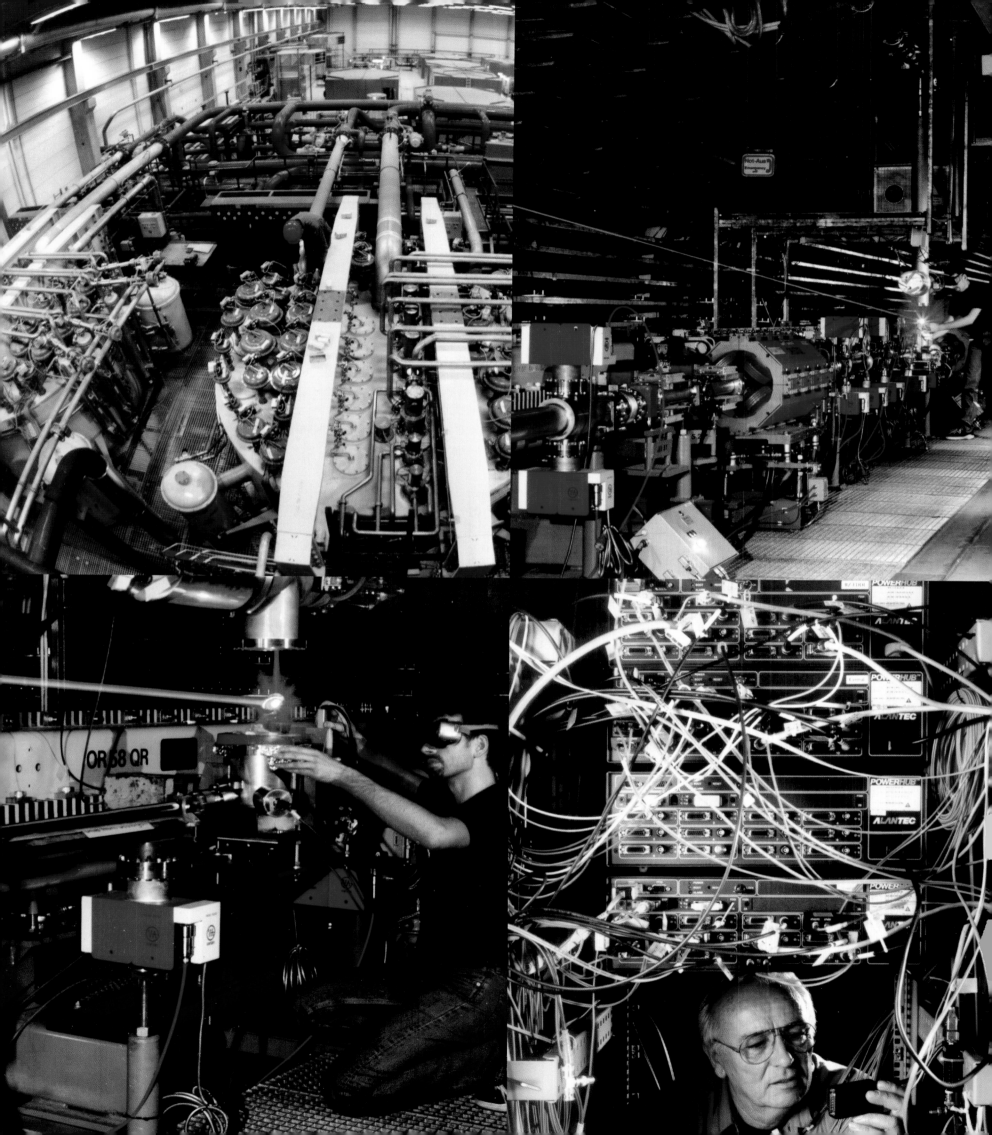

Animal behavior: lessons of survival

Konrad Lorenz (1903-1989)

Ethology is almost as closely associated with Konrad Lorenz as with his celebrated greylag geese. Lorenz's discovery of imprinting in animals marked the beginning of the science of ethology, the study of animal behavior by comparative methods.

1933

IN THE YEAR 1933

> Franklin D. Roosevelt's reform package, the *New Deal*, which is supposed to lead the country out of the economic crisis, comes into force.

> On February 1, the German President Paul von Hindenburg appoints Adolf Hitler as Chancellor. On March 23, with the Socialist Party the only opposition, Parliament passes the so-called *Enabling Act*. This Act allows the Government to enact laws without the consent of parliament. With the merging of the executive and legislative powers of the State, the Weimar Republic comes to an end.

> In the USA the eighteenth Constitutional Amendment establishing Prohibition is repealed.

△ When they leave the nest, birds such as geese will follow the first moving object they encounter after hatching and identify it as their mother.

The main basis of the newly-founded science of ethology in the 20th century was the observation of animal behavior in relation to specific questions. Scientists wanted to acquire information about the particular life patterns of different species. Investigations were based on the assumption that each element of behavior is based on two essential principles: conservation of the species, and rivalry within the species, or survival of the fittest. This thesis had already emerged from the theory of evolution in the 19th century. The ethological behavior patterns observed also provided the proof for the theory of evolution of Charles Darwin (1809–82).

However, observation preceded the discovery of ethology. The founder of ethology in the 20th century was Konrad Lorenz. Between 1933 and 1938, he studied the greylag goose at Altenburg in Austria and discovered the first relevant insights regarding animal behavior. Lorenz accompanied the geese throughout their life from their first day. In this way he discovered that shortly after leaving the nest they associated with the first moving object they encountered. In nature, this would normally be the mother-bird. He found that when the parents were intentionally kept away from the nest and replaced by another animal, a human being or even a moving object, the chicks would follow this "artificial parent."

Lorenz named this fixation on the animal's parent "imprinting." From his experiments with false imprinting, creating an artificial parent, Lorenz came to a remarkable conclusion: that nature had "automated" the behavior of the young birds to ensure the conservation of the species. Even before they had had any experiences of their own, the chicks followed the behavior that would ensure their survival, a behavior that was triggered in them by particular stimuli. According to Lorenz, imprinting was therefore a behavior innate in animals. Ethology calls this type of behavior "instinctive," in contrast with "learned" behavior.

The observations of Konrad Lorenz resulted in many more ethological findings, and his cooperation with the Dutch-British zoologist Nikolaas Tinbergen (1907–1988) proved to be particularly fruitful. Working together, the two men examined instinctive behavior mechanisms as well as the key stimuli that caused them. The *Kindchenschema* or "small children pattern" of appealing features is one of these mechanisms. Certain key stimuli such as a rounded body-form, a high forehead, large eyes, and a clumsy walk provoke protective reactions in the parent, so that, like animals, people have a "maternal instinct."

In 1973, Konrad Lorenz, Nikolaas Tinbergen and Karl von Frisch (1886–1982) received the Nobel Prize for Medicine for their outstanding achievements in the field of ethology. The explanation of animal behavior as an unconsciously displayed expression of survival strategies has also cast a new light on human behavior, so Konrad Lorenz's findings have also proved important in human ethology and psychology.

Konrad Lorenz with his greylag geese was the "father" of the study of animal behavior in the 20th century.

LSD: from psychotropic to hippy drug

Albert Hofmann (b. 1906)

IN THE YEAR 1938

> In Turkey, the President and founder of the State Kemel Ataturk dies.

> The *Queen Elizabeth,* the largest ship in the world, is launched.

> With the discovery of a more viscous ink, the ballpoint pen comes into use.

> Jews in Germany must register all their property, thus making it vulnerable to confiscation by the state.

The drug known as LSD (lysergic acid diethylamide) was originally a component of the poisonous fungus, ergot. Its stimulating effect on muscles and blood vessels has been known to medicine since antiquity. In 1938, the chemist Albert Hoffmann experienced its hallucinogenic side effects while carrying out experiments on himself.

Ergot is a parasitic fungus that is found particularly in rye plants. It grows in the ears of corn in place of the grain. Ergot contains alkaloids (poisonous nitrogenous compounds), tyramine histamine, and cholin. Because it stimulates the muscles of the womb, doctors in ancient times used it during childbirth and also for abortion. In addition, after ingestion, the fungus tightens the peripheral blood vessels and therefore raises the blood pressure. However, even in small doses, ergot is poisonous.

In the mid-1930s the chemist Albert Hoffmann was working for the Sandoz company in Basel, Switzerland, where he was experimenting with one of the substances found in ergot, lysergic acid. While searching for a medicine to stimulate the circulatory and breathing system, he manufactured lysergic acid diethylamide (LSD 25) for the first time. On April 19, 1943, he discovered the effect of the new substance on the psyche by conducting an experiment on himself. Hoffmann reported experiencing dizziness and anxiety, but also fantastic, colorful images that he could see with his eyes closed, and a feeling of great euphoria.

It was Dr Arthur Stoll (1887–1971) who carried out a systematic examination of LSD and its effects on humans in the psychiatric clinic of the University of Zurich. He was the first to write a protocol of an experiment on himself describing all the effects from euphoria to depression that consumers of LSD would later report. Hoffman's firm Sandoz put LSD on the market under the name "Delysid," and noted on the leaflet "For mental relaxation during analytical psychotherapy, particularly in the case of anxiety and obsessional neurosis."

Towards the end of the 1950s LSD developed from a medicine into a recreational drug for mass consumption, reaching the height of its popularity between 1964 and 1966. Enthusiastic hippies extolled the wonderful properties of the drug, but this could not disguise the growing number of mental breakdowns and suicides that were due to the drug's influence. In 1966, Sandoz felt obliged to remove the "medicine" from the market.

LSD is still controversial. Whether or not it can really help in psychotherapy has never been conclusively proved, and its use for medical purposes requires strict supervision at all times. The drug inspired the ethnologist Carlos Castaneda (b. 1931) to write a fulminating criticism of society, and Timothy Leary (b. 1920), the former assistant professor of psychology at Harvard University and later "drug crusader," also promoted the consciousness-expanding properties of the drug. But the side-effects of LSD consumption are not to be underestimated. They include changes in the thought processes and in the structure of the personality, which in the long term can lead to schizophrenic psychosis. In the 1980s and 1990s, cocaine and ecstasy displaced LSD and pushed it to the bottom of the drugs popularity list. However, the social problems caused by LSD are still extant today.

A model of the molecular structure of LSD. The side effects of the drug should not be underestimated.

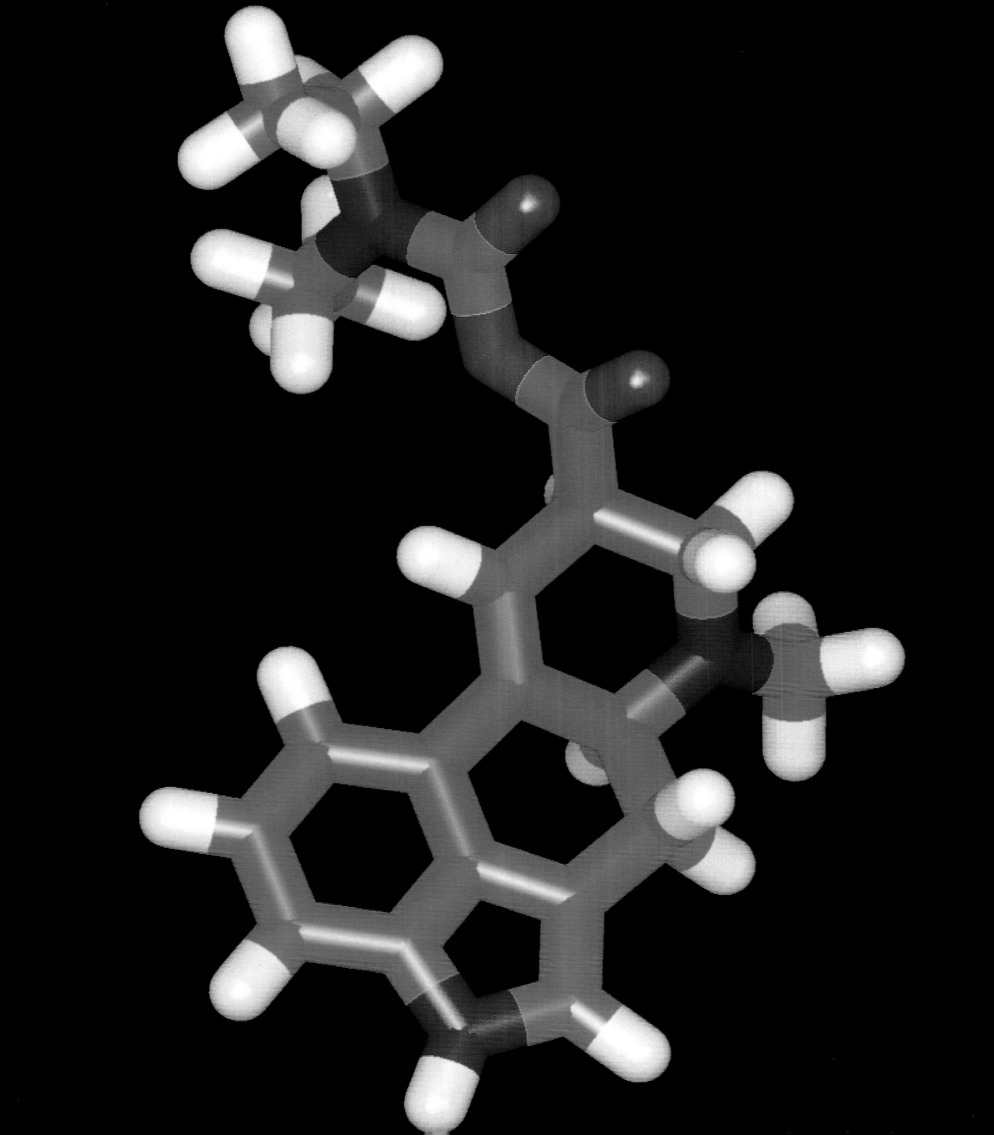

Nuclear fission: the indivisible becomes divisible

Otto Hahn (1879-1968), Friedrich Strassmann (1902-80)

Since ancient times, the atom has been regarded as the smallest indivisible unit of matter. When Otto Hahn and Friedrich Strassmann bombarded uranium with neutrons in 1938 they were actually just trying to produce transuranic elements. What they actually did was to trigger the splitting of the atom. This knowledge changed the world as well as nuclear physics.

1938

IN THE YEAR 1938

> After Austria's occupation by the German army, Adolf Hitler announces the annexation of Austria by Germany.

> In the Munich Agreement, Italy, France, and Great Britain give their consent to the German annexation of German Sudetenland in Czechoslovakia.

> In what is known as the "Crystal Night," units of Storm Troopers destroy Jewish businesses, synagogues, and houses. 91 people are killed and 26,000 are taken into custody and sent to concentration camps.

In 1934, the Italian physicist Enrico Fermi had bombarded uranium with neutrons and produced completely new elements. These "transuranic" elements were heavier than uranium, so Fermi assumed that the nuclei had absorbed neutrons. The chemist Otto Hahn, director of the Kaiser Wilhelm Institute for Chemistry in Berlin, continued the research work started by Enrico Fermi, together with the Viennese professor of physics Lise Meitner (1878–1968) and the chemist Friedrich Strassmann. In order to produce and isolate transuranic elements they also irradiated uranium with neutrons.

In 1938, while examining a specimen of irradiated uranium, Hahn and Strassmann (Lise Meitner had emigrated to Sweden in the meantime) found the elements barium and krypton instead of transuranium. Both of these elements, however, are lighter than uranium, not heavier. The only possible explanation they could find for this was that the uranium nuclei had split into smaller, lighter elements. Calculations of the energies used for the experiment confirmed this suspicion. The natural splitting of atoms – the decay of radioactive elements – had been known for a long time, but the results of Hahn and Strassmann's experiments proved that this reaction could also be caused artificially. The theoretical basis for this phenomenon was supplied by Lise Meitner and her nephew Otto Robert Frisch.

According to Meitner, the uranium nuclei starts to vibrate when irradiated by neutrons and changes its form to become elongated. Because of this, the repelling power of both poles of the nuclei is stronger than the forces that have so far held the nuclei together. Therefore, when fission takes place, not only are two lighter elements released, but also countless neutrons and what until then was thought of as an unbelievable amount of energy. Meitner explained her theory of the chain reaction during fission as follows. When the uranium nuclei is split, 2.5 neutrons on average are released. If these meet other nuclei, they split these too. For this reaction to become self-sustaining a "critical mass" has to be reached and then exceeded. There must be sufficient uranium available, or else too many neutrons will spin off unused so that the reaction slows down and stops.

In 1942, Enrico Fermi, who had in the meantime emigrated to the USA, produced the first controlled, self-sustaining chain reaction and proved Meitner's theory. In 1945, while the German atom bomb project was still in its infancy, the USA dropped two atom bombs on the Japanese cities Hiroshima and Nagasaki. Horrified by the terrible misuse of his discovery, Otto Hahn protested not only against the military use of atomic energy but against any escalation of armaments. However, the peaceful use of nuclear energy by controlling the chain reaction in piles, or reactors, has also proved very controversial because of the risks and the difficulty of safely disposing the waste.

The international symbol for radioactivity. It give warns of the risk of invisible radioactive radiation.

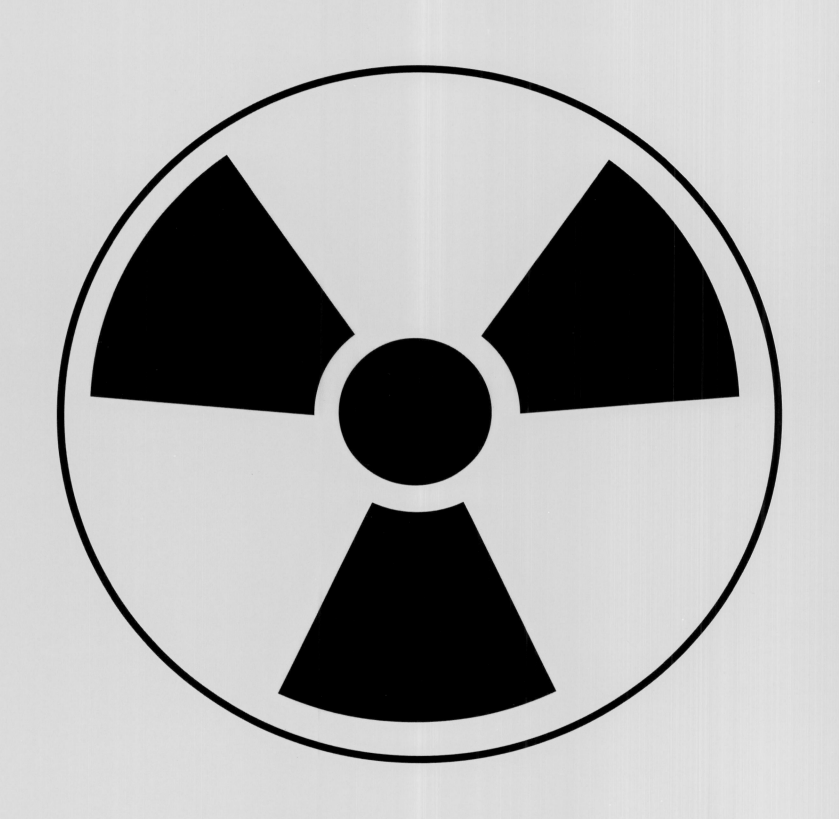

Jet aircraft: faster without a propeller

Sir Frank Whittle (1907-87)

In the 1930s a pioneering engineering achievement took place: the invention of the jet engine. It was the development of this new type of engine that turned the airplane into a means of fast mass transport.

1941

IN THE YEAR 1941

> Lieutenant-General Erwin Rommel becomes the Commander-in-Chief of the German troops in North Africa.

> Without declaring war, Germany attacks Russia. *Operation Barbarossa* has been planned since December of the previous year.

> The US President Franklin D. Roosevelt and the British Prime Minister Winston Churchill sign the Atlantic Treaty, which lays out their mutual policies for after the end of the war.

> Jews in Germany must now wear the Star of David. This is the start of the systematic genocide of the Jews.

> Without declaration of war, the Japanese air force attacks the military base at Pearl Harbor on the Hawaiian island of Oahu. The American Pacific fleet is temporarily put out of action by the attack. The next day the United States declares war on Japan.

The first planes were propeller aircraft with piston engines. But even before World War II, it was obvious that these engines had two serious disadvantages. They worked on the principle of an interrupted combustion process, and the movement of pistons and connecting rods was reciprocating rather than rotary. This created substantial out-of-balance forces, and it also meant that piston engines wore out very quickly at high speeds. Moreover, propeller planes only had a top speed of 500 mph. At such speeds the tips of the propeller blades were already moving at supersonic speed. At the same time the efficiency of the engine decreased rapidly with increasing speed, resulting in very high fuel consumption. Propeller aircraft were therefore only suitable for low-speed travel. Because of the wear and tear, relatively low speed, and high fuel consumption of propeller-driven engines, aviation experts began to look for alternatives.

Sir Frank Whittle (1907–87), an officer in the British Royal Air Force, was working on a completely new concept. At the beginning of the 1930s he developed the jet engine. This engine worked on the kickback or reaction principle. As the compressor vanes pushed the air out of the back of the engine, the plane moved forward. The concept of the jet engine has remained more or less unchanged to the present day. A multi-stage compressor sucks in air and forces it into the combustion chamber at high pressure. There the fuel is injected and ignited. In the extreme heat the air expands strongly and pushes through the next turbine at high speed into the open. The reaction of the outside air to the jet's thrust generates the forward movement of the engine. At the same time, the escaping air activates the blades of the turbines

that drive the compressor, which sucks in new air again. The decisive advantage of the jet engine compared to the traditional propeller engine lies in its steady fuel consumption. A further benefit is the load on its mechanical parts is continuous rather than intermittent. The rotating parts result in a higher performance with less noise and less wear and tear.

Whittle patented his revolutionary invention in 1930. By 1937 he had developed and built the first engine, which was tested on the ground. Britain thus became the first country in the world to have a jet engine. However, the first flight of a jet airplane took place in Germany where, completely independently of Whittle, Hans von Ohain had also developed a jet engine. In 1936 Ohain joined the aircraft manufacturer Ernst Heinkel and the first jet airplane in the world, the Heinkel He 178, was ready by 1939. This single-engine jet made its maiden flight in the same year, easily achieving speeds of 430 mph. The first flight of the British jet took place two years later.

In the post-war years civil aviation also benefited from the progress made in engine construction. The De Havilland Comet made its maiden flight in 1949 and became the first commercial jet airplane in the world in 1958, quickly followed by the Boeing 707. Since then jet engines and jet airplanes are constantly being improved. Today some 7,000 jet airplanes fly about one billion passengers round the earth each year. The invention of the jet airplane gave the world the mobility it enjoys today.

The jet engine worked on the principle of reaction. As the engine pushes the air backwards, the plane moves forward.

Nuclear power: unsuspected reserves of energy

Enrico Fermi (1901-54)

It was the chemist Otto Hahn who discovered how to split the atom. Then the physicist Enrico Fermi helped the Americans to build the atom bomb. His experiments, however, also proved the possibility of using the splitting of the atom for peaceful purposes, for obtaining energy.

1942

IN THE YEAR 1942

> The inhabitants of the Warsaw Ghetto are deported to the extermination camp of Treblinka.

> In Stalingrad, the German Sixth Army is surrounded by troops from the Soviet Union.

> At the Wann Lake Conference, representatives of the SS and the State discuss the final solution of the European "Jewish question."

> British troops under General Bernard Montgomery capture El-Alamein in North Africa.

△ The peaceful use of nuclear energy still involves some uncontrollable dangers even with the best safety precautions.

Before Otto Hahn, Enrico Fermi had split difficult atoms by bombarding them with neutrons and in doing so had artificially produced a series of radioactive substances from 1934 onwards. For this work he was awarded the Nobel Prize for Physics. When the Fascists took over in Italy, Fermi emigrated to the United States. Here the US government was noting the atom-splitting experiments of German chemists with growing concern. When even Albert Einstein warned of the German "uranium club," the American government initiated the Manhattan Project in 1942, whose task it was to build the first atom bomb.

Fermi was able to solve one of the biggest problems right at the start, the setting up of the chain reaction. It was only this avalanche-like increase in the number of split uranium nuclei that made an atom bomb possible. On December 2, 1942, on a sports field at the University of Chicago, Fermi succeeded in setting up a controlled, self-sustaining nuclear chain reaction. When splitting the atom (Fermi used the isotope uranium-235) an atomic nucleus with a large number of nucleons is split into two (usually radioactive) atomic nuclei with an average number of nucleons. This process releases energy and also superfluous neutrons that stimulate further reactions, thus setting up the chain reaction.

At this point the development of peaceful uses of nuclear power became separated from the military experiments. American scientists continued to work on the atom bomb, the first of which was dropped on Hiroshima in 1945. Parallel to this, Fermi was experimenting in another direction. He was controlling the chain reaction with cadmium rods. Cadmium soaks up excess neutrons and thus controls the reaction. Fermi's reactor was therefore a controllable atomic power station, but it did not produce more that 1 watt of power.

In 1951 the experimental reactor EBR 1 in Idaho produced electricity by nuclear fission for the first time. This was done (as it still is today) in the same way as it is in a "normal" thermal power station. A cooling agent is heated by the release of nuclear energy, and it then drives one or more turbines through a heat exchanger. These turbines drive dynamos creating electricity. However, the reactor does not only produce heat, it also creates radioactivity. Using nuclear power for energy, therefore, produces radioactivity as an undesirable by-product. In order to protect the environment, extensive, costly construction and security measures have to be taken.

There are other problems connected with the isotopes that can be split, such as plutonium or uranium. Plutonium, for instance, is extremely toxic and its half-life, that is, the time it takes for the number of its radioactive atoms to be reduced by half, is 24,000 years. The disposal and storage of radioactive nuclear waste is, therefore, the real (and very expensive) problem of the theoretically ecological, resource-saving nuclear energy. As a solution is not yet in sight, more and more nations are turning away from nuclear energy and placing their hopes in alternative methods such as solar, wind or water based energy.

Electricity is made from nuclear power in the same way as it is generated in a "normal" thermal power station.

Antibiotics: a victory against micro-organisms

Selman Abraham Waksman (1888-1973)

An antibiotic (from the Greek *anti* = against, *biotikos* = relating to life) is a metabolic product derived from bacteria, fungi, algae, lichen or higher orders of plants. It kills bacteria or obstructs their cell division. Before the discovery of this "wonder weapon," many more people died of bacterial infections than in wars.

By the mid-20th century vaccines against many different bacterial illnesses were available, but the problem of how to treat infected patients still remained. To combat bacteria, the "silent carriers" of diseases, effectively, scientists had to learn more about these micro-organisms. In 1872 the botanist Ferdinand Julius Cohn (1828–98) published a treatise in which he classified them systematically. Cohn also promoted further research by supporting the young physician Robert Koch (1843–1910). Koch was the first to breed anthrax bacilli successfully for use in laboratory experiments. In 1882 Koch discovered the tubercle bacillus (Koch bacillus).

But the scientist who actually discovered antibiotics was Alexander Fleming. In 1928 Fleming accidentally discovered that the mold *Penicillium notatum* destroyed bacterial cultures. Further research showed that certain strains of bacteria died when they came into contact with the mold. "Penicillin" inhibits the formation of the bacterial cell walls and it proved extremely beneficial at a time when cholera and gangrene were usually fatal to those infected. In the 1940s Howard Florey (1898–1968) and Ernst Boris Chain (1906–79) succeeded in producing pure penicillin, which became available in large quantities from 1945 onwards.

Although penicillin solved many problems it was not effective against tuberculosis. Other antibiotics such as tyrothricin, developed in 1939 from ray fungi, were too poisonous to be administered to the patient over a long period. There were other substances derived from ray fungi (Streptomycetes) that proved considerably better for use in medicine, including the treatment of tuberculosis.

The microbiologist Selman Abraham Waksman worked on this problem. Born in the Ukraine, Waksman had emigrated to the United States in 1910 since as a Jew he was not allowed to study in his home country. He studied microbiology and biochemistry at Rutgers University and at Berkeley, California. He then worked at the institute for soil microbiology and bacteriology at Rutgers University. His research concentrated on bacteria living in the soil, actinomycetes. Together with his assistant Albert Schatz, in 1944 Waksman succeeded in isolating the antibiotic streptomycin from these fungus-like bacteria that are involved in the process of composting the soil.

The scientists had found the first effective method for the treatment of tuberculosis, the most widespread infectious disease in the world. Ten years later, tuberculosis hardly existed any longer in the United States. In 1952 Waksman was awarded the Nobel Prize for Medicine for his discovery.

It is true that the therapeutic range of streptomycin is smaller than that of penicillin and it can cause poisoning if dosed incorrectly. But because streptomycin succeeded in practically eradicating the endemic presence of tuberculosis in industrial countries, it is a milestone in the history of medicine.

The development and industrial production of antibiotics, a milestone in the history of medicine.

Space travel: The discovery of new worlds

It was the development of powerful rockets as a transport system that made the exploration of space possible.

With the ability to leave the earth's atmosphere in a rocket, mankind's dream of reaching for the stars has come closer to realization. But what are people looking for so far away from the blue planet earth? The main incentives are to discover the origin of the earth, and whether there is life in the universe.

Space travel is still a young discipline, in spite of the fact that rockets have existed for hundreds of years. The firework rockets of early Chinese civilization were naturally very primitive. Nevertheless these early devices laid the foundation for modern rocket technology: the successor of the iron container filled with gunpowder weighing 11 lb with a range of about 1,000 yards contributed to the development of modern space travel.

By the 18th and 19th centuries the construction of these simple military rockets had not changed very much. The Russian mathematician and physicist Konstantin Ziolkowski was the first to draw up plans for a space vehicle. In 1883 he made the important discovery that rockets could also work in a vacuum, because their power was based on recoil. This meant that a rocket could operate without an atmosphere. In the 1920s Ziolkowski published a treatise in which he described the technical requirements for space in a very concrete manner. His theoretical treatise unleashed rocket fever throughout the world and experimental groups and space travel clubs sprang up everywhere. A little later, in 1926, the American Robert Goddard launched the first liquid fuel rocket in the world. Admittedly it did not fly far or for long, but it fired the imagination of technical experts everywhere.

The space race

Actual space travel only became possible with the military and technical advances of the mid-20th century. Inspired by the long-range carrier rockets that had been developed for delivering atomic weapons, the Soviet Union and the United States worked feverishly to produce a rocket with sufficient thrust to send a satellite or space capsule into space.

The USSR wins the first round

The Soviet Union won the race, causing great anxiety in America when they put the first satellite "Sputnik 1" into space orbit round the earth on October 4, 1957. This historic event marked the beginning of the space age. As a result the Americans poured enormous sums of money into their space travel program because, as a superpower the country wsa determined not to be left lagging behind in the field of military development. Barely six months later, on January 31, 1958, NASA launched the first American satellite into space.

America triumphs

But it was not long before the Soviet Union put further pressure on the Americans with a particularly brilliant technical performance. On April 12, 1961 the cosmonaut Yuri Gagarin set out on the first manned space flight. It was almost a year before the first American, John Glenn, circled the earth in a space capsule. For a time the United States found it difficult to get over these defeats, but on July 20,

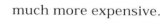

In the future large space stations orbiting close to the earth could provide a starting point for longer journeys into space.

1967, they succeeded in redressing the balance. On that day the US astronauts Neil Armstrong and Edwin Aldrin were the first people to land on the moon. This breathtaking event was watched on television by millions of people throughout the world. This "giant leap for mankind" gave manned space travel an enormous boost in the 1970s and 1980s. In 1981 the USA first sent the "Columbia" space shuttle into space. The Soviet Union kept the MIR space station continuously manned between 1986 and 2001.

Nowhere too far?

But in spite of these successes scientists have only explored a small section of the universe. The rockets that made flight into space possible were indeed a spectacular achievement. But at the same time, their range was very limited in comparison with the infinity of the universe. Because of the inconceivably vast distances of space, astronauts have only been able to concentrate on the part of space immediately surrounding the

earth, while satellites and unmanned space have been launched to reconnoiter the rest of the solar system. The infinitely large number of star systems remains outside the reach of man at present. With the technology available today, the journey to the nearest fixed star would take about 100,000 years.

The human body also limits the possibilities of manned space travel because the conditions in space are extreme in every respect. Weightlessness alone causes considerable strain to the body; for instance, astronauts "grow" from 1½ to 2½ in because of the reduced strain on their intervertebral discs. They also suffer from circulatory problems as well as muscle and bone wastage. During longer stays in space astronauts may also suffer from a permanent decrease in blood volume and red blood cells. This is one resaon why the space craft launched into space are mostly unmanned, and only 5 percent of all missions are manned. The other reason is that manned missions are

much more expensive.

Expensive but rewarding

Some of the immediate benefits of these extremely expensive flights into space have been found in weather and communications satellites, climatology research, and medical engineering. A large number of other disciplines have also benefited from space technology: air travel, computer sciences, electronics, medicine, telecommunications, energy, chemistry, robot technology, and automation technology have all profited from spin-offs of the space program.

But can the individual experience the universe? The American millionaire Dennis Tito went down in the history of space travel as the first space tourist in spring 2001. He traveled through space in a Russian Soyuz rocket. This pleasure cost the adventurous American about $20 million dollars, so for ordinary mortals-space travel remains the subject of dreams.

Mankind's age-old desire to travel towards the stars has been partly fulfilled in the last few decades. The journey to new worlds has begun but the ultimate destination is still far away. There are many financial and technical hurdles to be overcome before it is achieved.

"That's one small step for a man, one giant leap for mankind." The first man on the moon.

333

The atom bomb: the end of the age of innocence

Manhattan Project, Los Alamos USA (1942-45)

Discovering how to split the atom was a milestone in nuclear physics. Sadly, this scientific achievement was first used in war. In August of 1945, the first two atom bombs were dropped on the Japanese cities of Hiroshima and Nagasaki. Never before had a military power possessed a weapon with such terrible effect.

1945

IN THE YEAR 1945

> Adolf Hitler commits suicide on 30 April in his bunker under the chancellery building in Berlin. On 7 May the senior General Alfred Jodl signs Germany's unconditional surrender.

> Representatives from 51 nations meet in San Francisco to establish the United Nations, designed to maintain world peace.

> American president Franklin D. Roosevelt dies at the age of 63. His vice president Harry S. Truman follows him into office.

> After the dropping of the atom bomb on the Japanese cities Hiroshima and Nagasaki, Japan declares its unconditional surrender. World War II is officially over.

In 1938, the German chemists Otto Hahn (1879–1968) and Friedrich Strassmann (1902–80) split a uranium atom for the first time by bombarding it with neutrons. From 1939 onwards, scientists fleeing from the Nazi regime to the USA repeatedly warned the American president Franklin D. Roosevelt (1882–1945) that the Germans were capable of building a nuclear bomb, and of using it. In 1942, to prevent this danger, one of the largest secret scientific projects in history was called into being, the "Manhattan Engineer District," also known as the "Manhattan Project." About 150,000 people worked on the project, but only 100 top international scientists under the leadership of the physicist Julius Robert Oppenheimer (1904–67) knew what the true goal was – to build the first nuclear bomb.

The "recipe" for an atom bomb had been known since 1941. About 50 lb of fissionable uranium-235, the critical mass that is necessary to set up the chain reaction, is bombarded with neutrons. A single neutron splits the first atom and releases two or three other neutrons. These split further atoms and within fractions of a second, the number of atoms being split is growing increasingly rapidly. The chain reaction has begun. In a single gram of uranium-235 there are 23,000 kilowatt hours of useable energy. In practice, the critical mass is created by bringing two "uncritical" masses together in the atom bomb by exploding them conventionally. The task of the researchers in the Manhattan Project was to prevent an early explosion of the bomb after ignition in order to give the chain reaction time to build up completely, otherwise the fissionable material would merely scatter and the atom bomb evaporate without effect.

After Germany's surrender, the researchers took a decisive step. The first nuclear explosive device was detonated in the desert of New Mexico, USA, on July 16, 1945. It was named "Trinity." The violence of the explosion far exceeded the expectations of the participating scientists. In August 1945, in order to force the Japanese to capitulate, the USA dropped two atom bombs on the Japanese cities of Hiroshima and Nagasaki. Hundreds of thousands of civilians died, either immediately or during the following years as a result of the effects of the radiation. Horrified by these events, many of the participating scientists would have nothing more to do with the Manhattan Project.

However, they were not able to stop further developments. The dropping of the first atom bombs started an escalating worldwide nuclear arms race. At the beginning of the 21st century, at least 12 nations have the means to take part in a nuclear war. With the end of the Cold War, the acute threat from nuclear weapons has been minimized, but the danger is not past. Time after time, hostile nuclear powers such as India and Pakistan make the world apprehensive with their declarations of war.

The military use of nuclear power was at the forefront of scientific research carried out in the United States during the 1940s.

Photosynthesis: how plants live

Melvin Calvin (1911-97)

> In Nuremberg, trials against the leading war criminals are approaching their end. Twelve of the accused are condemned to death, seven are given prison sentences and three are acquitted.

> Heathrow, which would become the largest airport in the world, is opened in London.

> In a speech at the University of Zurich, Winston Churchill calls for the founding of a "United States of Europe."

> Great Britain and the USA merge their occupied territories in Germany.

In the mid-20th century it was possible to build jet aircraft, send pictures round the world electronically, and identify the materials of which far-distant stars were made. But the precise working of the process by which plants such as even the modest daisy feed themselves was still unknown.

Every plant uses carbon dioxide and produces oxygen; this process is measurable. But why is it necessary and how does it occur? The United States biologist Melvin Calvin had an ingenious yet simple idea that would answer these questions. He prepared carbon dioxide with a radioactive marker and followed its progress through the plant's organism. This enabled him to follow the fundamental processes of photosynthesis.

This photochemical process takes place in two stages. As a reaction to the light, the chlorophyll pigment in the chloroplasts – tiny green pellets in the plant tissue – absorb the sunlight. The absorption leads to a photolytic division of water with the release of oxygen and ATP (adenosine triphosphate) as well as the formation of reduced nicotinamide adenine dinucleotide phosphate (NADPH). The dark reaction transforms the previously produced carbon dioxide through enzyme reactions into pentose (single sugar in glucose) using energy supplied by the breakdown of NADPH and ATP.

This process is called the Calvin cycle after the scientist who discovered it. Each separate cycle uses up one carbon dioxide molecule, two NADPH molecules, and three ATP molecules. Three cycles produce a glyceraldehyde 3-phosphate. In turn, two of these molecules provide the starting material for the synthesis of both hexose and glucose. These produce the two most important forms of sugar for transport and storage: saccharose

and starch. At the end of these processes, nutrients and oxygen are produced that are used by humans and animals, while the carbon dioxide is broken down.

American and Japanese scientists believed that the first living organisms to carry out photosynthesis were found in purple bacteria, this making possible the development of a more advanced form of life on earth. An artificially produced photosynthesis could transform vast amounts of solar energy into easily usable matter. This is the reason why many scientists are concentrating their research on the development of an artificial molecule as a substitute for chlorophyll, but so far they have not succeeded in this objective.

Calvin's discovery made people aware of the importance of green plants – especially the vast forest regions of the earth – in maintaining the earth's balance. Unfortunately, by the time people realized this, large areas of forests had already been cleared, and even now the approach to forest clearing has not changed sufficiently. The seriousness of the destruction of forests is clearly illustrated by the example of a single large broad-leaved tree. This absorbs about 350 cu ft of carbon dioxide on a sunny day and produces enough oxygen to meet the daily requirement of 10 people. From the carbon dioxide it has absorbed, it produces roughly 26 lb of carbohydrate.

△ The chlorophyll in plants absorbs the sunlight as they react to light.

The discovery of the mechanism of photosynthesis explained the metabolism of plants.

Cells:
the structure of life

Albert Claude (1899-1983)

It was the microscope that gave scientists the first insight into the cell, the smallest component of living creatures and plants. But it was to take another 400 years before the structure and processes of cells were fully understood.

1950

IN THE YEAR 1950

> In the USA, Albert Einstein warns scientists against building the hydrogen bomb that president Harry S. Truman has ordered.

> The German Federal Republic joins the Council of Europe.

> South Africa decides to create segregated settlements for the various ethnic groups.

> North Korea sends troops into South Korea, the start of the Korean War. The American president Truman threatens the communist-governed North Korea with the atom bomb.

Cells are the basic components of every living being. In spite of numerous differences in structure and function, the cells of all living things have many characteristics in common. Complex chemical processes that take place in all cells contribute to the metabolism and the production of energy. Nearly all cells have the ability to increase through division. As a result of their particular surface structure, they are in contact with their surroundings and able to pick up and respond to certain stimuli. All cells contain genetic inheritance information that is stored in deoxyribonucleic acid (DNA); this guides the cells and enables them to divide and pass on their genetic information.

The basic structure of cells can be observed through an electron microscope. A liquid cytoplasm that is surrounded by a plasma membrane contains a series of organelles. These include the endoplasmic reticulum, robosomes, the Golgi apparatus, lysosomes, centrioles,and mitochondria. The mitochondria form the "power station" of the cell, producing the energy necessary for all the metabolic processes by synthesis of the universal biological fuel, adenosintriphosphate (ATP). In the middle of the cell is the cell nucleus containing the DNA molecules that store all the genetic information. The carriers of the hereditary dispositions or "genes" are the chromosomes.

It was the English scientist Robert Hooke (1635–1703) who first coined the concept of the "cell" in 1667. When examining a slice of cork under the microscope he observed its pore-like structure, and he found similar pores in elder pith and other parts of plants. He called these pores "cells" (from the Latin *cella* = chamber). But it was only in 1839 that the German botanist Matthias Schleiden (1804–81) actually described the cells as the basic element of the life of plants. His friend Theodor Schwann (1810–82) succeeded in demonstrating the existence of cells in animals, and the two scientists together discovered that the mother cells divide every time into two daughter cells. It was on the basis of this discovery that Schwann developed his famous cell theory for animals and plants, which stated that all living tissue consisted of cells. In 1854 Rudolf Virchow (1821–1902) completed this theory by adding that all living creatures or things consist of cells, and cells always descend from other pre-existing cells – in Latin *Omnis cellula e cellula*.

Since 1931 it had been possible to observe the structure of cells closely under the electron microscope, and in the 1950s scientists made some particularly important discoveries in the field. Albert Claude (1899–1983), a cytologist at the Rockefeller Institute in New York, succeeded in isolating and analyzing individual cell components for the first time in 1950. In 1974 he was awarded the Nobel Prize for Medicine (together with George Palade, b. 1912, and Christian de Duve, b. 1917) for his work on the structural and functional organization of cells, the basis of modern cell biology.

Using genetic engineering it is now possible to manipulate human cells. This means that reproducing a living human being by cloning is no longer a distant fantasy but an actual possibility.

Representation of plant cells according to Matthias Schleiden, dating from 1838.

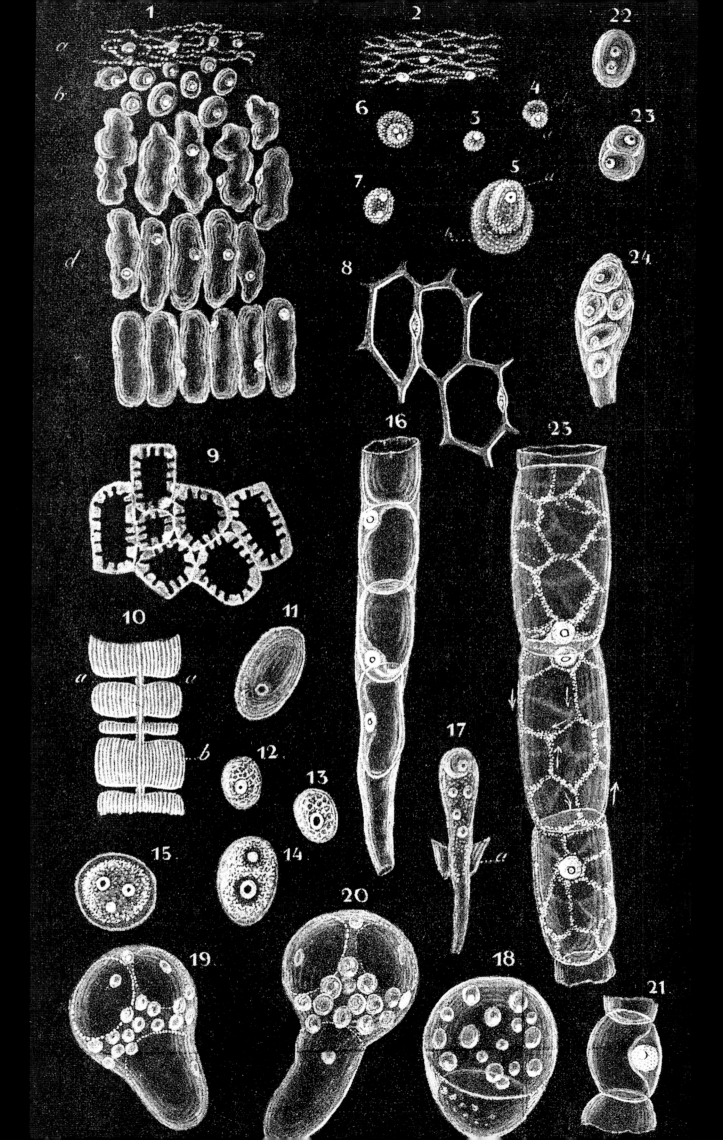

The double helix: the mystery of life is unraveled

Francis Crick (b. 1916), James Watson (b. 1928), Maurice Wilkins (b. 1916)

It is February 28, 1953. Two men are in a bar in the English university city of Cambridge and the whiskey is flowing. What have the scientists Francis Crick and James Watson to celebrate? At this moment they are the only people in the world who actually know how life works. They have decoded the secret of DNA and in doing so they have solved the mystery of heredity.

By the mid-19th century Gregor Mendel (1822–84), the father of genetics, had recognized that the individual units of heredity were passed on independently of each other and were combined again with fertilization. But a more detailed view of the nucleus of the human cell had to await the development of more powerful microscopes.

In 1869, the biologist Friedrich Miescher (1844–95) discovered a long molecule contained in the chromosomes of white blood corpuscles and the sperm cells of trout, to which he gave the name deoxyribonucleic acid or DNA. This vital component of chromosomes contains all the "genes." In 1944, the geneticist Oswald Theodore Avery (1877–1945) and his scientist colleagues succeeded for the first time in taking the DNA of an individual plant or animal and transferring it to something else. The information of the new DNA was itself transmitted to new generations, so it was recognized as the bearer of genetic information. Eight years later, the British chemist Alexander Todd (1907–97) and his colleagues had analyzed all the components of the molecule. But it was still unclear how these molecules were interconnected and what the construction of DNA looked like.

Francis Crick and James Watson discovered the answer to these questions in 1953. After Maurice Wilkins (b. 1916) had proved the correctness of their theory, the three scientists received the Nobel Prize for Medicine in 1962. They are recognized as the founders of modern genetics.

How did this come about? The scientists had recognized that DNA usually has the form of a "double helix." The double helix structure consists of two strands linked to form a twisting ladder. Each upright of the ladder is a chain consisting of phosphates and the sugar deoxyribose. Attached to this this sugar molecule, like half a rung of the ladder, is one of four nitrogenous bases: adenine, cytosine, guanine, and thymine. The combination of the phosphate, the sugar and the nitrogenous base is known as a "nucleotide." These nucleotides are the building blocks of life. A virus needs approximately 5,000 of them, while an individual human being has more than 5 billion.

How do the half-rungs form a whole? The reason why DNA forms a ladder structure rather than a cube is as follows. There are not four but only two possibilities for the nitrogenous bases to form a chemical bond together. Adenine only links with thymine, and cytosine only links with guanine. Ever after, in whatever sequence they arrange themselves, the genetic code of the ladder is always preserved. It forms the "building instruction book" for a living being, the genes being the individual chapters, fixing the eye color of a human being for example. Two months after their discovery Watson and Crick wrote in the magazine *Nature*: "It has not escaped our notice that the specific pairing we have postulated immediately suggests a possible copying mechanism for the genetic material."

The discovery of the structure of DNA helped to solve the mystery of heredity.

IN THE YEAR 1953

> Elizabeth II is crowned Queen of Great Britain and Northern Ireland.

> The People's Police of East Germany and Soviet troops crush the workers revolt.

> An armistice ends the Korean War. The country remains divided into the communist North and the western-oriented South.

> After the death of Josef W. Stalin, Georgiy M. Malenkov becomes the chairman of the Soviet Council of Ministers and Nikita S. Khrushchev First Secretary of the Central Committee of the Communist Party of the Soviet Union.

> A vaccine against polio is developed by Jonas Edward Salk.

Solar cells: free electricity from solar energy

Gerald Pearson (b. 1905)

> In a sensational verdict in the court case "Brown v. Alabama Board of Education" the Supreme Court in the USA declares segregation in public schools to be unconstitutional.

> Mao Zedong becomes president of the People's Republic of China.

> Algerian freedom fighters start bomb attacks against the French colonial power. This is the beginning of the Algerian War.

> The German national football team wins the World Cup.

In the long term it is inevitable that non-renewable, fossil sources of energy such as oil or gas will have to be replaced by renewable sources. Most conspicuous among these is the eternally available energy of the sun. In 1954, a Bell Telephone Company laboratories research team headed by Gerald Pearson made the breakthrough with the construction of the first solar cell.

The French physicist Alexandre Edmond Becquerel (1820–91) discovered in 1839 that light can generate energy when it illuminates certain materials. The photo-electric effect that he observed involves the release of positive and negative electrons within a solid body by introducing light.

At first it was not possible to use this electricity generated by light in a practical way, but in 1880, Charles Fritts coated vacuum photo cells with selenium. The resulting energy yield was only 1 or 2 percent, but one such cell could at least power the light meter of a camera.

The silicon cell, the key to effective generation of energy from sunlight, was eventually discovered by Gerald Pearson in the laboratories of the American Bell Telephone Company in the early 1950s. The silicon solar cell functions in a surprisingly simple way. Two electrically separated layers of silicon crystals are treated in such a way that a surplus of electrons is produced on one side and a deficiency on the other. When illuminated by the sun, an electric charge is created in both layers that is discharged through electrons. When Pearson and his team illuminated the treated silicon with light, they were already able to convert 6 percent of the light directly into energy.

The world was astounded when in 1954 the front covers of the newspapers showed a transistor radio powered by solar energy. The *New York Times* called it the beginning of a new era.

But the great disadvantage of a solar cell, or photovoltaic technology, compared to other sources of energy was the high cost of manufacture.

To begin with, cost did not matter much since solar cells were developed for use in space. In 1958, the US satellite *Vanguard* was the first to send radio signals from space with a one-watt cell. Today almost all satellites are powered by solar electricity. Down on earth, however, the thought was spreading that perhaps the future lay with atomic energy, and in any event oil and gas were still flowing plentifully and inexpensively. It was not until the oil crises of the 1970s that interest in renewable energy sources was aroused. New technology caused the price for solar electricity to fall from $200 to $5 dollars per watt within just a few years, and towards the end of the second millennium, solar cells made of gallium arsenide were able to convert 37 percent of the light falling on them into electricity.

Still, many researchers are doubtful about the solar cell. There are other ways of using sunlight to generate energy; for instance, by using solar heat to heat water to power conventional steam turbines, thus generating electricity in an ecologically friendly way. In the low-voltage area, however, and in places far from a public electricity supply, the solar cell is undoubtedly the power source of the future.

Solar cells play an indispensable role in space satellites.

Optical fibers: high speed data transfer

Narinder Singh Kapany

> The Federal Republic of Germany joins NATO.

> The Soviet Union, Poland, Romania, Hungary, Albania and Czechoslovakia sign a military treaty, the Warsaw Pact.

> In Germany the economic miracle is in full swing.

> South Africa withdraws from the United Nations to avoid protests against its apartheid politics.

In 1955, Narinder S. Kapany invented the optical fiber made of glass. He was following on from experiments made in 1870 by the physicist John Tyndall (1820–93). Kapany's discovery had far-reaching technical significance and forms the basis for the glass fiber broadband cable that is used in modern communications and data transfer technology.

There are countless uses for pictures sent "round the corner." In the 1920s, for instance, Heinrich Lamm had the idea of making a flexible apparatus from fine glass fibers that could be inserted into the stomach to convey pictures from inside it. Lamm did manage to send optical images, but only over a very short distance. The problem was that the glass itself absorbed almost all the light, which therefore reduced the quality of the image transmission.

After World War II, a group of Dutch scientists developed a better periscope for submarines using glass fiber. They were able to improve the light conductivity of the fibers by giving them a protective coat of clear varnish.

But the first truly operational glass-fiber cable was made by the Indian scientist Narinder Kapany in 1955. Kapany took a single glass fiber and stretched and twisted it in the form of a figure of eight several thousand times. Afterwards the fibers were bundled together. In this way he constructed a fiber-optic cable that was a perfect light-ray conductor with about 20,000 fine fibers bundled together in which all the fibers were all exactly the same.

A fiber-optic cable that transmits light is made up of a core and a casing. Both are made of transparent material but with different refractory properties, the most suitable being glass. As the refraction of the core is higher than that of the casing, the light rays are reflected at the border between the core and the casing. In this way, the impulse is preserved within the cable without losing any of its intensity.

The fiber-optic cable designed by Kapany revolutionized communications technology. In 1966 the American Charles Kao made the first telephone call using fiber-optic cable. In comparison to a copper or a coaxial cable, a significantly larger number of calls or television channels can be transmitted by a glass-fiber cable of the same circumference or less. This meant that even before television, computers, and the Internet radically changed everyone's lives, a medium was available that would be able to transmit the huge amounts of data these new technologies would require or generate.

Today, almost all digital information is transmitted by means fiber-optic cables. As well as their great capacity, they have the advantages of low cost in relation to their capacity, and immunity from electromagnetic interference. Today cables are made of more than one layer which slows down the refraction rate as it moves outwards. In simple cables, which are made of only a single core and the casing, some data may take longer than others to arrive at their destination, since they are entered into the cable at different angles in order to separate the signals. In cables of more than one layer, however, it is possible to send all data so that they arrive at the same time. Almost 10 billion bits per fiber per second can be transmitted.

The invention of fiber-optic cable revolutionized communication technology.

The contraceptive pill: the sexual emancipation of women

Gregory Pincus (1903-67), John Rock (1890-1984)

Any unwanted pregnancy raises the same difficult decision: to continue with the pregnancy or to have an abortion, which used to be a painful, dangerous, and often illegal procedure. The discovery of the contraceptive pill made it possible for women to avoid unwanted pregnancy.

△ Some 80 million women worldwide use the contraceptive pill to prevent unwanted pregnancies.

Less effective contraceptive methods have existed for thousands of years. In the past men used to use a kind of leather bag or goat's bladder as a condom, while women used tampons made of wool with a spermicide. Such methods were unreliable and unpleasant. If an unwanted pregnancy occurred, abortions carried out by back-street abortionists often resulted in sterility or even death. There had to be another solution.

Since 1850 scientists had acquired a certain knowledge of the female cycle and the formation of eggs in the ovary. In 1902 Ernst Henry Starling (1866–1927) and William Maddock Bayliss (1866–1924) discovered sex hormones, endogenous substances that also control reproduction. They concluded quite rightly that any interference with hormone production would affect conception. In 1928 American scientists discovered that the corpus luteum present in the ovary produces a hormone after ovulation that prevents the ripening of a new egg. This hormone is called progesterone. Estrogen, which was discovered a year later, controls menstruation and prepares the lining of the womb for the implantation of the fertilized ovum. Estrogen and gestagen, whose main component is progesterone, influence both sexuality and conception. In 1944 Werner Bickenbach (1900–74) carried out the first experiments on contraception using synthetic progesterone developed by the chemists of the Schering company. But oral administration did not have the desired result; the body broke down the progesterone, which therefore lost its effect.

In the 1950s the American feminist Margaret Sanger (1883–1966) and the biologist Katherine McCormick (1875–1967) gave a new impetus to the development of a hormonal contraceptive. In 1951 they won over the biologist Gregory Pincus (1903–67) to their cause. In the same year the chemist Carl Djerassi (b. 1923) succeeded for the first time in producing an effective synthetic oral contraceptive that he called norethindrone (norethisteron). Pincus and his colleagues were soon able to prevent ovulation and therefore also pregnancy in experimental animals by giving them this substance. In 1954 Pincus, in collaboration with the gynecologist John Rock (1890–1984), carried out the first successful clinical experiments on 50 women in Boston. In 1957 the contraceptive pill, an estrogen-gestagen preparation that was originally used to treat menstrual problems, was approved. The first contraceptive pill was launched in the United States in 1960 and in Britain two years later.

The contraceptive pill became known simply as the "pill." It was condemned not only by the Roman Catholic Church, which believed that intercourse should only take place with the aim to reproduce, but also by the more conservative members of society who feared that it would lower morality. On the positive side, the contraceptive pill radically changed society since it enabled women to play a part in society besides "bearing children and doing housework." The birth rate in industrial countries fell dramatically as a result of the pill. Currently about 80 million women use hormonal contraceptives to protect themselves from unwanted pregnancies.

Before the contraceptive pill there were no methods of preventing pregnancy that were completely reliable.

The laser: a thin beam of light for difficult tasks

Gordon Gould (b. 1920), Arthur Leonard Schawlow (1921-99), Charles Hard Townes (b. 1915)

> After the resignation of Anthony Eden due to the Suez Crisis, Harold Macmillan becomes the new Prime Minister of Great Britain.

> In the Eisenhower Doctrine, the American president Dwight D. Eisenhower states that the USA will provide military aid to countries in the Near East threatened by communism.

> In the USA racial turmoil assumes the proportions of a civil war. In Arkansas, police and a mob of whites stop nine African-American students from entering Little Rock Central High School. President Eisenhower orders army protection to take the "Little Rock Nine" to the school.

Albert Einstein described the principle of "stimulated emission" in 1917, when he considered stimulating matter energetically so as to cause it to release dynamic particles to the surroundings on its return to its original state. These could stimulate other atoms, ions, and molecules to release further particles that resembled them so far as energy, phase, and orientation were concerned. This made it possible to produce an extremely high, bundled energy density. Einstein's theory formed the basis for one of the most important inventions of the 20th century, the laser.

The acronym LASER stands for the words "light amplification by stimulated emission of radiation." This in itself explains the basic function of a laser. In a resonance chamber consisting of a reflective mirror and an opposing, partly permeable mirror, the laser-active material is exposed to extreme energy. In the case of the ruby laser this is provided by a quartz vapor lamp. This lamp stimulates the atoms in the ruby so that they produce photons (light particles). These in turn stimulate other atoms to emit new photons. Thus within a very short time a large mass of particles has been produced that are reflected back and forth by the mirrors. The process in the laser become stronger and a mass of particles that are identically aligned is developed. When the energy reaches a particular density, it is propelled outwards like a beam through the partly permeable side of the resonance chamber.

In the 1950s the American physicists Charles Hard Townes and Arthur Leonard Schawlow tried to build an apparatus in which energetically-stimulated gas emitted coherently bundled microwaves. In 1953 their colleague James Gordon built the first "maser," today's name for such an apparatus. Townes then had the idea of producing bundled beams of light waves instead of microwaves. In 1958 he and Schawlow applied for a patent for this process, but the US atomic physicist Gordon Gould had already registered similar findings with a notary in 1957 in order to ensure that he would be granted the patent later. However, after a lawsuit the court decided in favor of Schawlow and Townes. The first working laser was built by the physicist Theodore Maiman in 1960, and he also gave it its name.

The highly precise concentration of energy produced by a laser beam makes it possible to heat, melt, and even cut materials with extreme accuracy. Human tissue can be treated in this way without damaging the surrounding area, for instance when injecting blood vessels. Compact disc and DVD systems also depend on laser technology. Lasers are used to guide the giant drills used in making tunnels and to activate chemical reactions. An important application is in measurement. Laser rangefinders send the laser beam over a certain distance and record the reflection time. The distance is then calculated from the time interval and the speed of the light. This has enabled the distance between the moon and the earth to be calculated to within an accuracy of ± 8 in.

Laser technology is very versatile and has many applications in the field of research and technology.

Technical
UpDate
Report:
Lini-Guide

Electrode Design

Optical Coupling

Assembly Automation

Sputnik:
the beginning of the space age

Soviet Union

On July 29, 1955 the outgoing President of the United States Dwight D. Eisenhower said that the USA would launch a research satellite into orbit round the Earth within two to three years. A few days after Eisenhower's announcement the Soviet scientist Leonid Sedow countered by declaring that his country would put a much heavier satellite into orbit.

Leonid Sedow was undoubtedly sticking his neck out with his provocative statement. In 1955, the modified R-7 intercontinental rocket that was to serve as the launch vehicle for the satellite had not yet been built. Even worse, the first excavators had only just arrived at the launch site in Baikonur. It soon became clear to all concerned that the planned heavy satellite of over 1 ton could be never operational by the envisaged date, the late summer of 1957.

In order to beat the USA in any case, they therefore constructed a very much smaller, lighter test satellite. "Sputnik Zelmi," the "traveller of the world," was an aluminum ball with a diameter of almost 2 ft weighing a little over 175 lb. Although the tests of the R-7 rocket had been very variable, the scientists dared to launch the Sputnik on October 4, 1957. Despite some problems, the R-7 took off on schedule. A few minutes later, Sputnik radioed the first signals from space. The mission was successful and the race against the USA had been won.

The shock in the United States was enormous. Nobody had seriously believed that the allegedly technically inferior USSR could make its announcement come true. The Americans were immediately afraid that the opponent in the east was ahead of them not only in the space race but also in the arms race. While they worked feverishly on their own satellite program, Sputnik circled round the earth for 57 days. Even before it re-entered the atmosphere and burnt up, the Soviet scientists launched Sputnik 2 into space on November 2, 1957. On board was the dog "Laika," who became celebrated as the first creature in space. The data radioed to the ground station provided the first biomedical measurements to the scientists. Before the second Sputnik burnt up after 162 days in orbit, the Americans made their first launch on January 31, 1958.

The cylindrical satellite "Explorer 1" weighed only 31 lb and had a diameter of 6 in with a length of 6 ft 6 in. Measuring instruments inside it provided data about cosmic radiation and mini-meteorites for 112 days. The second US satellite launch in March of the same year confirmed that the earth is not quite spherical but is slightly flattened at the poles.

In comparison with the two superpowers of the Cold War, Europe began to launch its own satellites into space very late. The European space organization ESA started its first launches in 1983. The artificial orbital satellites served military and technological purposes as well as scientific ones. The civilian use of satellites includes the transfer of telephone conversations, television programs and digital pictures. The artificial earth satellites send pictures from space for weather forecasting and make it possible to determine a vessel's position at sea to within a few meters. In 1989 a private rocket was launched for the first time, putting a British television satellite into space. With modern launch systems such as the American "space shuttle" that came into use in 1984, satellites have not only been put into orbit but also recovered and repaired.

Thousands of satellites are now orbiting the earth in the wake of Sputnik, the first satellite to be launched.

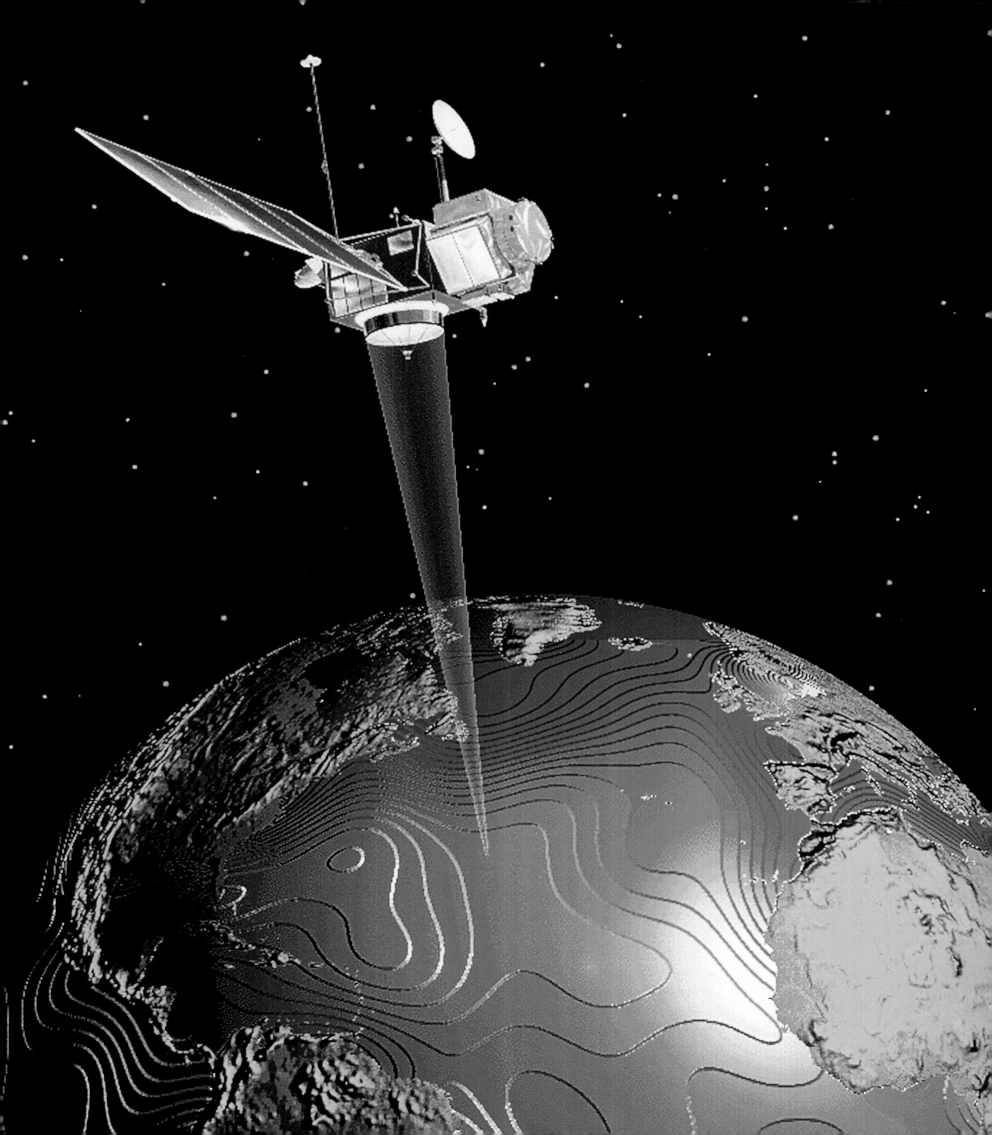

Quarks: the smallest components of matter

George Zweig, Murray Gell-Mann (b. 1929)

For a long time protons, neutrons and electrons were believed to be the smallest units in the atomic nucleus. In 1931 Wolfgang Pauli proved that when a neutron decays a completely new particle is produced, the neutrino. But in spite of this discovery the fundamental particle of the universe remained unknown. It is now thought that the smallest particles are quarks and leptons.

To achieve an overall view of all other particles, research into sub-atomic particles was divided into three categories: bosons without mass, leptons (which include electrons and neutrinos), and hadrons. In 1964, while attempting to arrange the particles into a system similar to the periodic table, the United States nuclear physicists Murray Gell-Mann and George Zweig came independently to the same conclusion, that hadrons must be made up of even smaller particles.

Gell-Mann called these particles "quarks," after the saying "Three quarks for muster Mark" quoted in James Joyce's novel *Finnegan's Wake*. Joyce hated exact sciences and loved what was difficult to comprehend. Gell-Mann perceived these new particles as similarly intangible and inexact.

Later scientists succeeded in proving the existence of quarks by bombarding protons with high-energy electrons. The method resembled that developed by Rutherford who bombarded the atomic nucleus with alpha particles, thereby proving that the nuclear mass was heterogeneous. But quarks are probably a thousand times smaller than the atomic nucleus.

Gell-Mann and Zweig started from the assumption that there were three different kinds of quarks into which all the hadrons then known could be classified. Today it is known that there are six different quarks, called up (u), down (d), charm (c), strange (s), bottom (b), and top (t). Every mass that is visible and exists under normal conditions is made up of the first two quarks. The particles of the other four quarks are unstable and decay very quickly.

Each quark is complemented by an anti-quark that resembles it but has a negative charge instead of a positive one. For instance, a proton, the positively charged particle in the atomic nucleus, consists of a d-anti-quark and two u-quarks. Quarks are bound together by very strong forces and their existence uncombined has never been proved. But it is assumed that they were present when the universe came into being.

As far as leptons are concerned, scientists have been unable to prove the existence of smaller particles. Based on today's knowledge, all particles that have so far been identified are made up of quarks and leptons. They are bound together by strong forces whereby they exchange correlational particles that belong to the boson category.

But even with this so-called standard model, scientists are not able to explain all natural phenomena, such as gravitation. There is no doubt that future generations of nuclear physicists will still have many questions to answer.

The European nuclear research centre CERN is one of the places where quarks are being investigated.

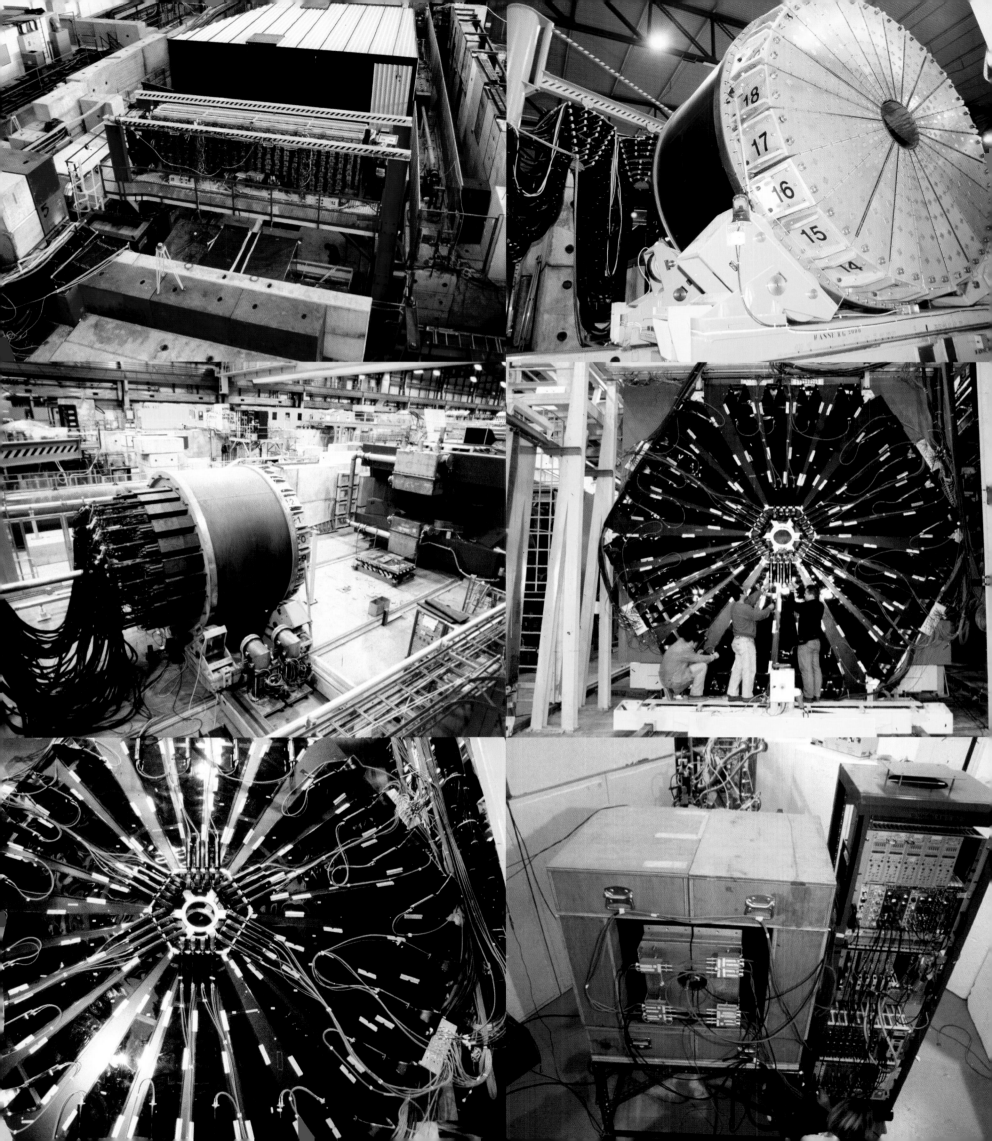

The internet:
the world becomes a village

Advanced Research Projects Agency (ARPA)

No other medium has changed the form of mass communication in the way the Internet has. Never before has information been exchanged so quickly and over such great distances. The idea of a handful of visionary computer experts in the 1950s is now standard equipment for PC users.

1969

IN THE YEAR 1969

> The French president Charles de Gaulle resigns after a defeat in the referendum instigated by himself.

> In West Germany Willy Brandt becomes Chancellor.

> The press reports of the massacre of civilians by American soldiers at My Lai in South Vietnam leads to worldwide protests and riots in the USA.

The Internet was a child of the Cold War. The point of departure was the strategic planning on the part of the US government that would enable communications between the authorities and the military in the event of nuclear war. When in 1957 the Russians launched a satellite, Sputnik, into space, President Dwight D. Eisenhower (1890–1969) took steps to make sure that such an "accident" did not happen again. The newly founded research institute Advanced Research Projects Agency (ARPA) was given the task of co-ordinating technological research nationwide.

Several scientists contributed their ideas to the development of a process for transmitting information for scientific and military application. Paul Baran recognized that a national network of communication through computers would have to fulfill at least two criteria: first, there could be no central control station, since if it broke down communications would be cut off, and secondly, the individual components of the network would have to be fully functional and able to work individually. Every nodal point of the net should therefore have the possibility of creating, transmitting and receiving data. The practical application of these requirements was achieved by packet switching. This technique separated the data into individual "packets," each packet showing the "sender" and the "recipient."

In 1962, Joseph Licklider (b. 1915) took over ARPA and pushed forward research on computer networks. At a conference on information systems in Virginia in 1964, he and a young computer genius Larry Roberts argued that computer networks were *the* research task of the future. Larry Roberts led the first practical experiments with larger networks at the Massachusetts Institute of Technology (MIT) in 1966.

From 1968, ARPA sponsored the project of a computer network with a common data source at the University of California in Los Angeles (UCLA). Within the framework of this project, a "network team" was formed that constructed a network via telephone lines between four points: UCLA, the University of California in Santa Barbara, the Stanford Research Institute, and the University of Utah. With this, ARPAnet, the precursor of the Internet, was born.

In October 1972 the first public demonstration of the network was given at an international symposium on computer communications held in Washington, USA. By 1977, 111 computers were already connected to the ARPA network. Independently of the ARPA network, Usenet/News was developed, which transmitted e-mails via telephone lines and offered open forums for discussion on every imaginable subject.

In 1984, the National Science Foundation established a successor for the seriously overloaded ARPA network, NFSNet. From the early 1990s, with the development of Hyper Text Markup Language (HTML) and various browser software, the World Wide Web began its triumphant progress as the true medium of the masses.

Tim Berners-Lee is recognized as the creator of the World Wide Web. At the CERN research facility he wrote the first web browser and related software.

The microprocessor: a whole computer on a single chip

Marcian Edward Hoff (b. 1937)

Before the development of the microprocessor, there were two types of computers. "Mainframes" filled whole rooms, had extremely high current consumption, and cost several million dollars. "Minicomputers" were somewhat handier – one could be carried in an automobile trunk.

In 1969 the Japanese company Busicom commissioned the electronics company Intel to develop a programmable calculating machine, a pocket calculator. Intel would design and produce a solid state programmable calculator using 12 semiconductor components. Semiconductors chips are space-saving electronic circuits that accommodate many functions on a single component. By 1969, the industry was already using simple chips. This Intel job would today have been forgotten long ago if Marcian Edward Hoff had not collaborated on it. This college graduate had just joined Intel as an electronics engineer. He had the idea of using four chips instead of the 12 originally planned, connected to an as yet undeveloped all-round logic chip.

The client Busicom turned down the suggestion when it was presented, but Intel's boss Robert Noyce (1927–90) allowed his electronics engineer to continue further research into the project. Noyce had in mind the development of a universal programmable chip that could be put into the most varied calculating machines. In mid-1969, Hoff and Noyce received support from their colleague Stan Mazor. Together, they designed a first circuit, the so-called "Hoff circuit." The first microprocessor was born, at least on paper. A microprocessor is the extremely miniaturized calculating and control unit of a computer. One or more semiconductors each about ¼ in square are contained in what is known as a Dual in-Line Integrated Circuit (DILIC) with 18 to 64 connecting pins.

This time, Intel was able to convince the Japanese client. Busicom bought the rights to use the microprocessor planned by Intel for about $60,000. Mazer, Hoff, and their colleague Frederico Faggin, (b. 1941) then built the first prototypes. This was given the name 4000 and was followed by the improved types 4001, 4002, and 4003. With the 4004 microprocessor in 1971 the first fully operational example was ready for mass production. This first "computer on a chip" had 2,300 MOS transistors to carry out about 4,000 functions. "MOS" stands for "Metal Oxide Semiconductor" and refers to the three basic layers in the construction of a MOS-transistor: metal as a current conducting material, silicon oxide as an insulating material, and silicon as the semiconductor. A single 4004 microprocessor of 1971 had the same performance as the first electronic computer "Eniac" of 1946. But in contrast with that gigantic device, the 4004 chip was just the size of a matchbox.

It soon occurred to the Intel team that the 4004 could also be put to use in other areas. In 1970 Intel gave Busicom a price reduction in exchange for the return of the rights to the world's first microprocessor. As things turned out, this was good business. In the 1970s, microprocessors were used mainly in devices for production technology and calculating machines. The areas of application were widened as technological improvements were made to the chips. Today the best known use of the microprocessor is in the personal computer or PC.

Microprocessors made possible the successful development of the modern information technology.

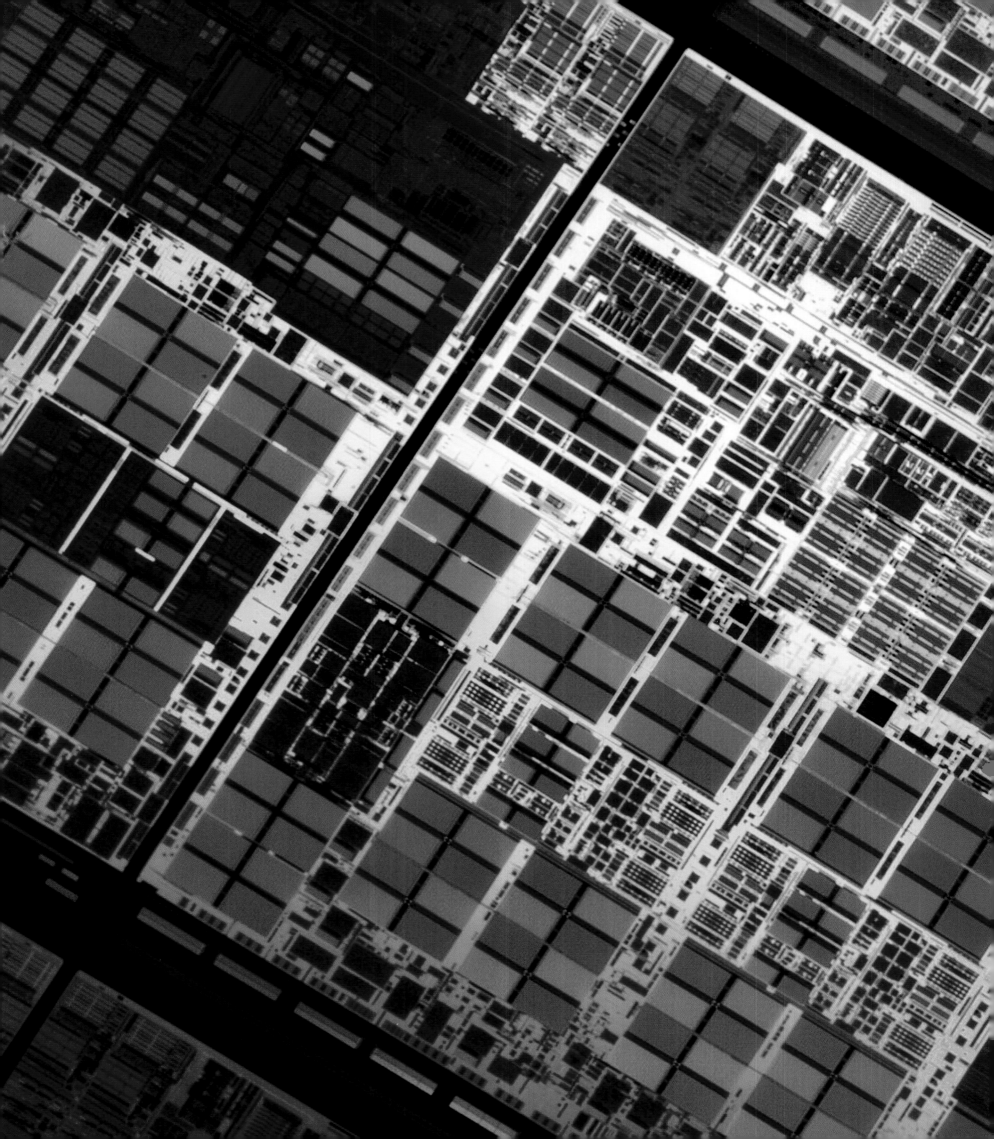

Moon landing: "The Eagle has landed"

Apollo 11

In 1869, Jules Verne wrote his fantastic story *From the Earth to the Moon*. Exactly 100 years later, fiction became reality. On July 21, 1969, the astronauts Neil Armstrong and Edwin Aldrin were the first people to set foot on the moon. A human dream had been realized.

IN THE YEAR 1969

> In the USA the republican Richard M. Nixon is sworn in as new president.

> Muammar al-Gaddafi overthrows the Libyan King Idris I and declares the republic of Libya.

> In Germany homosexuality between adults is no longer forbidden.

> Olof Palme becomes the new Prime Minister of Sweden.

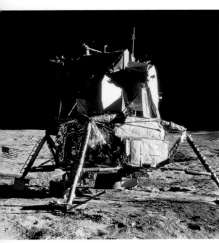

△ The first landing on the moon and the following missions were more than a symbolic act, they also served scientific purposes.

The moon, 238,855 miles from the earth, remained an impossible dream for mankind for a long time. The distance could be shortened optically by using a telescope, but it was not until after the mid-20th century that space technology was far enough advanced to make it possible to send a human being to the moon. In 1945 science began to work on a feasible foundation for such a project, the development of a booster rocket. The venture into space was therefore only a matter of time.

The first triumph in this sector was achieved by the Russian space program in 1957 with the launching of their satellite *Sputnik 1*. Four years later, the Russian astronaut Yuri Gagarin (1934–68) was the first man in space with the space capsule *Wostock 1*. In 1961, president John F. Kennedy (1917–63) declared that landing man on the moon was a national responsibility and gave NASA's specially established Apollo program top priority.

First of all, careful and costly preparations had to be made. Unmanned moon probes explored space (*Ranger*, *Lunar Orbiter*, and *Surveyor*). Scientists tested how well astronauts performed in a weightless environment with manned flights around the Earth (the Mercury and Gemini programs). The precise controlling of the capsule when re-entering the Earth's atmosphere also had to be examined. The actual moon-landing program began in 1965. To start with, the first unmanned Apollo missions tested the new space rocket in orbit. Several space rocket units and a corresponding booster rocket were necessary for the program. With the development of Saturn 5, a three-stage, 2,900 ton booster rocket, NASA was getting close to achieving its aim. In 1968, Apollo 8 and Saturn 5 were successful in putting the first manned rockets into orbit around the moon. Seven months and three test flights later the critical moment arrived.

On July 16, 1969, the space shuttle *Columbia* started its journey from the John F. Kennedy Space Center in Florida, USA. On board were the astronauts Neil Armstrong (b. 1930), Edwin Aldrin (b. 1930) and Michael Collins (b. 1930). After they had reached orbit around the moon, Armstrong and Aldrin transferred from the main unit to the moon-landing shuttle *Eagle* and were the first to step onto the moon's surface on 21 July 1969. The Apollo 11 mission was a success. Five hundred million viewers followed what was probably the most spectacular adventure in history live on television. When he stepped onto the moon's surface, Neil Armstrong spoke the now legendary words: "That's one small step for a man, one giant leap for mankind."

The moon landing was more than the symbolic conquest of space; it also served scientific purposes. The astronaut's job was to collect stones, make a photographic record, and to construct small research stations. These provided information on solar wind, magnetic fields, and the warmth conductivity of the ground as well as investigating the possibility of an atmosphere surrounding the moon. Nevertheless, it was man's landing on the moon that remained the greatest achievement in people's memories.

With the landing on the moon, the impossible was seen to be possible.

The Christian interpretation of the history of creation was completely revolutionized by the theory of evolution.

Anthropology:
In search of mankind's origin

Where do we come from?

This question must be among the oldest that mankind has ever asked itself. Until the 19th century the answer had been quite straightforward. Each culture had its own myths about its origin. Christianity believed in the Creator who had made the earth and all the species on it in six days. Man was special in God's creation. But should the Bible be interpreted literally? Even before Charles Darwin destroyed this image of creation in 1859 with his work *The Origin of Species Through Natural Selection*, fossil finds had led scientists to alternative answers from the middle of the 18th century onward.

The first, albeit erroneous, theory of evolution, that is, the concept that species have changed and developed since their origin, was put forward by Jean-Baptist Lamarck (1744–1829). He assumed that each individual possessed an internal drive towards perfection. On the other hand, Darwin's view was that natural selection ensured the appropriate adaptation of creatures to their surroundings, and consequently the phylogenetic development of the species. His contemporaries protested against the concept that "man was descended from the apes" but gradually they had to accept Darwin's theory under the weight of evidence.

In fact, it was through genetics, whose principles were based on Mendel's Laws

Charles Darwin´s theories on the evolution of species laid the foundations for modern anthropology.

of 1866, that evolution through heredity was finally explained. Darwin's basic theory gradually developed into today's synthetic Darwinism, most importantly by taking the principle of mutation into account. Although even the Catholic Church recognized the theory of evolution in 1996, there are still people who reject it. Creationists, Biblical fundamentalists, still firmly believe that all species were created by God because hardly any transitional forms between species have been found to support the idea of continuous development. So the question asked is where the "missing links" are to be

found. The sketchiness is indisputable, but many fossils of transitional forms have been discovered such as *Archaeopteryx*, the link between two species that has both reptilian and bird-like characteristics.

The path to man

The study of the specific development of man from the origin of the species forms the basis of anthropology, the "study of man." It compares genes, cultures, skills, behavior, and social systems of past and present populations. Based on remains that have been found, scientists have put forward the following theories.

The first known hominid (man-like creature) appeared over 4.4 million years ago as *Ardipithecus ramidus*, followed by various species of the *Australopithecus* genus. They walked partly upright and lived together in groups. The "single species hypothesis" held that only one species existed at any one time in the evolution of man, who would therefore-have developed along a straight line into modern man. But this theory has long become outdated: each new discovery increasingly confirms that there was a wide range of different species existing at the same time.

Homo habilis is generally considered to be the first species that is the actual ancestor of present-day man. He was

known to have the skills necessary to make stone tools, thus displaying foresighted thinking and planning abilities. He was probably followed, both chronologically and as a tool maker, by the "man from the Rudolfsee," *Homo rudolfensis*, who lived about 2.5 million years ago. It was his descendant, *Homo erectus,* whose skeleton strongly resembles that of human beings today, who first discovered fire. *Homo erectus* then developed into primitive forms of *Homo sapiens* that also includes Neanderthal man. These cavemen first appeared in Europe over 150,000 years ago. He distinguished himself as "human-like" in that he buried his dead. But DNA analyses of Neanderthal fossils have revealed that his species is different from that of modern man.

Homo sapiens sapiens is at least 100,000 years old with origins that can clearly be traced back to Africa. From there he traveled to all parts of the Old World where he undoubtedly came across Neanderthal man. After co-existing for a while modern man finally drove out Neanderthal man about 30,000 years ago, apparently because of his superior skills of adaptation. *Homo sapiens sapiens* is distinguished by his rather modern behavior. Sophisticated tools, body decoration, and the elegant ornamentation of items of practical use reveal an outstanding sense of the artistic and an aesthetic approach that goes far beyond the mere skill of surviving.

Three steps towards man

An upright walk, increased brain volume, and well-developed speech were the three milestones that marked the development of man. Two-leggedness was lit-

erally the first step of hominid adaptation and it was probably the result of changes in the environment. Forests became reduced to steppes so that it was advantageous to look out for enemies and sources of food from a raised position. This also helped the brain and body cool in a more efficient manner.

Today the human brain has a volume of about 85 to 90 cu in. The chimpanzee's brain is only 24 cu in, which means that its size is similar to that all the species of the *Australopithecus* genus. The brain only began to increase in size with the development of the genus *Homo* but it was the change in brain structure that was more important. This is because awareness and learning, intelligence and integration skills were all linked to the development of the "gray cells" in the cerebral cortex that was divided into two lobes with specific functions in different areas.

This brain structure also affected the third step in the development of man, language. It is true that, based on brain casts of the skull's inner walls, the brain of *Homo habilis* was already divided into areas with specific functions, but the verbal communication of Neanderthal man and *Homo erectus* was very limited.

As shown by reconstructions of their speech organs and the simulation of their articulation potential, they were unable to produce important vowel sounds. They lacked the appropriate speech organs that would have provided space for a voice box because they had an unusually deep-lying larynx. Such a structure had considerable disadvantages because it increased the danger of choking and

made breathing difficult. This clearly shows how important speech skills must have been from an evolutionary point of view.

That speech is a characteristic of modern man is also suggested by studies of apes that have been carried out by scientists since the 1960s. Admittedly apes only have limited speech skills, but they are able to learn sign language after intensive training. They understand and use a few hundred signs but they remain at this level, which is below that of any normal young child. Speech is evidently a human characteristic that is not only the result of the human being's social nature but is also linked to his awareness, ability to reason, and power of imagination. Because such inner developments appear to be linked to the origins of (modern) man, it is important to find external expressions of these inner developments.

The cellphone: always within reach

Deutsche Bundespost

Mobile wireless communication has been possible since the end of the 19th century, but participation was limited. The attempt to connect mobile telephones to the fixed network was first made by German Railways in 1927. They set up a public train telephone in a first-class carriage between Berlin and Hamburg and later on other routes. The technical equipment took up a whole compartment.

After World War II it became more and more important in the business world to be reachable at all times. Many business men and women wanted to be constantly available to everyone in the public network. In 1946, the USA was the first country to set up a mobile radio network. The telephone weighed almost 40 lb and its accumulator batteries lasted for just eight minutes.

A prerequisite for mobile telephones is a closely woven network of transmitting and receiving stations that receive the signals sent by the mobile telephones and then establish a connection with the fixed network. Today, a smooth transmission between the different radio transmitters and networks is possible even if the user leaves one receiving area and moves into another. This had not always been possible. From 1958, the German Post Office offered a car telephone service called the A-net. This covered about 80 percent of Germany, but it was divided into many unconnected radio areas. Due to the high purchase cost and the extensive apparatus involved, only about 10,000 customers took advantage of the service. Still, the A-net was the largest mobile telephone network of its kind in the world at that time.

The breakthrough came when the Post Office introduced the fully automatic B-net in 1972. With this, the caller had to know the area in which the person being called was located in order to dial the correct area code. In 1986, the C-net developed by the German company Siemens was introduced. In this case all users could be reached under one area code. A year later, Siemens put the first truly mobile telephone on the market. It could be used outside a car and was about the size of a portable radio.

In 1982, the Conference of the European Post and Telecommunications Organization founded a project group with the name GSM (Groupe Speciale Mobile) in order to establish a standard for the implementation of a unified European digital cellphone network. After international acceptance of this standard, the name was changed to Global System for Mobile Telecommunications. The GSM standard began to be introduced in the early 1990s. The decisive impulse for the spread of mobile cellphones was digital technology. This improved the quality of transmission considerably and reduced susceptibility to interference.

Ever smaller and more powerful cellphones are being equipped with ever greater technical possibilities, and most importantly, are now within most people's means. The UMTS (Universal Mobile Telecommunication System) standard is making possible the cable-free broadband transmission of video sequences, Internet and Intranet pages. The WAP (Wireless Application Protocol) technology in use today offers access to the Internet via a mobile phone, and it is already possible to use cellphones for sending short text messages. However, the future of mobile telephony may lie in space. It is expected that satellites will soon make the earthbound transmitting and receiving stations a thing of the past.

In some European countries the number of cellphones has overtaken the number of landlines in only a few years.

Computerized axial tomography: seeing through someone

Godfrey Newbold Hounsfield (b. 1919), Allan MacLeod Cormack (b. 1924)

The technique of computerized axial tomography (CAT) developed by the English scientist Godfrey Newbold Hounsfield and his American colleague Allan MacLeod Cormack gave doctors a completely new view of the interior of the human body. X-rays scan the body layer by layer and a computer then calculates an overall picture from the individual cross-sections. This procedure makes the diagnosis of injuries to the body's soft internal organs much easier.

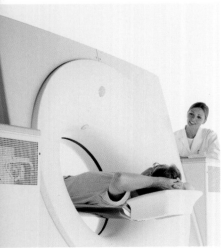

△ In computer tomography the X-rays examine the body layer by layer. The computer then produces an overall picture.

Computer tomography – "tomography" means representation in layers – is based on the principle of the X-ray machine. CAT (computer axial tomography) also involves scanning the human body with X-rays. The basis of both is that X-rays diminish in strength as they penetrate a body. The denser the human tissue is, the more the rays are weakened, so that the image on film recorded by the radiation on the exit side becomes lighter. So bones or teeth appear as the lightest parts in an X-ray, since they have the densest tissue. Different tissue thicknesses are recorded on an X-ray film as gray tones varying between white and black. If a doctor suspects a bone fracture, a conventional X-ray can easily confirm or deny it. However with injuries to internal organs such as the lung, the lighter image of the rib cage and spinal column lying above it "obscures" the lung and impedes the diagnosis. The main problem of traditional X-rays is that the rays are transmitted in only one direction and create an image without any representation of depth.

How can doctors avoid this problem? One possibility is to turn the patient and take individual X-rays from different directions. But ideally these pictures would be combined in an overall image to facilitate diagnosis by the doctor. The scientists Godfrey Newbold Hounsfield and Allan MacLeod Cormack had this exciting idea. In 1972 they developed an X-ray machine that moves itself round the patient and scans the body layer by layer. The thickness of each body layer to be scanned is adjustable and is usually between 1/16 and 3/8 in depending on the precision required. From the superimposed tissue thicknesses of the scans of the individual cross-sections, the computer calculates a median value and presents this as an image.

The advantage of computerized axial tomography (CAT) is that it makes it possible to produce images of smaller tissue structures for examination by doctors without distracting superimposition. Soft tissue parts such as nerves, muscles, the spinal cord, and other organs appear directly in high contrast resolution. The contrast can be improved if a contrast medium is administered to the patient before the CAT scan is made. The two scientists received the Nobel Prize for Medicine in 1979 for their achievement.

Since the invention of CAT scanning scientists have continued to improve the technique, particularly by reducing the radiation to which the human body is exposed. The exposure time needed for one CAT scan has been reduced from five minutes to less than 500 milliseconds. CAT scanners are simple to operate, quicker and more economical than newer high-tech procedures. It is therefore the normal method used for initial examination in cases of acute bleeding, head injuries and strokes.

Computer tomography gives doctors a better view of the organs inside the human body.

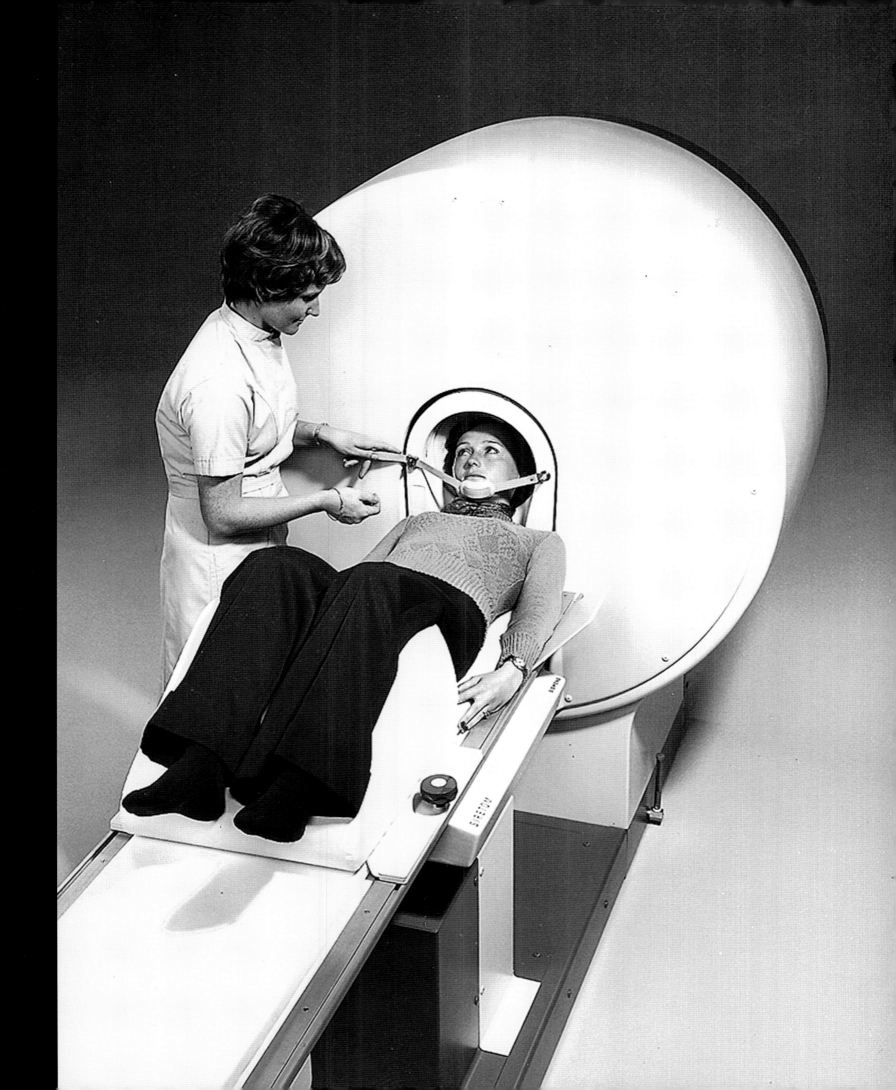

The first test tube baby: giving nature a helping hand

Louise Brown (b. 1978)

IN THE YEAR 1978

> The Volkswagen factory stops production of the "VW Beetle" in Germany.

> At Camp David, USA, the Prime Minister of Israel Menachem Begin and the President of Egypt Anwar El Sadat sign a peace treaty between their two countries.

> In Afghanistan, the pro-Soviet military leaders overthrow the government in a coup and sign a treaty of mutual assistance with the USSR.

> After only 34 days in office Pope John Paul I dies. The Polish cardinal Karol Wojtyla succeeds him as John Paul II.

Until the end of the 1970s, the only possibility for couples who wanted children but could not have any of their own was to adopt one. Then medicine came up with the process of *in vitro* fertilization, in which the egg was brought together with the sperm and fertilized in a laboratory.

On July 25, 1978 in Cambridge, England, the first "test tube" baby in the world Louise Brown, was born. This child's conception had not taken place by the natural process of the sexual act between her parents but by so-called *in vitro* fertilization. In this process, the female ovaries are stimulated with hormones. Then two or three eggs are removed and put into a test tube with male sperm, which fertilizes it. The fertilized egg is then implanted in the mother's womb where, if all goes well, it develops as a normal embryo.

The commonly used terms "artificial insemination" and "test tube baby" are actually misleading. The fertilization of the egg proceeds essentially as it does in nature, and the baby does not grow in a test tube or a laboratory vessel made of glass, but in the body of a woman in the normal way.

The process sounds simple but there are a number of health risks involved for the woman. Apart from the side-effects of the hormone treatment itelf, she must take a number of other things into account: the possibility of ovarian pregnancy, miscarriage, and multiple births. The reason for the last risk is that two or three eggs are usually implanted to increase the chance of success, and if they are all successful twins or triplets are born. The extraction of the egg is almost 100 percent successful, but the possibility of a pregnancy is only about 10 to 20 percent. The chances of a birth without complications are reckoned at between 4 to 6 percent. Taking these figures into account, doubt as to the effectiveness of *in vitro* fertilization is perhaps justified.

However, many couples who cannot have children naturally – either because the composition of the sperm is faulty or there is a malformation of the female ovaries – decide to try this method. After the successful conception of Louise, there was much public debate not only on the medical value of *in vitro* fertilization but also on its ethical, theological, and legal aspects. Psychologists try to discover if there is not another problem hidden behind the unfulfilled and urgent wish for a child in counseling talks.

Additional to this problem is the question of under which "authority" the control and use of still-undeveloped human life falls. In some countries it is forbidden to store fertilized eggs, but legislators in France and the USA for example see no ethical problem in freezing embryos for possible use in further attempts.

In 1998, on her 20th birthday, photographs of an evidently healthy and happy Louise Brown circled the globe. Since 1978, research has made further progress in the field of reproductive medicine. As human genes have now been largely decoded and the first sheep, "Dolly," has been cloned, it now appears to be within the realms of possibility to clone human beings. The first test tube baby was just the beginning of medical intervention in nature.

The first test tube baby was followed by many others.

Laptop and palmtop: mobile communication without limits

Epson, Hewlett Packard

Riding in a train, flying in an airplane or sitting in a hotel room almost anywhere on earth – with a laptop or a palmtop there are practically no limits to mobile communication. These types of computer are so small and light that they can easily be carried in a briefcase. The fact that the electricity is supplied by accumulator batteries making an extension cord superfluous makes them even more flexible.

IN THE YEAR 1982

> For the first time the USSR and the USA negotiate the actual disarmament of existing weapons and not merely arms limitations. In Geneva START (Strategic Arms Reduction Talks) begin.

> In Germany, a vote of no-confidence against Chancellor Helmut Schmidt of the socialist party is successful and Christian social democrat Helmut Kohl is elected new Chancellor.

> The British Falkland Islands are occupied by Argentine troops and Britain declares war on Argentina. After two months Argentina has to surrender.

> In the USA a death sentence is carried out by a poison injection for the first time.

In the early 1980s, technology progressed so far that almost everyone could afford a computer. The computers of that time made data processing theoretically possible in every household or office, but not elsewhere. The sheer weight of the monitor, the fragile components, and countless cable connections "bound" the user to the desk. The demand for a mobile computer grew.

In 1982, the Epson company put a computer on the market, the HX-20, that had a rechargeable battery and could be used everywhere without needing to be plugged in. It was the size of a sheet of typing paper, only 2 in, high and was the first to earn the name of "laptop" as it truly could fit on a lap. It weighed only 3.5 lb and had a flat liquid crystal display (LCD) screen instead of a CRT monitor. This could display 20 x 4 characters, which was sufficient for the demands of the time. An internal tape drive stored data on the computer and there was also a built-in printer. A fully charged set of batteries enabled the HX-20 to work for up to 40 hours; this is still an impressive length of time today.

After the successful Epson HX-20, many other firms followed with even more powerful laptops. Whether in conferences, waiting rooms, in airplanes or on construction sites, laptops allow people to work more flexibly. The reason that desktop PCs are still in the majority today lies in the higher price of a laptop in relation to its performance. The small size of the casing forces manufacturers to use expensive, space-saving building methods, and the construction of the flat screen is relatively costly.

In 1991 saw a new generation of computers appeared on the market. Known as "palmtops," they fit in the palm of the hand. This had been made possible by the development of more powerful, compact, and versatile computer components. The first such model was the 95LX palmtop from Hewlett Packard. Despite its diminutive size, it was a fully functioning computer on which the then current operating system MS-DOS 3.2 could be installed. Two AA batteries were all it needed.

The palmtop was a complete success. In the course of its development manufacturers added more and more ingenious features. Entering data is often carried out with a stylus, either operating a virtual keyboard on the screen, or writing directly, interpreted by handwriting recognition software. Connecting a palmtop to the Internet opens up the myriad possibilities of the net, including e-mail communication.

The development of laptops and palmtops is still continuing. Their future may be influenced by the improvement in cellphone mobile communication. The variety of options offered by these devices could easily make the acquisition of a portable laptop computer unnecessary.

The dramatic development of mobile computing is still continuing.

The personal computer: a computer for everyone

Steven Wozniak (b. 1950), Steve Jobs (b. 1955)

The construction of a light, practical, small, economical computer was the idea behind the development of the PC or "personal computer." IBM started selling a computer with this name in 1981. But the Apple Lisa was the first example of the computer design that is universal today, with a mouse and a graphical user interface.

1983

IN THE YEAR 1983

> Germany permits the stationing of American medium-range missiles on its territory.

> A South Korean passenger airplane crossing USSR air space crashes and all 269 people on board are killed.

> The Hamburg magazine *Stern* publishes the supposed diaries of Adolf Hitler which are soon proved to be a hoax.

> Lech Walesa, the leader of the forbidden Polish trade union Solidarity, is awarded the Nobel Peace Prize.

The history of the computer actually began when people started to formulate mathematical processes precisely. In the 17th century arithmetical operations were first expressed as mechanical rules of calculation. Over the following centuries, increasingly complex calculating machines were created, such as punched card tabulators. In the mid-20th century, companies such as IBM built the first program-controlled calculating machines using relays. The computers after World War II used electronic vacuum tubes as switching elements, which gave them faster perfomance (by the end of the 1950s several tens of thousand addition operations per second were possible). With the development of the transistor and integrated circuits the size was progressively reduced, and in the early 1970s the first microprocessors arrived.

1981 saw the appearance of IBM's "personal computer" on the market. With it, data could be entered with a keyboard, read on a monitor, printed out, and saved on floppy diskettes. For secure, rapid storage of "large" quantities of data (then just a few megabytes), users could connect the first hard disks to the PC. Just as importantly, extensive office software became available for the PC. The $4,000-dollar computer became generally accepted on the market and developed into the forerunner of almost all the personal computers that followed. Today the MS-DOS operating system and PC hardware architecture are still the basis of most computer systems.

The Apple company established itself in the growing computer industry beside enterprises such as Commodore, Sinclair, and Atari. Steve Jobs (b. 1955) and Steven Wozniak (b. 1950) started this computer manufacturing company in 1976. Even with its earliest models, the company valued user-friendliness. The Apple II of 1977 was the first personal computer to be sold completely assembled rather than as a kit. The then revolutionary floppy disk drive and simple expansion capability meant that the $1,200-computer sold like hot cakes. The VisiCalc electronic spreadsheet made the Apple II attractive not only for programmers but also for use in numerous offices.

But the first PC with an interface similar to that used today was the Apple Lisa of 1983. It was the first mass-produced computer to have a mouse and a graphical user interface. The mouse was a small hand appliance with a rotating ball and button that was connected to the computer by a cable; moving it intuitively on the mouse mat moved the cursor or mouse pointer to commands that were graphically represented on the screen. When the user clicked the mouse button, the Lisa executed the chosen command. The results were easily, quickly, and securely stored on the hard disk, which was provided as standard. Despite the advanced features of the Lisa, its success was prejudiced by its high price of $20,000, and the lead established by the IBM-PC that had been introduced two years earlier. Some years later the graphic user interface became universal on the Windows platform.

The principle goes back a long way. The Apple Lisa was the first "real" PC with mouse and graphic interface, a milestone on the computer's way to becoming a mass medium.

HIV virus: on the track of a deadly virus

Luc Montagnier (b. 1932), Robert Gallo (b. 1937)

At the beginning of the 1980s, the US Department of Health reported some remarkable statistics. There was an unusually high incidence of young homosexual men suffering from a rare form of cancer, Kaposi's sarcoma, as well as from an unusual variant of pneumonia.

1984

IN THE YEAR 1984

> The USSR starts to position missiles in East Germany.

> The British Prime Minister Margaret Thatcher and Zhao Ziyang, the Chairman of the Chinese Communist Party, agree that Great Britain will hand the crown colony Hong Kong back to China in 1997.

> Poisonous gases escape from a leak in a pesticide factory in the Indian state Bhopal. More than 2,000 people die and thousands more are blinded by the poison gas.

> In Europe forests continue to die because of acid rain.

Blood samples from the patients showed that the percentage of T-helper cells – the leucocytes, which play an important role in the immune defense – had sunk almost to zero. From 1982 onwards, the symptoms also began to appear in heterosexual adults and newborn babies. The cause of this hitherto unknown disease was not, therefore, linked to homosexuality. As the sickness attacked the immune system in particular, it was given the name Acquired Immuno-Deficiency Syndrome, AIDS.

In October 1984, the virologist Luc Montagnier in Paris identified a virus as the cause of the symptoms. At the same time, the American scientist Robert Gallo demanded that he should be named as the discoverer. In order to mediate the quarrel, both were awarded the distinction. The virus was given the name Human Immunodeficiency Virus, HIV.

How does this treacherous virus go about its work? Research was not long in finding out more. HIV takes over the control center of the immune system and destroys the T4 cells (helper cells). In this way the virus paves the way for other infections that under normal circumstances are less harmful. Even a harmless cold can be dangerous for a person infected with HIV. A patient in the terminal stages of immune deficiency disease does not die "of AIDS," but succumbs to a serious form of an infection such as pneumonia, toxoplasmosis, tuberculosis or cancer. Scientists call these "opportunistic" infections, since they take advantage of the weakness of the organism.

Shortly after these discoveries, the way the disease was transmitted was also found. HIV was transferred through the exchange of bodily fluids such as blood, semen, vaginal discharge, and mother's milk. Infection by saliva is unlikely. The risk of infection increases in proportion to the presence of various other factors, such as injury to the mucous membranes. The greatest danger is posed by unprotected sexual contact and the communal use of injection needles by drug users. Today, an AIDS test can show the existence of HIV antibodies in the blood, but not until a few weeks after the patient has been infected with the disease.

Even though research has made great progress since the discovery of the disease, AIDS is still incurable. Medication can merely inhibit the outbreak of the immune deficiency and relieve the symptoms to some extent. The most important goal of a possible therapy is to increase the number of the T4 (helper) cells in the blood. As the virus is constantly changing (science now distinguishes between HIV0, HIV1 and HIV2), the development of a vaccine has proved particularly difficult.

Many people in the industrial, countries do not appear to be aware of just how dangerous this disease is. However, it has taken on epidemic proportions in the developing countries: 70 percent of all those infected worldwide live in Third World countries, and 80 percent of AIDS victims are Africans. HIV is now the number one cause of death in Africa.

Photograph of a giant cell resulting from fusion with an HIV-producing cell.

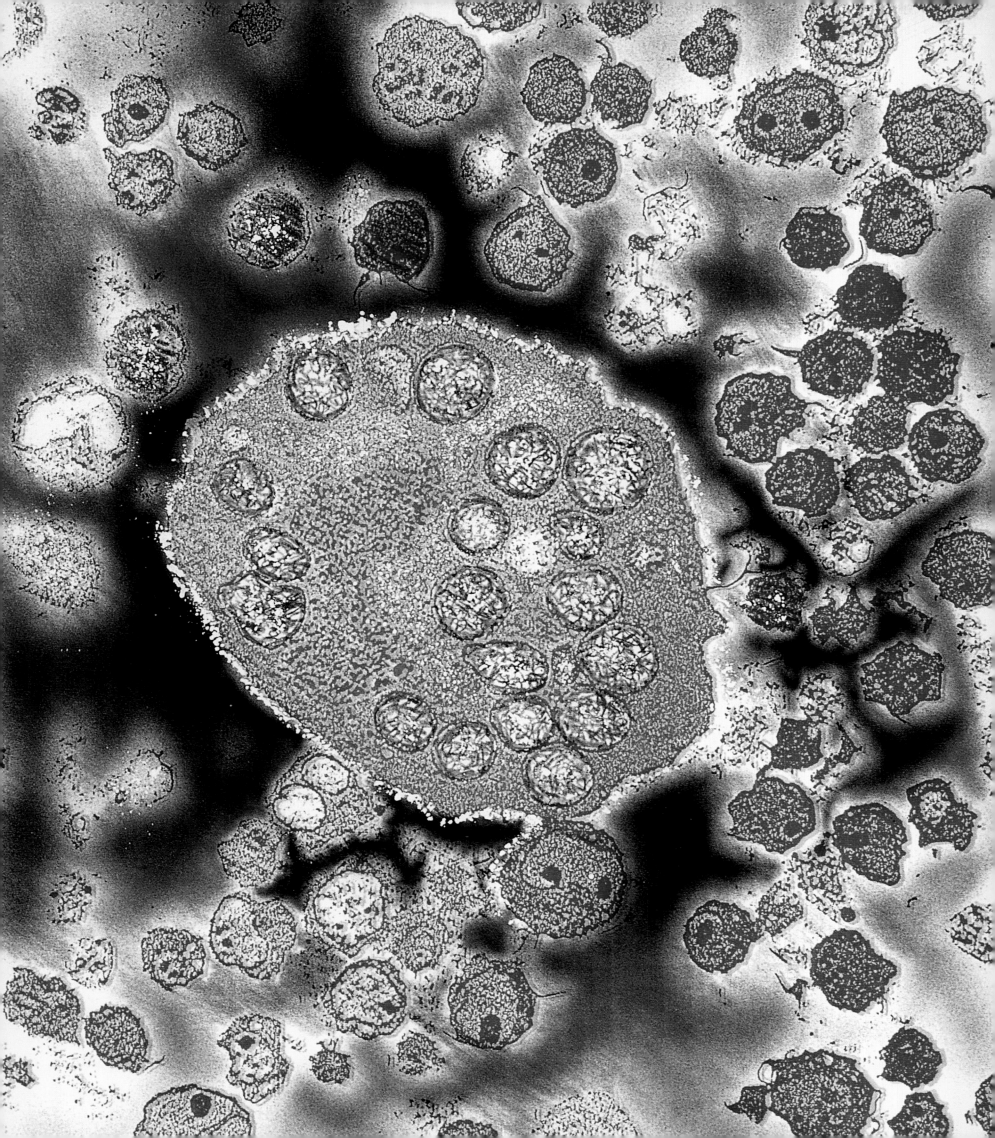

The Mir space station: about life in space

Soviet Union and Russia

The race in science and technology between the two great powers USA and USSR shaped the years of the Cold War, and of course the period also included the first manned space flights. Which nation would be the first to establish a space station?

Before the Soviet MIR ("peace") space station mission, several attempts were made to set up a scientific research station in space. In April 1971, the Soviet space authority launched the 18-ton Saljut 1 into space. The astronauts Georgij Dobrowolskij, Wladislaw Wolkow, and Viktor Pazajew succeeded in entering Saljut 1 on the second attempt and they carried out physical, chemical, and biological experiments over a period of 24 days. On the return trip to earth all three tragically lost their lives as a result of a leak in the air supply. A second space station, Saljut 2, went out of control in 1973. Up to 1982, Soviet scientists launched a total of seven smaller space stations of the Saljut type in space. Saljut 7 also involved other participants from France, Cuba, and India. The only United States space station in those years was the Skylab that was visited three times between 1973 and 1974.

All these stations were small and only habitable for a short time, but the Soviet space authority was striving to develop a large station that would have a longer lifespan. Its plan involved the construction of a main core with several detachable modules through which energy, air, and technical equipment could be supplied, and this design was intended to ensure that the station was usable and expandable indefinitely.

On February 19, 1986, the plan succeeded when the main part of MIR was launched into space. One year later, the Kwant laboratory module docked with it. Kwant contained four X-ray telescopes among other things, with the aid of which the cosmonauts observed the recently discovered supernova 1987 AT. After the attachment of further research modules, the station was finally completed in 1986. Weightlessness on board the space station enabled medical, technical, and pharmaceutical experiments to be carried out that could only be managed with great difficulty on earth. These included, for instance, the manufacture of large semiconductor crystals, flawless glasses, extremely strong magnets, and also certain medications such as insulin. By staying a whole year in space, from 1987 to 1988, the two cosmonauts Wladimir Titow and Musa Manarow created a new record.

With the end of the Soviet Union, international personnel used the MIR space station more and more. The German astronauts Klaus-Dieter Flade (1992), Ulf Merbold (1994), Thomas Rider (1995), and Reinhold Ewald (1997) were among the members of the different teams. In 1995, the American space shuttle docked with MIR for the first time. Altogether, over 100 astronauts visited the station.

By 1999 however the MIR space station was becoming technically obsolete and the Russian space authority could no longer afford its annual overhead of $250 million dollars. On March 23, 2001, MIR was shifted out of its orbit and directed to crash into the Pacific Ocean, an event that was transmitted throughout the world by the media.

More than one hundred space travelers visited the MIR space station between 1986 and 2001.

Superconductivity: it cannot go faster

**Johannes Georg Bednorz (b. 1950),
Karl Alexander Müller (b. 1927)**

In the 19th century, the physicist Georg Simon Ohm (1789–1854) discovered that, depending on its length, diameter, and composition, an electrical conductor offers resistance to electric current. Since that time, electrotechnology has been working to prevent the loss of current due to resistance.

The first scientific breakthrough in this direction came from the physicist Heike Kamerlingh Onnes (1853–1926), who in 1911 discovered the phenomenon of superconductivity. When the temperature of certain conductive materials falls below a transitional temperature, the electrical resistance suddenly falls to zero. Mercury is one of 26 elements that have this characteristic. The application of superconductors is not a simple matter: to achieve the desired effect, the temperature of the material has to be close to absolute zero (0 Kelvin/-273.15 C°/-459.67 F°). In order to reach this temperature the conductors have to be cooled with liquid helium, but this uses more energy than distributing electricity with conventional conductors. Another problem is that superconductors are particularly sensitive to external electric currents.

For decades, scientists have wrestled with this problem. Then in 1986 the physicists Johannes Georg Bednorz and Karl Alexander Müller from the IBM Zurich Research Laboratory in Switzerland discovered a material known as "Zurich oxide." This ceramic alloy becomes a superconductor at temperatures of about -32 F°. Such values can be reached using liquid nitrogen, which is a much less expensive cooling material than liquid helium. In addition, the new ceramic alloys were much less sensitive to external disturbances than the earlier metallic superconductors.

Superconductivity is also opening up new possibilities in medicine. At the moment, for instance, science is working on the development of SQUIDs (Superconducting Quantum Interference Device), which are superconductive sensors. When laid on the surface of the body, SQUIDs measure the magnetic fields caused by the electrical current from the heart or brain. The sensors register deviations from the norm, identifying where the change has taken place and how large it is. The use of SQUIDs could mean a breakthrough in giving early warning of thrombosis.

There are other areas which also benefit from the extreme sensitivity of SQUIDs. Mineral resources and metal fatigue in bridges or airplane parts both cause miniscule distortions in an electrical field. Geologists and engineers can identify these with sensors, thus locating the mineral deposits or the faulty metal.

As well as the progress in metrology, superconductivity is revolutionizing many technical applications. It speeds up electrical switching circuits, reduces the level of interference by one-tenth, makes possible a more compact mode of construction for individual components, and increases the power of processors. A superconductor also decreases the amount of electricity lost between the generator of electricity and the consumer. The trend is continuing in favor of "high temperature" (or less low-temperature) superconductors, since materials with higher critical temperatures are still being discovered.

Superconductivity is a phenomenon found in certain elements at a temperature near absolute zero, -273° C (-459.67 F°).

-273,15 °C

Supernova : the death of a star

Chile

1987

IN THE YEAR 1987

> The German Christian Democrat Uwe Barschel resigns shortly after the victory of the Social Democrats. The press agent publicizes the fact that Barschel was about to launch a smear campaign against a challenger. Weeks later Barschel is found dead in a Geneva hotel, whether from suicide or murdered is still unknown.

> In Washington DC, US president Ronald Reagan and the Soviet party leader Mikhail Gorbachev sign a treaty agreeing to the destruction of all medium-range nuclear missiles.

> The 19-year-old German Matthias Rust flies to Moscow in his Cessna plane and lands in the middle of Red Square.

In the year 1054 Chinese astronomers observed the explosion of a star in the constellation of Taurus. The remnants of this cosmic catastrophe, a "supernova," can still be seen expanding today as the Crab Nebula. Until 1987, only two other supernovas had been sighted with certainty since the observation in China, in 1572 and in 1604. With no event to observe, scientists have used technical equipment to explore the secret of the exploding stars.

The term "nova" describes a variable star that suddenly shines more brightly, then slowly fades to its original level at which it continues to exist. Early astronomers first perceived only the brightness and believed they had discovered a new star (Latin *nova* = new). The cause of this appearance is an excessive production of helium in the outermost layers of the heavenly body. The extremely rapid expansion of the gas causes many smaller explosions, and a brilliant atmosphere originates around the star. With a "supernova," an especially intense nova, the brightness of the star can reach 100 million times its terminal brightness.

The most recent supernova was discovered by Ian Shelton, a scientist of the Chilean Las Campanas Observatory, on February 24, 1987 in the Large Magellanic Cloud. This supernova was exceptionally bright and only reached its maximum brilliance on the 88th day. Studies of this phenomenon were carried out using the most modern methods, enabling scientists to make significant discoveries. It was realized that in contrast with the smaller explosions of a nova, a supernova destroys the star or at least fundamentally changes it.

Such stars sometimes reach a luminosity 100 million times brighter than the sun and would deliver as much energy in few days or weeks as the sun in several millions of years. Then, they fade for ever. Usually little of the star remains apart from an extending cloud of debris – such as the Crab Nebula. A rapidly rotating neutron star sometimes originates inside it, known as a "pulsar."

Although scientists know even less about supernovas than they do about novas, they have already discovered one interesting aspect. There are two different types of supernovas. The first and brighter phenomenon is presumed to originate through double stars. One of the two takes matter from its companion, making it extremely unstable and eventually leading to a thermonuclear explosion. The second, slightly less bright type, of which the 1987 appearance was an example, marks the end of the development of a star of sufficient mass. All its energy reserves are exhausted, and the star falls into gravitational collapse in itself. The outer layers of the star are repelled at speeds of 3,000 to 6,000 miles per second. Only such explosions generate the heaviest chemical elements and hurl them into space.

From the remnants of the supernovas new stars are formed, containing heavier chemical elements than older heavenly bodies. From their observation of supernovas, scientists expect to learn more about the history and development of the cosmos. The sun of the earth's solar system is not threatened with the fate of a supernova, since its mass is too small for it to end in this way.

New celestial bodies may be formed from the debris of a supernova.

The Hubble space telescope: the stars become closer

United States of America

The equipment with which astronomers observe the heavens are more susceptible to disturbance the more sensitive they are. Turbulence in the atmosphere and the background brightness on the earth impair and distort the view of distant heavenly bodies. In order to avoid such complications, astronomers had the idea of simply transfering their observation devices into space.

The United States National Aeronautics and Space Administration (NASA) and the European Space Agency (ESA) together developed what was until then the largest star-observing telescope, the Hubble Space Telescope. It was named after the astronomer Edwin Powell Hubble (1889–1953), who in the year 1924 had calculated the distance of the Andromeda nebula. By this he had proved for the first time that other galaxies existed outside the Milky Way. With the Hubble telescope, these galaxies were seen about ten times more clearly than they could be observed by large telescopes on earth under the clearest viewing conditions.

On April 24, 1990 the space shuttle Discovery launched the Hubble telescope on its orbit 370 miles from the earth. The instrument is 43 ft long and it is much more than a simple telescope. Essentially it is a multi-functional observatory for the observation of the cosmos. The main mirror of the Hubble has a diameter of nearly 8 ft. Among the telescope's equipment is a wide-angle planet camera, a special camera for weak radiation, two high-resolution spectrographs, and several highly sensitive measuring instruments with which the distance of the stars can be determined with great accuracy. Solar cells provide the necessary power. The equipment is remotely controlled from the earth, and engineers visit the observatory every 30 months to service and maintain it. Before Hubble was fully operational, a crew from the space craft Endeavour in 1993 had first to remedy a mistake in the grinding of the main mirror, for example.

The data collected from the Hubble on-board computer is delivered by communication satellites to the Space Telescope Science Institute in Baltimore, which was specifically equipped to handle the scientific findings of the telescope. By using Hubble's findings, scientists hope to be able to observe distant galaxies, to learn more about the life of stars and the formation of planetary systems, to find planets in the sphere of other stars, and to calculate the age of the universe by measuring the speed of its expansion.

Astronomers from numerous countries send suggestions for observations to Baltimore, from which about 300 are selected each year. For example Hubble took fascinating pictures of the appearance of a supernova in 1987, and the impact of fragments of the comet Shoemaker-Levy 9 on Jupiter in 1994. Using methods of spectral analysis, scientists could more precisely determine the chemical composition of Jupiter's atmosphere. Hubble's original pictures are black and white, but those presented to the public are reworked in colour by computer.

The Hubble mission will probably end in about 2010, but the pictures it has sent from space are so informative that NASA and ESA are already planning a successor that will be even larger and more effective, but less expensive than the Hubble Space Telescope.

Orbiting at an altitude of 370 miles (600 km), the Hubble telescope has been sending pictures from space since 1993.

The man from Similaun: a Stone Age story

Konrad Spindler (b. 1939)

Since the excavations of Pompeii and Herculaneum, buried by the eruption of Vesuvius in AD 79, no archaeological find has illustrated the way of life of man's early ancestors so clearly as the Ice Man, or "Ötzi." The body of the frozen man found in the Ötztal Alps is particularly well preserved and has therefore provided scientific knowledge that was previously unobtainable.

In September of 1991, a married couple from Nuremberg, Germany, who were on a mountain hike in the Ötztal Alps in Tyrol, Austria, reached the Similaun glacier. Arriving at the partly melted glacier cap, the hikers made a discovery that froze the blood in their veins. They saw the upper body of a corpse frozen in a hollow. They took it to be a victim of a mountain climbing accident. The couple informed the manager of a nearby lodge, who called the mountain rescue team. After a police doctor had also been called, the men began to free the corpse from the ice with pick axes. They were not particularly careful, since at this point nobody thought that the body would have archaeological significance.

Several days after these events, the professor for early and pre-history at the University of Innsbruck, Konrad Spindler, received notification of the find. Spindler dated the weapons and equipment carried by the man to the transitional period from the Neolithic to the Copper Age (3,350–3,100 BC). The sensational value of the Ice Man as Europe's oldest preserved body was realized. The corpse from the glacier caused a furore among scientists as well as in the media. In order to clarify precisely the rights of ownership, the Similaun glacier was resurveyed. It was officially determined that the Ice Man had been found on the Italian side.

The finding of the Ice Man, or Ötzi, was the first time that a relatively well-preserved body of a prehistoric human being was found as well as a complete skeleton. Investigation brought to light completely new knowledge of life in the alpine region 5,000 years ago. Similaun Man was 40 to 50 years of age and was not in good health at the time of his death. Fur-lined clothes and padded shoes were insufficient to shield him from the icy temperatures at such high altitudes. The Ice Man carried various objects with him. He had a bronze axe, which was rare at that time, a small dagger with a flint blade as well as other weapons, tools, and some provisions. He also had a vessel for carrying live coals and some medicine for wounds. An incomplete bow and some unfinished arrows showed that Ötzi had been disturbed while whittling.

The question still unanswered is what drove this lonely wanderer into such hostile altitudes. Attempts at an explanation range from the theory that he was an explorer looking for metal deposits or a safe passage over the Alps, to the light-hearted notion that he was a lover being chased by a rival. The pollen found adhering to his clothes proved with a high degree of certainty that he had come from the south Tyrolean valley of Vintschgau. Equipment similar to this man's has been found in that upper Italian region and the stone of his weapons originated in the stone quarry there. Recently, scientists have found an arrowhead embedded close to his shoulder blade. Was the man murdered? The mystery of the Ice Man's death has probably been taken with him to the grave.

This bronze axe that "Ötzi" carried with him was a very valuable piece of equipment 5000 years ago.

Dolly the cloned sheep: pros and cons of genetic engineering

Ian Wilmot (b. 1945)

1996

IN THE YEAR 1996

> In the Afghan civil war the radical Islamic Taliban takes over Kabul and forms a temporary government.

> Prince Charles and Princess Diana are divorced.

> Peruvian rebels of the "Tupac Amaru" movement occupy the Japanese embassy in Lima, Peru. They take 490 hostages and demand the release of 400 imprisoned supporters.

> Shortly after take-off, an airplane of the Turkish airline Birgen Air falls into the sea close to the coast of the Dominican Republic. All 189 passengers and crew lose their lives in the accident.

It was not just the scientists who held their breath for a short moment on July 5, 1996. With the birth of the cloned sheep Dolly, Scottish scientists presented a lamb to an astonished world public that was identical to its "mother" down to the last hair. Whether this was the fulfilment of a bold dream or a vision of horror is still a question of heated debate.

Ian Wilmot, embryologist and leader of the research team at the Roslin Institute in Scotland, had been trying to clone a living creature for some time. In 1996, he extracted an egg cell from a female sheep and removed the genetic material, the DNA. Next, Wilmot implanted genetic material from the udder of a second sheep into the egg cell and activated the cell to split as if it had been fertilized. Wilmot then implanted the cluster of cells into the womb of a third sheep. This "surrogate mother" gave birth to a healthy lamb in the summer of 1996 – Dolly. As the artificial creation of genetically identical progeny is called reproductive cloning, Dolly was described as a cloned sheep.

The birth of Dolly was the climax of a development that had started in 1859 with Charles Darwin (1809–82) and his theory of evolution. By 1930, the German scientist Hans Spemann (1869–1941) had produced the first artificial clone by halving the embryo of a salamander with a hair. Scientists recognized nucleic acids (deoxyribonucleic acid or DNA) as the carrier of genetic material in 1944, and Francis Harry Compton Crick (b. 1916) and James Dewey Watson (b. 1928) decoded the structure of DNA in 1953. For this, and for the explanation of the chemical mechanisms by which the cells pass on their genetic substance when they divide, they were awarded the Nobel Prize for Medicine in 1962. The year 1973 marked the birth of genetic engineering, when for the first time it became possible to combine the DNA from two different organisms. This was a prerequisite for the cloning of a mammal in the embryonic stage. In 1982, scientists in the USA managed to split cow embryos and since the mid-1980s, the splitting of animal embryos has become routine in the USA and in Europe. But Dolly was the first clone to be started with a single cell.

Will genetic scientists soon be cloning human beings? The technology today is so advanced that nothing actually stands in the way of this happening. But there is a heated debate raging over the ethics of this process. When in March 2001 scientists in the USA and Italy announced they would be cloning humans in the near future, Germany and France petitioned for a UN initiative against it. In August of the same year, the US House of Representatives passed a general law against cloning humans. However, before November of 2001, the first human embryos existed, produced by American scientists who wanted to obtain stem cells for the development of genetic therapy against cancer. Worldwide, scientists were announcing further cloning experiments with human cells.

Today, in most of the industrialized countries cloning is only permitted to a limited degree for medicinal purposes. In such cases internal organs are to be reproduced. They can then be implanted without any danger of them being rejected by the recipient. It may even turn out that clones cannot live up to the expectations made of them by their proponents: the young sheep Dolly is already suffering from the infirmities of her old "mother:" she has arthritis.

The artificial creation of identical offspring was successfully achieved for the first time with a sheep.

BSE prions: nature's revenge

Stanley Prusiner (b. 1942)

In 1984, the English veterinary surgeon David Bee examined a cow in Sussex that had attracted attention with its curious stumbling gait. Bee could find no reason for the odd behavior of "Cow no. 133," but six weeks later the animal died.

IN THE YEAR 1997

> Princess Diana dies in a car crash in Paris.

> Peruvian soldiers end the occupancy of the Japanese embassy in Lima, Peru. They free 71 hostages but one hostage, two officers and all 14 rebels are killed in the operation. The rebels had freed most of the hostages during the 126 days of the embassy's occupation.

> In Britain, the Labour Party wins the election. Tony Blair becomes new Prime Minister.

Over the following two years more and more vets and farmers observed similar cases of cows that foamed at the mouth and started to sway when they walked. The stricken animals displayed disorders in coordination and motor activity, loss of orientation, and a collapse of the central nervous system. In the autopsies, the brains of the animals were found to be riddled with holes like a sponge.

In 1986, British scientists found the agent of this abnormal behavior. The cows had fallen victim to an unknown disease that the researchers called Bovine Spongiform Encephalopathy or BSE. However, it was soon dubbed "mad cow disease" by the public.

The American scientist Stanley Prusiner had first indicated that such diseases as BSE existed in 1984. In contrast to viral or bacterial infections, BSE is carried by another type of organism that is composed of protein and has a complex structure. Prusiner called them "prions." Infection can be caused either by contagion or by heredity. In 1997 Prusiner was awarded the Nobel Prize for Medicine for his research on prions.

How BSE originated is unclear. One theory supposes that scrapie-infected animal meal was the culprit. Scrapie is a sheep disease that is also caused by prions. In the mid-1970s, almost 100,000 sheep caught this disease in Britain. They were slaughtered, and the carcasses were processed into animal meal and fed to cattle. For a long time animal meal was regarded as a high-quality, protein-rich feed concentrate. Cattle fed with it reached slaughter weight more quickly than on a diet of grass and hay alone.

But how did the disease organism overcome the species barrier between sheep to cattle? Perhaps the unnatural feeding was responsible for this; cows are ruminant vegetarians, and nature has not equipped them to eat animal protein. However, with an eye to economic considerations, the agricultural industry turned them into meat eaters and even cannibals, in that scraps from the slaughter of cattle were also processed into animal meal and fed to cows. Officially, more than 200,000 head of cattle are infected with BSE worldwide. In Germany there were 183 certified cases by June of 2002. However, according to experts, the number of unreported cases is estimated at 800,000 animals worldwide that were slaughtered, processed and eaten before the outbreak of the disease.

Prion diseases are not actually new. They occur in other species of animals and also in humans. In 1920, the neurologist Hans-Georg Creutzfeldt (1885–1964) and his colleague Alfons Jakob (1884–1931) discovered a sickness in humans that runs a course similar to that of BSE and is invariably fatal, Creutzfeld-Jakob disease. In the mid-1990s, the first known cases of a human illness similar to the Creutzfeld-Jakob disease (CJD) appeared. This also attacked young people, which is not usually the case with Creutzfeld-Jakob. It rapidly became evident that BSE can infect humans too.

Animal feed containing cattle scraps turned cows into carnivores, thus contributing to the spread of BSE.

El Niño: stormy weather

European Centre for Medium-Range Weather Forecasts and the Max Planck Institute for Meterology

> After 156 years, the crown colony of Hong Kong is returned to the People's Republic of China. However, for the next 50 years it will have special administrative status with a high degree of autonomy.

> The human bones found in the Bolivian village of Vallegrande in the Andes are identified as the remains of the Cuban revolutionary Che Guevara. Forensic medical analysis confirms this. In 1967, Guevara had been shot while trying to instigate a revolution in Bolivia.

> The Tour de France is won by the German Jan Ullrich.

During the last century Peruvian fishermen awaited the arrival of "El Niño," "the Christ child," with a certain ambivalence. At Christmas time the trade winds disappeared and the fish moved away from the warmer seas with disastrous consequences for the fishermen.

"El Niño" is not a child born in recent times - the Spanish conquistadors mentioned a similar phenomenon in 1567. Every three to seven years there is a complete reversal of climatic conditions along the coast of South America. Normally the seas are much cooler in the east Pacific than they are in the west Pacific. This leads to the development of a high pressure area along the South American coastline, and low pressure with a lot of rain in northern Australia and south-east Asia. The strong trade winds blow from east to west and drive the surface water, warmed by the sun, westward from South America. "El Niño" reduces the strength of the trade winds until they almost disappear. Warm water then flows from west to east, resulting in a rise of temperature in the eastern Pacific of up to 50° F. This is followed by periods of heavy rain in South America and drought in south-east Asia and Australia. The economic consequences for the regions affected, such as crop failures, are usually catastrophic.

Often, "El Niño" is accompanied by its sister "La Niña," "the little girl," which further increases the difference between the cold water in the east Pacific and the warm water in the west Pacific, thus triggering devastating cyclones.

El Niño was particularly violent in 1982/83 and took both weather scientists and the general population completely by surprise. But in 1997 climate experts at the European Centre for Medium-Range Weather Forecasts in Reading, England, and the Max Planck Institute for Meteorology in Hamburg, Germany, gave warning of the El Niño effect as early as the beginning of the year. Using an ocean-atmosphere model, the experts succeeded in interpreting the first signs of the arrival of El Niño much earlier. One of the most important parameters is the temperature of the surface water in the eastern Pacific that begins to change one year ahead of the El Ninō events. With such advance warning the countries affected can take protective measures, for instance by adapting the country's agriculture to these climatic anomalies.

It appears, however, that both El Niño and La Niña are becoming stronger and more frequent. It is thought that this may be caused by the slow change in climate, but experts are unable to prove this theory. In any event, research into the El Niño phenomenon highlights the importance of the oceans on the climate. Meanwhile, weather experts have also noticed a slight El-Niño effect over the Atlantic. Many meteorologists believe that this too will become stronger in the future and that the storms that now rage over the Atlantic will hit south-west Europe in a few years.

△ Computer image of climate changes in the east Pacific and along the coast of South America.

It was only when weather data from space became available, for instance from space stations, that global weather phenomena such as El Niño could be forecast.

Expedition to Jupiter: the discovery of an unknown world

Galileo space probe, in flight from 1989 to 1999

IN THE YEAR 1997

> Timothy MacVeigh is found guilty of causing an explosion in a government administrative building in Oklahoma City, USA, in which 168 people died. He is condemned to death.

> The Catholic nun Mother Teresa dies in Calcutta, India. The work of her order Missionaries of Charity was widely acclaimed.

> In front of the Temple of Hatshepsut in Egypt, Islamic extremists kill 58 foreign tourists and four Egyptians with machine guns and knives.

In the 17th Century Galileo Galilei (1564–1642) saw the planet Jupiter for the first time through his telescope. Nearly 400 years later, the space probe "Galileo" on what was until then the longest planetary mission would transmit fascinating pictures of the planet from space. These showed the surface structures of the moons orbiting Jupiter.

When Galileo Galilei observed the planet Jupiter with a telescope in 1610, the scientist recognized the heavenly body as a rotating sphere that was surrounded by four moons. With improvements in technology, astronomers have since identified cloud structures in the atmosphere of the Jupiter, in which a never-diminishing tornado has raged for centuries. The surface of the planet is a single sea of liquid hydrogen.

However, astronomers' thirst for knowledge of the researcher of the heavens was not yet satisfied. In December 1973, the space probe Pioneer 10 traveling through the solar system came within 81,650 miles of Jupiter, and in 1974 Pioneer 11 came within 26,000 miles of the planet. In 1979 the space probes Voyager 1 and Voyager 2 sent back several thousand photographs of the planet. On them could be seen a system of rings and close-up views of the moons Amalthea, Io, Europa, Ganymede, and Callisto. With these pictures, scientists even identified two new moons.

On October 19, 1989 NASA launched the spacecraft Galileo, named after the discoverer of the planet. Its journey to Jupiter lasted virtually as long as its planning phase. From the beginning of the project in May 1977, the start date was postponed again and again, and the configuration of the probe and its carrier were constantly altered. Galileo was eventually launched on its six-year journey in October 1989.

Six months before Galileo reached Jupiter, the space controllers released an atmosphere probe from the spacecraft, which penetrated Jupiter's atmosphere in December 1995. During its one-hour mission it conveyed basic physical and chemical information as well as meteorological data from Jupiter's upper atmosphere. A little later Galileo itself went into orbit round Jupiter. The scientific goals of the observation of Jupiter primarily included the description and understanding of various weather phenomena as well as the Aurora Borealis. The little inner satellites Metis, Adrastea, Amalthea, and Thebe were found to be the cause of the form and appearance of Jupiter's very weak ring system, and indeed of its very existence. A camera on board the Galileo probe, the SSI (Solid State Imaging Experiment) delivered many astonishing pictures, including the first pictures of the rotation of the earth. This camera had a CCD chip with a resolution of 800 x 800 pixels and a lens with a focal length of 59 in and an aperture of 6.95 in. It sent very detailed pictures of the cloud structure of Jupiter and the surface of the moons, revealing for example active volcanos on Io.

Galileo itself became an orbital satellite and orbited Jupiter 11 times during the two-year primary mission. On the basis of its great success, NASA extended the mission by two more years. This expansion was known as the "Galileo Europa Mission" or "GEM" and involved 15 further Jupiter orbits.

The Galileo space probe orbited Jupiter, the largest planet of the solar system, for two years on its primary mission.

The human genome; the mystery is finally unraveled

Craig Venter (b. 1946)

The complete decoding of the human genome, the description of individual hereditary factors, was an event that was comparable in its significance to the landing on the moon in 1969. By means of this genetic "map," the science of molecular medicine may be able to develop cures for genetic diseases such as cancer, Alzheimer's, and osteoporosis.

IN THE YEAR 2000

> The prosecuting attorney's office begins investigations into the dealings of former German Chancellor Helmut Kohl. Between 1993 and 1998 Kohl accepted cash donations of two million Deutschmarks which he placed in private accounts. He refuses to name the donor.

> In Austria, Wolfgang Schüssel is elected the new Chancellor. His conservative party enters into a coalition with Jörg Haider's right-wing populist party.

> The Serbian dictator Slobodan Milosevic is overthrown by a coup after he annuls the results of the presidential and parliamentary elections. The new president is Vojislav Costunica, the leader of the democratic opposition.

> George W. Bush is the winner in the most controversial presidential elections in American history. After misleading ballots and an antiquated automatic ballot-counting process result in protests in Florida, the Supreme Court votes against counting ballots by hand.

In order to find out more about genetic illness and to open up new paths of diagnosis and therapy, scientists in the USA founded the Human Genome Organization (HUGO) in 1988. Its goal was to decode the human genetic makeup. A genome is what experts call the simple set of chromosomes and its full complement of genes. Chromosomes, which are visible under a microscope, are carriers of genetic information, DNA (deoxyribonucleic acid). There are 46 chromosomes in human body cells, but only 23 in the egg and sperm cells. With the fusion of the egg and sperm, there are again 46. The chromosomes are made up of 22 pairs of autosomes and one pair of sex chromosomes, the male one 46,XY, and the female 46,XX. The spiraling ladder of DNA is contained in the chromosomes. The "rungs" of the ladder are made up of the base pairs adenine-thymine and guanine-cytosine. This "horizontal" order is determined, since only these combinations are possible. The key to the genome must therefore lie in the "vertical" order of the rungs, A, T, G and C, and the task was to solve the riddle of this sequence.

The Human Genome Project was initially led by James Watson (b. 1928), who had discovered the structure of DNA in 1953. By 1992 the researchers had cataloged chromosome 23 and the Y-chromosome which, in the case of humans, determines the male sex. The American scientist and businessman Craig Venter took part in the competition for the complete decoding of the human gene with his biotech company Celera Genomics. In the end, Venter won the race. In June of 2000 he announced to the gathered world press that he had already decoded 99 percent of the human genome.

In January 2001, the researchers of the Human Genome Project presented their results. According to these, humans have about 26,000 to 40,000 genes (hitherto it had been assumed to be over 100,000), about twice as many as a fruit fly or a worm. Still, heredity shows that the human being is a much more complex creature, and human genes are constructed in a far more complicated way than those of an animal. According to the researchers, most mutations (changes in genes) occur during the production of sperm cells, while the rate of mutation in the creation of the egg is only about half of that. On the human gene landscape there are also "deserts," fields in which there are no, or very few, genes. Only about 2 percent of the genes make essential proteins for the control of bodily functions. On the other hand, so-called "hot spots" show a lot of activity.

The expected equation of "one gene for one disease" was not to be realized. It will probably still be some time before enough is known to make possible a quick operation on the genetic substance to "cure" genetic diseases. Whether or not such manipulation is ethical is an open question, but anyone who suffers from a genetic disease would probably answer "yes."

Medicine is hoping to achieve important breakthroughs in the treatment of hereditary diseases by making use of the decoding of the human being's genetic make-up.

What holds the world together

The Greek philosophers

Amazingly, philosophers in ancient Greece had already imagined that all matter was made up of tiny, identical pieces. Leucippus (*c.* 450–370 B.C.) and his pupil Democritus (*c.* 460–370 B.C.) called these elementary particles of all matter "atoms" (Greek *atoma* = indivisible) and founded the school of the so-called "atomists." They believed that the atoms were indestructible and would exist for ever. They were so small that they could not be seen, and apart from the void they were the only existing things. The world was created by their movements, their collisions with one another, and their accumulation. The characteristics of objects were determined solely by the adhesion of atoms. Changes arose through movements within the accumulations of atoms. A question often discussed among the "atomists" was whether individual atoms were truly identical. The philosopher Anaxagoras was of the opinion that every substance was composed of different atoms. Empedocles however thought that there were just four kinds of atom, one for each of the four elements, earth, air, fire, and water.

Modern atomic theory

These thoughts from ancient Greece were forgotten for 2,000 years. It was not until the 17th century that philosophers again started to discuss nature's miniscule building blocks. René Descartes (1596–1650) supposed that these elementary particles, which he called "corpuscles," had differing mass, variegated movement and individual characteristics that could be calculated mathematically. Atomic theory, upon which modern physical science is based, was developed in 1803 by the British chemist and physicist John Dalton (1766–1844). According to Dalton, matter is composed of atoms of various weights that are related in simple ways. Each chemical element is made up of atoms belonging to one of these weight classes. Chemical substances are combinations of different atoms. If the connections are decomposed, the atoms are released unchanged. In 1808, in his book *A New System of Chemical Philosophy*, Dalton tried to give the atomic weights of the known elements in relation to each other. As his starting point he took the hydrogen atom, which he gave a value of "1."

All these theories presupposed that atoms were solid pieces of matter. However, Antoine Henri Becquerel (1852–1908) discovered in 1896 that uranium salts give off rays that could penetrate solid matter and could only be screened by lead. Marie Curie (1867–1934) and her husband Pierre (1859–1906) found further radiating elements, polonium and radium. This radiation, they discovered, could not be caused by the chemical or physical condition of the original substance (which does not visibly change) but had to come

from the interior of the matter itself. At the same time the British physicist Joseph John Thompson (1856–1940) discovered the electron, a particle with considerably less mass than the atom.

Atom models

With these discoveries, the question of what constitutes the smallest components of nature and the composition of the atom had to be asked anew. Around the turn of the century scientists were discussing various alternatives as to how the interior of the atom might look. It was the intensive series of experiments by the New Zealand-born British physicist Ernest Rutherford (1871–1973) that led to the construction of a model of an atom that is still valid today. Now it was clear that the atom was composed of a shell around which negatively charged electrons circled, surrounding a nucleus, in which neutrons and positively charged protons were found. However, the model still did not explain all the powers that are in effect within an atomic nucleus. For instance, the accelerated movement of a charge of electrons would release energy in the form of light, gradually lose its speed of movement, and eventually fall into the nucleus.

The Danish physicist Niels

**Marie Curie
(1867-1934)**

**Albert Einstein
(1878-1955)**

394

Bohr tried to explain these paradoxes in 1913. He postulated that the electrons would take on specific states of energy. Only when in the transitional phase from an energy-rich orbit to an energy-poor one would the electron be able to emit light. Normally, however, electrons are in an energy-poor and therefore stable state. Only when energy is added to the system does it enter for a short time into a stimulated, but unstable, state. Bohr assumed that several electrons circulate around the nucleus at a regular distance and therefore create an "electronic shell." According to the quantum theory developed by Max Planck (1858–1947) in 1900, processes at molecular, atomic, and sub-atomic levels do not take place continuously but are sporadic.

In 1905, Albert Einstein (1878–1955) recognized that light not only appeared in the form of waves of energy but also had particle characteristics. Some physical processes can only be explained if the wave characteristics of light are assumed, and others only if its particle characteristics are taken as a basis. Einstein called these particles of light "photons." In 1923, Louis de Broglie (1892–1987) posed the question of whether or not, conversely, particles such as electrons or protons might also have wave characteristics. Experiments then proved that this was indeed the case. In 1927, Werner Heisenberg (1901–76) postulated the theory that the position and impulse of an elementary particle such as an electron can never be determined at the same time, since observation will influence the behavior. It was Erwin Schrödinger (1887–1961) who found out that the space in which an electron is to be found with the greatest probability can be calculated.

In practice the scientific discoveries in the field of nuclear physics have both negative and positive aspects. The energy released by the atom bomb placed mankind on the edge of a social abyss. At the same time the peaceful application of nuclear energy could provide a source of energy for mankind for thousands of years to come, if the problems of handling nuclear waste are overcome.

The power of the atom

Scientists also asked themselves questions about the "nuclear force" holding the protons and neutrons together in the nucleus of the atom. To overcome this force, they bombarded the atomic nuclei with highly energetic particles. In these experiments, and in cosmic radiation, over 200 so-called elementary particles have been discovered. These tiny, subatomic "building blocks" usually have a life span of under one hundred-millionth of a second. Therefore, according to the currently accepted theory, the components of the nucleus are held together by interchanging their forces.

The confusing variety of elementary particles is difficult to classify into a system. Today they are usually ordered according to the force that they belong to, as hadrons, leptons, and bosons. Each particle has a corresponding anti-particle that carries the opposite charge. In 1963, the American physicists Murray Gell-Mann and George Zweig postulated that hadrons are composed of even more fundamental elementary particles. Today, these parti-

cles, which Gell-Mann called "quarks," are regarded as the smallest unit of an atomic nucleus. However, the development of a unified "field theory," in which all the particles and forces that have been discovered will fit, has still not been achieved.

There is also the question of the practical application of these discoveries, particularly the utilization of the enormous energy released in atomic processes. In the early 1930s, the French couple Frédéric and Irène Joliot-Curie succeeded in manufacturing artificial radioactive elements (isotopes) by bombarding stable, non-radioactive elements with certain particles. Later, the Italian physicist Enrico Fermi created radioactive elements not occurring naturally that are heavier than uranium (transuranium elements). Today these are used as indicators in medicine, biology, chemistry and technology.

In 1939 the scientists Otto Hahn and Fritz Strassmann succeeded in splitting the atom. With this achievement, the way was opened for the military as well as the peaceful use of atomic energy.

Index

Subject index

Acknowledgments

1 Bayer AG; 2 Twinbooks, Munich; 6 Stockbyte; 9 Twinbooks, Munich; 11 Twinbooks, Munich; 12 Twinbooks, Munich; 13 Arrow, Ötzi Dorf Umhausen; 15 Egyptian lamp and stand, Twinbooks, Munich; 16 Aswan High Dam, Twinbooks, Munich; 17 Egyptian irrigation system, Twinbooks, Munich; 18 Loom from Crete, Twinbooks, Munich; 19 Roman loom, Photo: Römerstadt Augusta Raurica; 20 Constellation, Twinbooks, Munich; 21 Sky map, Twinbooks, Munich; 22 Getty Images; 23 Rottweil window sundial, Wuppertaler Uhrenmuseum; 24 Suspension bridge, Twinbooks, Munich; _25 Bridge building, Twinbooks, Munich; 26 Stonehenge, Twinbooks, Munich; 27 Megalith grave near Stora Köpinge, Ystad, InterPhoto, Munich; 28 Stone Age vessel, Ötzi Dorf Umhausen; 29 InterPhoto, Munich; 30l Nicolaus Copernicus, Twinbooks, Munich; 30r Galileo Galilei, Twinbooks, Munich; 31t Sunspots, Getty Images; 31m Hubble space telescope, Getty Images; 31b Isaac Newton, Twinbooks, Munich; 32 Papiermaking, Basler Papiermühle; 33 Colored engraving: Papierherstellung, Basler Papiermühle; 35 Shield, Altuna Sweden (7th c.), InterPhoto, Munich; 37 Twinbooks, Munich; 38 Jan van Eyck: The Madonna of Chancellor Rolin (c. 1425), Detail, Twinbooks, Munich; 39 Throne, Tutankhamun and his consort, Silvestris/PhotoPress, Schmidbauer; 40 Corbie Psalter, initial (8-9th c.), Twinbooks, Munich; 41 Attic vase: chariot and lions (8-7th c.BC), Twinbooks, Munich; 42 Twinbooks, Munich; 43 Pyramids of Gizeh, InterPhoto, Munich; 44 Twinbooks, Munich; 45 Computer graphic, Getty Images; 46 Egyptian scales, Twinbooks, Munich; 47 Petrus Christus: St Eloi in his workshop (1449), Twinbooks, Munich; 49 Louis Jean Francois Lagrenée: Vulcan's forge, DuMont archive; 51 Chinese compass, Twinbooks, Munich; 53 Twinbooks, Munich; 55 Solar eclipse, Getty Images; 56 Roman aqueduct, Twinbooks, Munich; 57 Pont du Gard, Languedoc, InterPhoto, Munich; 58 Chaldeic cuneiform script, Twinbooks, Munich; 59t Medieval house book: scholar at his desk (15th c.), Twinbooks, Munich; 59b Canterbury mnuscript (early 12th c.), Twinbooks, Munich; 60 German shop (c. 1520), Twinbooks, Munich; 61 Twinbooks, Munich; 63 Sculpture of Hippocrates, Twinbooks, Munich; 65 DuMont archive; 67 Twinbooks, Munich; 69 Twinbooks, Munich; 71 Twinbooks, Munich; 73 DuMont Archiv; 75 Twinbooks, Munich; 76 Windmill in Greece, Twinbooks, Munich; 77 Jacob van Ruysdael: The mill on the road near Duurstede, detail (1670), Twinbooks, Munich; 78 Twinbooks, Munich; 79 Twinbooks, Munich; 81 Amethyst scepter, Mörchnerkar/ Zillertal, Photo: Hermann Brunner; 83 Hans Holbein the elder: The ambassadors, detail (1533), DuMont archive; 84 Baquet, Etruscan wall painting, Twinbooks, Munich; 85 DuMont archive; 86 Makind hourglasses, Wuppertaler Uhrenmuseum; 87t Chinese water clock, Wuppertaler Uhrenmuseum; 87b Stockbyte; 88 Twinbooks, Munich; 89 Twinbooks, Munich; 91 Clockwork, Stockbyte; 92 Twinbooks, Munich; 93 Quinten Massys (1465/66-1531): Canon Stephan Gardiner, Twinbooks, Munich; 94 Twinbooks, Munich; 95 Sulfur, volcano, Vulcano, InterPhoto, Munich; 97 Silvestris/PhotoPress, Bott; 99 Wall painting, Herculaneum, Twinbooks, Munich; 100 Johannes Gutenberg, Twinbooks, Munich; _101 Twinbooks, Munich; 102 Nicolaus Copernicus, Twinbooks, Munich; 103 Sun, Getty Images; 105 Twinbooks, Munich; 106 Twinbooks, Munich; 107 Leonardo da Vinci (1452-1519): Anatomical drawing, DuMont archive; 108 Leaning Tower of Pisa, Twinbooks, Munich; 109 Galileo in Pisa Cathedral, Twinbooks, Munich; 110 Twinbooks, Munich; 111 Historic microscope, Carl Zeiss Jena GmbH; 112o Gottfried Wilhelm Leibniz, Twinbooks, Munich; 112u René Descartes, Twinbooks, Munich; 113 Quinten Massys: The moneychanger and his wife, Detail (1514), Twinbooks, Munich; 114 Hans Sebald Beham: German city life (c. 1550), Twinbooks, Munich; 115t Calculating machine (1623), source: IBM; 115b Eniac Computer, US Army photo; 117 Twinbooks, Munich; 119 Leonardo da Vinci (1452-1519): Anatomical drawing, DuMont archive; 120 Stockbyte; 121 Jupiter, Getty Images; 122 Planetary orbits, Twinbooks, Munich; 123 Johannes Kepler, Twinbooks, Munich; 125 Observatory, Nice, Twinbooks, Munich; 127 Submarine, Howaldtswerke Deutsche Werft AG, Kiel; 129 Calculating machine (1623), source: IBM; 131 Twinbooks, Munich; 133 Descartes in Amsterdam, Twinbooks, Munich; 134 Otto von Guericke, Twinbooks, Munich; 135 The Magdeburg hemispheres, Twinbooks, Munich; 137 W. Hecht: The die is cast (c. 1870), InterPhoto, Munich; 139 Red blood corpuscles, D. Scharf/Peter Arnold, Inc./OKAPIA Munich; 140t Postman (18th c.), Twinbooks, Munich; 140b Gabriel Metsu (1629-1667): The letterwriter, Twinbooks, Munich; 141o Stockbyte; 141u Twinbooks, Munich; 142 Gottfried Wilhelm Freiherr von Leibniz, Twinbooks, Munich; 143 Twinbooks, Munich; 145 Isaac Newton, Twinbooks, Munich; 146 Edmund Halley, Twinbooks, Munich; 147 Halley's comet, Getty Images; 149 Blood pressure measurer, InterPhoto, Munich; 151 Twinbooks, Munich; 152 Immanuel Kant, Twinbooks, Munich; 153 Meteorite in the Milky Way, Getty Images; 154 Benjamin Franklin, Twinbooks, Munich; 155 Lightning Miyuki Shishido, Photo: Hans Schremmer, www.himmelsfarbe.de; 156 Galen and Hippocrates, Fresko Anagni (c. 1255), Twinbooks, Munich; 157 Rembrandt van Rijn: The anatomy lesson of Dr Tulp (1632), DuMont archive; 159 James Watt's steam engine, Twinbooks, Munich; 160 Twinbooks, Munich; 161 Twinbooks, Munich; 162 Twinbooks, Munich; 163 Balloon of the Montgolfier brothers, Twinbooks, Munich; 165 Mechanical loom (early 19th c.), Twinbooks, Munich; 166 Galvani's frog's leg experiment, Twinbooks, Munich; 167 Twinbooks, Munich; 168 Middle Rhine Master: The paradise garden (c. 1420), Twinbooks, Munich; 169l Florence Nightingale (1855), Twinbooks, Munich; 169r Computer tomography, Siemens AG; 169t Getty Images; 170 Vaccination (c. 1830), Twinbooks, Munich; 171 Master of Alkmaar: Feeding the hungry (1540), Twinbooks, Munich; 172 Pierre Simon Laplace, Twinbooks, Munich; 173 Illustration of a black hole, Getty Images; 175 Twinbooks, Munich; 176 High-pressure steam engine, DuMont archive; 177 Twinbooks, Munich; 179 Twinbooks, Munich; 181 Twinbooks, Munich; 182 Arc lamp, Twinbooks, Munich; 183 Twinbooks, Munich; 185 Lilienthal, Fliegeberg (16.8.1894), Otto Lilienthal Museum archive, www.lilienthal-museum.de; 187t Draisine, Twinbooks, Munich; 187b Crank-wheeled bicycle (c. 1860), Zweirad Museum Havel-Auen-Werder; 189 Dinosaurier-Freilichtmuseum Münchehagen; 191 Twinbooks, Munich; 193 Twinbooks, Munich; 194 Jan Vermeer: The soldier and the laughing woman (c. 1655-60), Twinbooks, Munich; 195lt Vasco da Gama, Twinbooks, Munich; 195mt Christoph Kolumbus, Twinbooks, Munich; 195rt Roald Amundsen, Twinbooks, Munich; 195b Stanley meets Livingstone in Afrika (1872), Twinbooks, Munich; 197 Stockbyte; 198 Stockbyte; 199 Advertising poster, Schreibmaschinenmuseum Peter Mitterhofer, Partschins; 201 Morse code machine, Twinbooks, Munich; 202 Eniac Computer, US Army photo; 203 Stockbyte; 205 Faraday in his laboratory in London, Twinbooks, Munich; 206 Twinbooks, Munich; 207 Honoré Daumier: Patience is the virtue of a donkey (1839), Twinbooks, Munich; 208 Sun corona, Getty Images; 209 Sun, Getty Images; 211 Twinbooks, Munich; 212 Charles Darwin, Twinbooks, Munich; 213 Twinbooks, Munich; 215 Neanderthal Museum; 216 Mendel monument in Brünn, Twinbooks, Munich; 217 Twinbooks, Munich; 219 Advertisement, Robert Bosch GmbH; 220 Robert Wilhelm Bunsen, Twinbooks, Munich; 221 Spectral analysis, Twinbooks, Munich; 222 Carmina Burana: Summer landscape (13the c.), Twinbooks, Munich; 223 Arrival of lions at London Zoo (1876), Twinbooks, Munich; 224t Botanical garden in London (1852), Twinbooks, Munich; 224b Sebastian Münster's Cosmography (1550), Twinbooks, Munich; 225 Microscope picture of DNA, Bayer AG; 226 Twinbooks, Munich; 227 Twinbooks, Munich; 229 Getty Images; 230 Suez Canal, Twinbooks, Munich; 231 Alfred Nobel, Twinbooks, Munich; 233 Periodisc table according to Mendeleyev, Twinbooks, Munich; 235 Bacteria culture under the magnifying glass, Bayer AG; 237 Picture of the earth, computer graphic, Getty Images; 239 Benz's patent motor car, Daimler Benz archive; 241 Advertisement for Edison's phonograph, Twinbooks, Munich; 243 Louis Pasteur, Twinbooks, Munich; 245 InterPhoto, Munich; 247 British troops in Burma (1887), Twinbooks, Munich; 248 BASF Aktiengesellschaft; 249 New York skyscrapers, Twinbooks, Munich; 250t Hare shoot, Castile (early 12th c.), Twinbooks, Munich; 250b The deaths of Marshals Clermont and Champagne (14th c.), Twinbooks, Munich; 251 British troops in WWII, Twinbooks, Munich; 253 Vertical punched-card sorting machine by Hollerith (1908), source: IBM; 255 Bert Kaempfert with phonograph (1961), InterPhoto, Munich; 256 DuMont archive; 257 Guglielmo Marconi with telegraph (1930), Twinbooks, Munich; 259 Louis and Auguste Lumiere, Film Museum Berlin, Deutsche Kinemathek; 260 Wilhelm Konrad Röntgen, Twinbooks, Munich; 261 Twinbooks, Munich; 263 Siegmund Freud, Twinbooks, Munich; 265 Marie Curie with her daughter Irène, Twinbooks, Munich; 267 Work on AIDS research, Bayer AG; 268 Twinbooks, Munich; 269 The airship Hindenburg crashes in flames (1937), Twinbooks, Munich; 271 Knossos, Palace of Minos, InterPhoto, Munich; 272 Red blood corpuscles, Twinbooks, Munich; 273 Twinbooks, Munich; 275 Wright biplane, Twinbooks, Munich; 276 Passage of Moses through the Red Sea (c. 1100), Twinbooks, Munich; 277lt Cambridge station (1848), Twinbooks, Munich; 277rt London in the 1880s, Twinbooks, Munich; 277b Twinbooks, Munich; 279 Twinbooks, Munich; 281 Human brain, Twinbooks, Munich; 283 Christian Weber, www.integrativ.ch; 285 Stockbyte; 286 Microscope image of chromosomes, Max-Planck-Gesellschaft; 287 John Fox Images; 288 Getty Images; 289 Vitamin C, crystal image, Roche Vitamine GmbH; 291 Twinbooks, Munich; 292 Alfred-Wegener Institut für Polar- und Meeresforschung; 293 Twinbooks, Munich; 294 Twinbooks, Munich; 295 Assembly line, Robert Bosch GmbH; 297 Sinking of the Titanic, Twinbooks, Munich; 299 Albert Einstein, Twinbooks, Munich; 300 Twinbooks, Munich; 301 Bee dance, Deutscher Imkerbund e.V. Wachterberg-Villip; 302 M. Santos Dumont and his aircraft in Paris, Champs Elysées, Twinbooks, Munich; 303l Louis Blériot (1909), Twinbooks, Munich; 303r Stockbyte; 304 Weather chart, Deutscher Wetterdienst; 305 Weather satellite image, EUMETSAT; 306 Fluorescent nerve image, Max-Planck-Gesellschaft; 307 Twinbooks, Munich; 309 Twinbooks, Munich; 311 Space shuttle, Getty Images; 313 Bacteria culture, Bayer AG; _315 InterPhoto, Munich; 317 RAMAC IBM 305 (1958), source: IBM; 319 Desy, Deutsches Elektronen-Synchotron; 320 Getty Images; 321 Konrad Lorenz, InterPhoto, Munich; 323 LSD modell, molecule structure, Kjeld Olesen/OKAPIA Munich; 325 Twinbooks, Munich; 327 Stockbyte; 328 Stockbyte; 329 Gundremmingen nuclear power station (t) and Biblis (b), RWE Power AG; 331 Bayer AG; 332 Twinbooks, Munich; 333t Space station graphic, Getty Images; 333lb Twinbooks, Munich; 333rb Twinbooks, Munich; 335 Detonation of an atom bomb, Getty Images; 336 Getty Images; 337 Getty Images; 339 Twinbooks, Munich; 341 Molecular model, 3-dimensional DNA structure, Bayer AG; 343 Weather satellit e graphic, Getty Images; 345 Optical fiber, Stockbyte; 346 Twinbooks, Munich; 347 Hieronymus Bosch: The garden of delights, detail (c. 1485) photo Artothek J.S. Martin und Hans Hinz; 349 InterPhoto, Munich; 351 Illustration of a satellite, Getty Images; 353 CERN, European Organisation for Nuclear Research; 355 Tim Berners Lee (July 11, 1994), CERN, European Organisation for Nuclear Research; 357 Microprocessor, source: IBM; 358 Luna module, Getty Images; 359 Getty Images; 360t Creation of Eve, fresco (late 12th c.), Twinbooks, Munich; 360m Charles Darwin, Twinbooks, Munich; 361 Gorilla, Twinbooks, Munich; 363 Stockbyte; 364 Examination with CAT machine, Siemens AG; 365 Siemens AG; 367 John Fox Images; 369 Siemens AG; 371 Apple; 373 Microscope image of an AIDS cell, Bayer AG; 375 MIR space station over the Pacific, Getty Images; 377 Exploding gas globule, Getty Images; 379 Hubble telescope, Getty Images; 381 Tool, Ötzi Dorf Umhausen; 383 Twinbooks, Munich; 385 Silvestris/Hollweck; 386 NASA, R. B. Husar, Washington University ; 387 Space station over the Pacific, Getty Images; 389 Galileo probe in space, Getty Images; 391 Twinbooks, Munich; 393 Laboratory, Max-Planck-Gesellschaft; 394l Marie Curie, Twinbooks, Munich; 394r Albert Einstein, Twinbooks, Munich; 395l Atom bomb explosion (1945), Digital Stock; 395r Stockbyte

Concept and creation: Twin Books, Munich
Text: Karl-Heinz Asenbaum, Dr. Thomas Barth, Andreas Faber, Claudia Fink, Dr. Bernhard Fritscher, Katharina Geiger, Esther Grau, Axel Hilterhaus, Dr. Christa Kordt, Birgit Kremser, Sandra Papadopoulos, Christa Pöppelmann, Dr. Andrea Rottloff, Annerose Sieck, Anja Voss
Editorial: Sonya Mayer, Christina Fröhlich, Dr. Thomas Rosky
Translation: Rosetta International, London, UK
Picture research: Thomas Martin, Claudia Sandtner, Christiane Fritsche, Simone Steger
Design: H3A GmbH, München
Proofreading: Laura Grec, Eva Munk, Emily Sands

ISBN 90 366 1700 6